❯Amos™ 7.0 User's Guide

James L. Arbuckle

For more information, please contact:

Marketing Department	Amos Development Corporation
SPSS, Inc.	1121 N. Bethlehem Pike, Suite 60 - #142
233 S. Wacker Dr., 11th Floor	Spring House, PA 19477, U.S.A.
Chicago, IL 60606-6307, U.S.A.	URL: *http://amosdevelopment.com*
Tel: (312) 651-3000	
Fax: (312) 651-3668	
URL: *http://www.spss.com*	

Amos 7.0 User's Guide
Copyright © 1995–2006 by Amos Development Corporation
All rights reserved.
Printed in the United States of America.

1 2 3 4 5 6 7 8 9 0   09 08 07 06

ISBN-13: 978-1-56827-386-0
ISBN-10: 1-56827-386-X

Contents

Part I: Getting Started

1 Introduction   1

2 New Features   7

3 Tutorial: Getting Started with Amos Graphics   11

Part II: Examples

1   Estimating Variances and Covariances   27

5   *Unobserved Variables*   *85*

6   *Exploratory Analysis*   *105*

7 *A Nonrecursive Model* 133

8 *Factor Analysis* 141

9 *An Alternative to Analysis of Covariance* 149

10 Simultaneous Analysis of Several Groups 163

11 Felson and Bohrnstedt's Girls and Boys 179

12 Simultaneous Factor Analysis for Several Groups 199

13 Estimating and Testing Hypotheses about Means 213

17   Missing Data   273

24 Multiple-Group Factor Analysis   367

25 Multiple-Group Analysis   381

29 Estimating a User-Defined Quantity in Bayesian SEM — 441

30 Data Imputation — 465

31 Analyzing Multiply Imputed Datasets — 473

Introduction

Amos is short for **A**nalysis of **MO**ment **S**tructures. It implements the general approach to data analysis known as **structural equation modeling** (SEM), also known as **analysis of covariance structures**, or **causal modeling**. This approach includes, as special cases, many well-known conventional techniques, including the general linear model and common factor analysis.

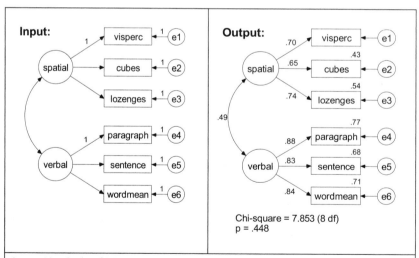

Amos (Analysis of Moment Structures) is an easy-to-use program for visual SEM. With Amos, you can quickly specify, view, and modify your model graphically using simple drawing tools. Then you can assess your model's fit, make any modifications, and print out a publication-quality graphic of your final model. Simply specify the model graphically (left). Amos quickly performs the computations and displays the results (right).

Structural equation modeling (SEM) is sometimes thought of as esoteric and difficult to learn and use. This is incorrect. Indeed, the growing importance of SEM in data analysis is largely due to its ease of use. SEM opens the door for nonstatisticians to solve estimation and hypothesis testing problems that once would have required the services of a specialist.

Amos was originally designed as a tool for teaching this powerful and fundamentally simple method. For this reason, every effort was made to see that it is easy to use. Amos integrates an easy-to-use graphical interface with an advanced computing engine for SEM. The publication-quality path diagrams of Amos provide a clear representation of models for students and fellow researchers. The numeric methods implemented in Amos are among the most effective and reliable available.

Featured Methods

Amos provides the following methods for estimating structural equation models:

- Maximum likelihood
- Unweighted least squares
- Generalized least squares
- Browne's asymptotically distribution-free criterion
- Scale-free least squares

Amos goes well beyond the usual capabilities found in other structural equation modeling programs. When confronted with missing data, Amos performs state-of-the-art estimation by full information maximum likelihood instead of relying on ad-hoc methods like listwise or pairwise deletion, or mean imputation. The program can analyze data from several populations at once. It can also estimate means for exogenous variables and intercepts in regression equations.

The program makes bootstrapped standard errors and confidence intervals available for all parameter estimates, effect estimates, sample means, variances, covariances, and correlations. It also implements percentile intervals and bias-corrected percentile intervals (Stine, 1989), as well as Bollen and Stine's (1992) bootstrap approach to model testing.

Multiple models can be fitted in a single analysis. Amos examines every pair of models in which one model can be obtained by placing restrictions on the parameters of the other. The program reports several statistics appropriate for comparing such models. It provides a test of univariate normality for each observed variable as well as a test of multivariate normality and attempts to detect outliers.

Amos accepts a path diagram as a model specification and displays parameter estimates graphically on a path diagram. Path diagrams used for model specification and those that display parameter estimates are of presentation quality. They can be printed directly or imported into other applications such as word processors, desktop publishing programs, and general-purpose graphics programs.

About the Tutorial

The tutorial is designed to get you up and running with Amos Graphics. It covers some of the basic functions and features and guides you through your first Amos analysis.

Once you have worked through the tutorial, you can learn about more advanced functions using the online Help, or you can continue working through the examples to get a more extended introduction to structural modeling with Amos.

About the Examples

Many people like to learn by doing. Knowing this, we have developed 31 examples that quickly demonstrate practical ways to use Amos. The initial examples introduce the basic capabilities of Amos as applied to simple problems. You learn which buttons to click, how to access the several supported data formats, and how to maneuver through the output. Later examples tackle more advanced modeling problems and are less concerned with program interface issues.

Examples 1 through 4 show how you can use Amos to do some conventional analyses—analyses that could be done using a standard statistics package. These examples show a new approach to some familiar problems while also demonstrating all of the basic features of Amos. There are sometimes good reasons for using Amos to do something simple, like estimating a mean or correlation or testing the hypothesis that two means are equal. For one thing, you might want to take advantage of the ability of Amos to handle missing data. Or maybe you want to use the bootstrapping capability of Amos, particularly to obtain confidence intervals.

Examples 5 through 8 illustrate the basic techniques that are commonly used nowadays in structural modeling.

Example 9 and those that follow demonstrate advanced techniques that have so far not been used as much as they deserve. These techniques include:

■ Simultaneous analysis of data from several different populations.

■ Estimation of means and intercepts in regression equations.

■ Maximum likelihood estimation in the presence of missing data.

■ Bootstrapping to obtain estimated standard errors. Amos makes these techniques especially easy to use, and we hope that they will become more commonplace.

Tip: If you have questions about a particular Amos feature, you can always refer to the extensive online Help provided by the program.

About the Documentation

Amos 7.0 comes with extensive documentation, including an online Help system, this user's guide, and advanced reference material for Amos Basic and the Amos API (Application Programming Interface). If you performed a typical installation, you can find the *Amos 7.0 Programming Reference Guide* in the following location: *C:\Program Files\Amos 7\Documentation\Programming Reference.pdf*.

Other Sources of Information

Although this user's guide contains a good bit of expository material, it is not by any means a complete guide to the correct and effective use of structural modeling. Many excellent SEM textbooks are available.

■ *Structural Equation Modeling: A Multidisciplinary Journal* contains methodological articles as well as applications of structural modeling. It is published by:

Lawrence Erlbaum Associates, Inc.
Journal Subscription Department
10 Industrial Avenue
Mahwah, NJ 07430-2262 USA
www.erlbaum.com

- Carl Ferguson and Edward Rigdon established an electronic mailing list called *Semnet* to provide a forum for discussions related to structural modeling. You can find information about subscribing to Semnet at *www.gsu.edu/~mkteer/semnet.html*.
- Edward Rigdon also maintains a list of frequently asked questions about structural equation modeling. That FAQ is located at *www.gsu.edu/~mkteer/semfaq.html*.

Acknowledgments

Numerous users of preliminary versions of the program provided valuable feedback, including Stephen J. Aragon, Chris Burant, David Burns, Morton Kleban, Sik-Yum Lee, Michelle Little, and Tor Neilands. John Raz performed testing. Pat O'Neil edited this book.

A last word of warning: While Amos Development Corporation and SPSS have engaged in extensive program testing to ensure that Amos operates correctly, all complicated software, Amos included, is bound to contain some undetected bugs. We are committed to correcting any program errors. If you believe you have encountered one, please report it to the SPSS technical support staff.

James L. Arbuckle
Ambler, Pennsylvania

New Features

Estimation for Ordered-Categorical and Censored Data

Amos 7.0 performs Bayesian model fitting for ordered-categorical data and for censored data

Ordered-Categorical Data

As an example of ordered-categorical data, consider the response scale

A. Disagree
B. No opinion
C. Agree

Prior to version 7.0, Amos required assigning numeric scores to the three responses, for example, *A = 1, B = 2, C = 3*. Although Amos 7.0 permits assigning numeric scores to the three responses, it can also employ a model in which there is a continuous underlying *agreement* scale that is broken up into three contiguous intervals. The observed categorical response is related to the unobserved numeric variable by the following rule: If a respondent's level of agreement is in the lowest interval, the response is *A*; in the middle interval, the response is *B*; in the highest interval, the response is *C*. The distribution (across respondents) of the underlying numeric agreement score is assumed to be normal.

7

Censored Data

Censored data occurs when you know that a measurement exceeds some threshold, but you do not know by how much. (There is a less common kind of censored data where you know that a measurement falls below some threshold, but you do not know by how much.) As an example of censored data, suppose you watch people as they try to solve a problem and you record how long each person takes to solve it. Suppose that you do not want to spend more than 10 minutes waiting for a person to reach a solution so that if a person has not solved the problem in 10 minutes, you call a halt and record the fact that *time to solve* was greater than 10 minutes. If five people solve the problem and two do not, the data from seven people might look like this:

Case	Time to solve
1	6
2	2
3	9
4	>10
5	4
6	9
7	>10

In Amos 6.0, you could either treat the observation for cases 4 and 7 as missing, or you could substitute an arbitrary number like 10, 11, or 12 for cases 4 and 7. Treating cases 4 and 7 as missing has the effect of biasing the sample by excluding poor problem solvers. Substituting an arbitrary number for a censored value is also undesirable, although the exact effect of substituting an arbitrary number is impossible to know.

In Amos 7.0, you can take advantage of all the information you have about cases 4 and 7 without making assumptions other than the assumption of normality.

Data Imputation for Ordered-Categorical and Censored Data

Ordered-categorical measurements and censored measurements provide partial information about the value of an underlying continuous numeric variable. They provide more information than you would have if the measurement was missing, but less information than you would have if the numeric value was directly observed. In this sense, an ordered-categorical or censored measurement is somewhere between observed and missing.

Amos 7.0 can impute numeric values for ordered-categorical, censored, and missing measurements in the same way that Amos 6.0 can impute numeric values for missing measurements. The resulting completed dataset (also called an **imputed dataset**) can be used as input to other programs that require complete numeric data. In this way, non-numeric data can be converted to numeric data.

Estimation of Posterior Predictive Distributions

Amos 7.0 can estimate posterior predictive distributions for missing data values and for scores on unobserved numeric variables that underlie ordered-categorical and censored measurements.

In a latent variable model, there are three types of unknown numeric values:

■ Parameter values and functions of parameter values; for example, regression weights and correlations

■ Missing data values

■ Partially missing data values such as ordered-categorical or censored measurements

In a Bayesian analysis, these three types of unknowns are all treated in the same way. The state of knowledge about any unknown quantity is represented by a posterior density that shows which values are probable. In the case of data values that are missing or partially missing, the posterior density is called a **posterior predictive distribution**.

No Bayesian Prerequisites

The new capabilities in Amos 7.0 employ Bayesian estimation. If you have used Amos before, you do not need any background in Bayesian estimation to get started with Example 32 and Example 33. Afterwards, you may want to look at Example 26 through Example 31 to find out more about Bayesian estimation with Amos; however, you can go straight to Example 32 and/or Example 33 if you are primarily interested in censored data or ordered-categorical data.

For further reading, Gelman, Carlin, Stern, and Rubin (2004) provide general coverage of Bayesian estimation including the type of algorithm (Markov Chain Monte Carlo, or MCMC) that Amos uses. Jackman (2000) gives a brief nontechnical introduction to Bayesian estimation and MCMC algorithms. Scheines, Hoijtink, and

Boomsma (1999) discuss Bayesian SEM. S.Y. Lee and X.Y. Song have many relevant papers on Bayesian estimation for complex SEM models, including Lee and Song (2003, 2004)

Tutorial: Getting Started with Amos Graphics

Introduction

Remember your first statistics class when you sweated through memorizing formulas and laboriously calculating answers with pencil and paper? The professor had you do this so that you would understand some basic statistical concepts. Later, you discovered that a calculator or software program could do all of these calculations in a split second.

This tutorial is a little like that early statistics class. There are many shortcuts to drawing and labeling path diagrams in Amos Graphics that you will discover as you work through the examples in this user's guide or as you refer to the online Help. The intent of this tutorial is to simply get you started using Amos Graphics. It will cover some of the basic functions and features of Amos and guide you through your first Amos analysis.

Once you have worked through the tutorial, you can learn about more advanced functions from the online Help, or you can continue to learn incrementally by working your way through the examples.

If you performed a typical installation, you can find the path diagram constructed in this tutorial in the following location: *C:\Program Files\Amos 7\Tutorial*. The file *Startsps.amw* uses an SPSS data file. *Getstart.amw* is the same path diagram but uses data from a Microsoft Excel file.

Tip: Amos 7.0 provides more than one way to accomplish most tasks. For all menu commands except Tools → Macro, there is a toolbar button that performs the same task. For many tasks, Amos also provides keyboard shortcuts. The user's guide demonstrates the menu path. For information about the toolbar buttons and keyboard shortcuts, see the online Help.

About the Data

Hamilton (1990) provided several measurements on each of 21 states. Three of the measurements will be used in this tutorial:

- Average SAT score
- Per capita income expressed in $1,000 units
- Median education for residents 25 years of age or older

You can find the data in the *Tutorial* directory within the Excel 8.0 workbook *Hamilton.xls* in the worksheet named *Hamilton*. The data are as follows:

SAT	Income	Education
899	14.345	12.7
896	16.37	12.6
897	13.537	12.5
889	12.552	12.5
823	11.441	12.2
857	12.757	12.7
860	11.799	12.4
890	10.683	12.5
889	14.112	12.5
888	14.573	12.6
925	13.144	12.6
869	15.281	12.5
896	14.121	12.5
827	10.758	12.2
908	11.583	12.7
885	12.343	12.4
887	12.729	12.3
790	10.075	12.1
868	12.636	12.4
904	10.689	12.6
888	13.065	12.4

The following path diagram shows a model for these data:

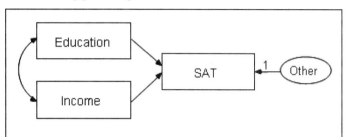

This is a simple regression model where one observed variable, *SAT*, is predicted as a linear combination of the other two observed variables, *Education* and *Income*. As with nearly all empirical data, the prediction will not be perfect. The variable *Other* represents variables other than *Education* and *Income* that affect *SAT*.

Each single-headed arrow represents a regression weight. The number 1 in the figure specifies that *Other* must have a weight of 1 in the prediction of *SAT*. Some such constraint must be imposed in order to make the model **identified**, and it is one of the features of the model that must be communicated to Amos.

Launching Amos Graphics

You can launch Amos Graphics in any of the following ways:

- Click Start on the Windows task bar, and choose Programs → Amos 7→ Amos Graphics.

- Double-click any path diagram (**.amw*).

- Drag a path diagram (**.amw*) file from Windows Explorer to the Amos Graphics window.

- Click Start on the Windows task bar, and choose Programs → Amos 7→ View Path Diagrams. Then double-click a path diagram in the View Path Diagrams window.

- From within SPSS, choose Analyze → Amos 7 from the menus.

Creating a New Model

▶ From the menus, choose File → New.

Your work area appears. The large area on the right is where you draw path diagrams. The toolbar on the left provides one-click access to the most frequently used buttons. You can use either the toolbar or menu commands for most operations.

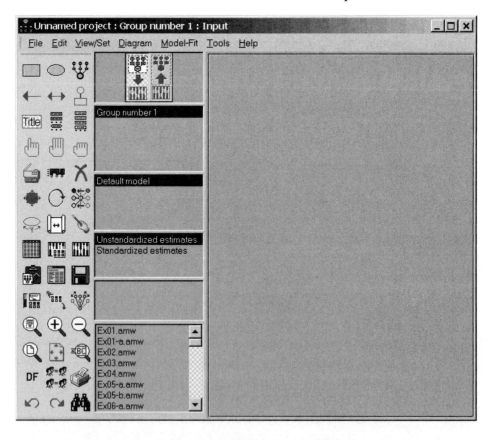

Specifying the Data File

The next step is to specify the file that contains the Hamilton data. This tutorial uses a Microsoft Excel 8.0 (**.xls*) file, but Amos supports several common database formats, including SPSS **.sav* files. If you launch Amos from the Analyze menu in SPSS, Amos automatically uses the file that is open in SPSS.

▶ From the menus, choose File → Data Files.

▶ In the Data Files dialog box, click File Name.

▶ Browse to the *Tutorial* folder. If you performed a typical installation, the path is *C:\Program Files\Amos 7\Tutorial*.

▶ In the Files of type list, select *Excel 8.0 (*.xls)*.

▶ Select *Hamilton.xls*, and then click Open.

▶ In the Data Files dialog box, click OK.

Specifying the Model and Drawing Variables

The next step is to draw the variables in your model. First, you'll draw three rectangles to represent the observed variables, and then you'll draw an ellipse to represent the unobserved variable.

▶ From the menus, choose Diagram → Draw Observed.

▶ In the drawing area, move your mouse pointer to where you want the *Education* rectangle to appear. Click and drag to draw the rectangle. Don't worry about the exact size or placement of the rectangle because you can change it later.

▶ Use the same method to draw two more rectangles for *Income* and *SAT*.

▶ From the menus, choose Diagram → Draw Unobserved.

▶ In the drawing area, move your mouse pointer to the right of the three rectangles and click and drag to draw the ellipse.

The model in your drawing area should now look similar to the following:

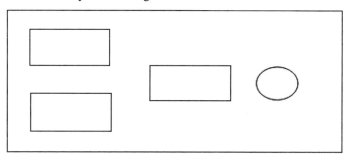

Naming the Variables

▶ In the drawing area, right-click the top left rectangle and choose Object Properties from the pop-up menu.

▶ Click the Text tab.

▶ In the Variable name text box, type Education.

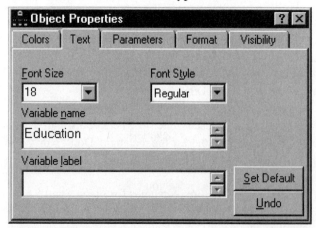

▶ Use the same method to name the remaining variables. Then close the Object Properties dialog box.

Your path diagram should now look like this:

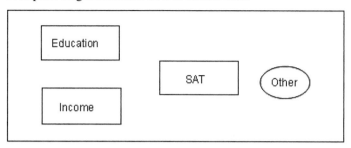

Drawing Arrows

Now you will add arrows to the path diagram, using the following model as your guide:

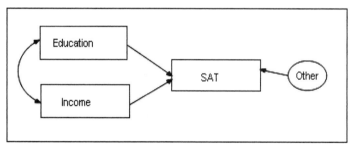

▶ From the menus, choose Diagram → Draw Path.

▶ Click and drag to draw an arrow between Education and SAT.

▶ Use this method to add each of the remaining single-headed arrows.

▶ From the menus, choose Diagram → Draw Covariances.

▶ Click and drag to draw a double-headed arrow between Income and Education. Don't worry about the curve of the arrow because you can adjust it later.

Constraining a Parameter

To identify the regression model, you must define the scale of the latent variable *Other*. You can do this by fixing either the variance of *Other* or the path coefficient from *Other* to *SAT* at some positive value. The following shows you how to fix the path coefficient at unity (1).

▶ In the drawing area, right-click the arrow between Other and SAT and choose Object Properties from the pop-up menu.

▶ Click the Parameters tab.

▶ In the Regression weight text box, type 1.

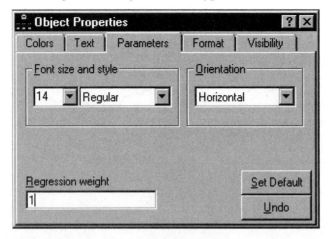

▶ Close the Object Properties dialog box.

There is now a 1 above the arrow between Other and SAT. Your path diagram is now complete, other than any changes you may wish to make to its appearance. It should look something like this:

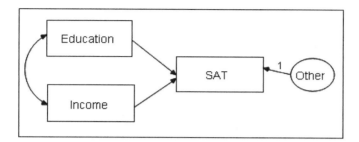

Altering the Appearance of a Path Diagram

You can change the appearance of your path diagram by moving and resizing objects. These changes are visual only; they do not affect the model specification.

To Move an Object

▶ From the menus, choose Edit → Move.

▶ In the drawing area, click and drag the object to its new location.

To Reshape an Object or Double-Headed Arrow

▶ From the menus, choose Edit → Shape of Object.

▶ In the drawing area, click and drag the object until you are satisfied with its size and shape.

To Delete an Object

▶ From the menus, choose Edit → Erase.

▶ In the drawing area, click the object you wish to delete.

To Undo an Action

▶ From the menus, choose Edit → Undo.

To Redo an Action

▶ From the menus, choose Edit → Redo.

Setting Up Optional Output

Some of the output in Amos is optional. In this step, you will choose which portions of the optional output you want Amos to display after the analysis.

▶ From the menus, choose View → Analysis Properties.

▶ Click the Output tab.

▶ Select the Minimization history, Standardized estimates, and Squared multiple correlations check boxes.

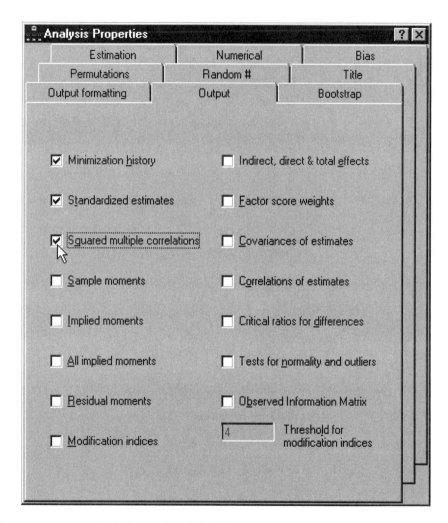

▶ Close the Analysis Properties dialog box.

Performing the Analysis

The only thing left to do is perform the calculations for fitting the model. Note that in order to keep the parameter estimates up to date, you must do this every time you change the model, the data, or the options in the Analysis Properties dialog box.

▶ From the menus, click Analyze → Calculate Estimates.

▶ Because you have not yet saved the file, the Save As dialog box appears. Type a name for the file and click Save.

Amos calculates the model estimates. You can watch the progress of calculations in the panel to the left of the path diagram, but the calculations happen so quickly that you may see only the summary after calculations are complete.

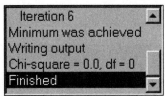

Viewing Output

When Amos has completed the calculations, you have two options for viewing the output: text and graphics.

To View Text Output

▶ From the menus, choose View → Text Output.

The tree diagram in the upper left pane of the Amos Output window allows you to choose a portion of the text output for viewing.

▶ Click Estimates to view the parameter estimates.

Regression Weights: (Group number 1 - Default model)

			Estimate	S.E.	C.R.	P	Label
SAT	<---	Income	2.156	3.125	.690	.490	
SAT	<---	Educatn	136.022	30.555	4.452	***	

Standardized Regression Weights: (Group number 1 - Default model)

			Estimate
SAT	<---	Income	.111
SAT	<---	Educatn	.717

Covariances: (Group number 1 - Default model)

			Estimate	S.E.	C.R.	P	Label
Income	<-->	Educatn	.127	.065	1.952	.051	

Correlations: (Group number 1 - Default model)

			Estimate
Income	<-->	Educatn	.485

Variances: (Group number 1 - Default model)

			Estimate	S.E.	C.R.	P	Label
Income			2.562	.810	3.162	.002	
Educatn			.027	.008	3.162	.002	
Other			382.736	121.032	3.162	.002	

Squared Multiple Correlations: (Group number 1 - Default model)

		Estimate
SAT		.603

To View Graphics Output

▶ Click the Show the output path diagram button .

▶ In the Parameter Formats pane to the left of the drawing area, click Standardized estimates.

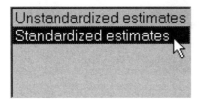

Your path diagram now looks like this:

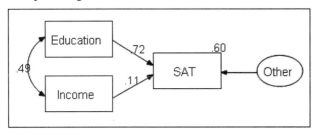

The value 0.49 is the correlation between *Education* and *Income*. The values 0.72 and 0.11 are standardized regression weights. The value 0.60 is the squared multiple correlation of *SAT* with *Education* and *Income*.

▶ In the Parameter Formats pane to the left of the drawing area, click Unstandardized estimates.

Your path diagram should now look like this:

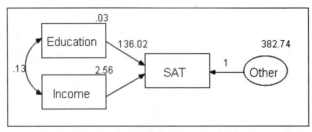

Printing the Path Diagram

▶ From the menus, choose File → Print.

The Print dialog box appears.

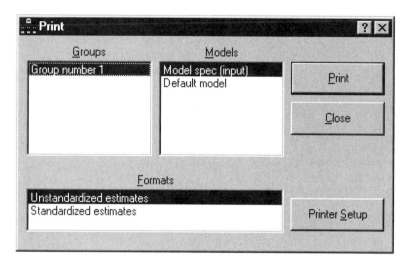

▶ Click Print.

Copying the Path Diagram

Amos Graphics lets you easily export your path diagram to other applications, such as Microsoft Word.

▶ From the menus, choose Edit → Copy (to Clipboard).

▶ Switch to the other application and and use the Paste function to insert the path diagram. Amos Graphics exports only the diagram; it does not export the background.

Copying Text Output

▶ In the Amos Output window, select the text you want to copy.

▶ Right-click the selected text, and choose Copy from the pop-up menu.

▶ Switch to the other application and and use the Paste function to insert the text.

Example

1

Estimating Variances and Covariances

Introduction

This example shows you how to estimate population variances and covariances. It also discusses the general format of Amos input and output.

About the Data

Attig (1983) showed 40 subjects a booklet containing several pages of advertisements. Then each subject was given three memory performance tests.

Test	Description
recall	The subject was asked to recall as many of the advertisements as possible. The subject's score on this test was the number of advertisements recalled correctly.
cued	The subject was given some cues and asked again to recall as many of the advertisements as possible. The subject's score was the number of advertisements recalled correctly.
place	The subject was given a list of the advertisements that appeared in the booklet and was asked to recall the page location of each one. The subject's score on this test was the number of advertisements whose location was recalled correctly.

Attig repeated the study with the same 40 subjects after a training exercise intended to improve memory performance. There were thus three performance measures before training and three performance measures after training. In addition, she recorded scores on a vocabulary test, as well as age, sex, and level of education. Attig's data files are included in the *Examples* folder provided by Amos.

Bringing In the Data

▶ From the menus, choose File → New.

▶ From the menus, choose File → Data Files.

▶ In the Data Files dialog box, click File Name.

▶ Browse to the *Examples* folder. If you performed a typical installation, the path is *C:\Program Files\Amos 7\Examples*.

▶ In the Files of type list, select *Excel 8.0 (*.xls)*, select *UserGuide.xls*, and then click Open.

▶ In the Data Files dialog box, click OK.

Amos displays a list of worksheets in the *UserGuide* workbook. The worksheet *Attg_yng* contains the data for this example.

▶ In the Select a Data Table dialog box, select Attg_yng, then click View Data.

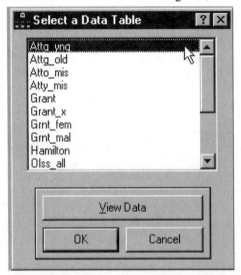

The Excel worksheet for the *Attg_yng* data file opens.

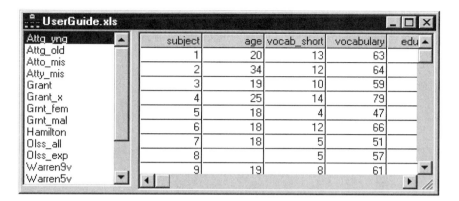

As you scroll across the worksheet, you will see all of the test variables from the Attig study. This example uses only the following variables: *recall1* (recall pretest), *recall2* (recall posttest), *place1* (place recall pretest), and *place2* (place recall posttest).

▶ After you review the data, close the data window.

▶ In the Data Files dialog box, click OK.

Analyzing the Data

In this example, the analysis consists of estimating the variances and covariances of the *recall* and *place* variables before and after training.

Specifying the Model

▶ From the menus, choose Diagram → Draw Observed.

▶ In the drawing area, move your mouse pointer to where you want the first rectangle to appear. Click and drag to draw the rectangle.

▶ From the menus, choose Edit → Duplicate.

▶ Click and drag a duplicate from the first rectangle. Release the mouse button to position the duplicate.

▶ Create two more duplicate rectangles until you have four rectangles side by side.

Tip: If you want to reposition a rectangle, choose Edit → Move from the menus and drag the rectangle to its new position.

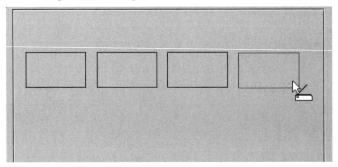

Naming the Variables

▶ From the menus, choose View → Variables in Dataset.

The Variables in Dataset dialog box appears.

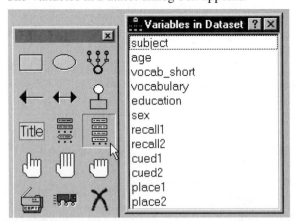

▶ Click and drag the variable *recall1* from the list to the first rectangle in the drawing area.

▶ Use the same method to name the variables *recall2*, *place1*, and *place2*.

▶ Close the Variables in Dataset dialog box.

Changing the Font

▶ Right-click a variable and choose Object Properties from the pop-up menu.

The Object Properties dialog box appears.

▶ Click the Text tab and adjust the font attributes as desired.

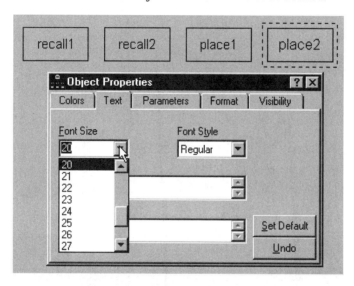

Establishing Covariances

If you leave the path diagram as it is, Amos Graphics will estimate the variances of the four variables, but it will not estimate the covariances between them. In Amos Graphics, the rule is to assume a correlation or covariance of 0 for any two variables that are not connected by arrows. To estimate the covariances between the observed variables, we must first connect all pairs with double-headed arrows.

▶ From the menus, choose Diagram → Draw Covariances.

▶ Click and drag to draw arrows that connect each variable to every other variable.

Your path diagram should have six double-headed arrows.

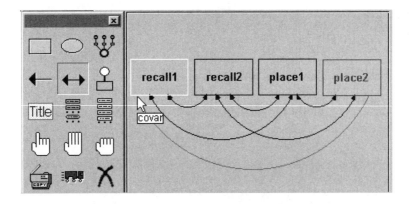

Performing the Analysis

▶ From the menus, choose Analyze → Calculate Estimates.

Because you have not yet saved the file, the Save As dialog box appears.

▶ Enter a name for the file and click Save.

Viewing Graphics Output

▶ Click the Show the output path diagram button .

Amos displays the output path diagram with parameter estimates.

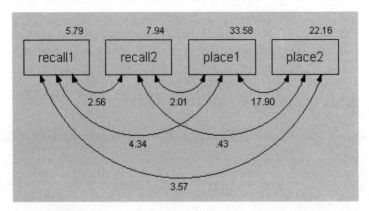

In the output path diagram, the numbers displayed next to the boxes are estimated variances, and the numbers displayed next to the double-headed arrows are estimated covariances. For example, the variance of *recall1* is estimated at 5.79, and that of *place1* at 33.58. The estimated covariance between these two variables is 4.34.

Viewing Text Output

▶ From the menus, choose View → Text Output.

▶ In the tree diagram in the upper left pane of the Amos Output window, click Estimates.

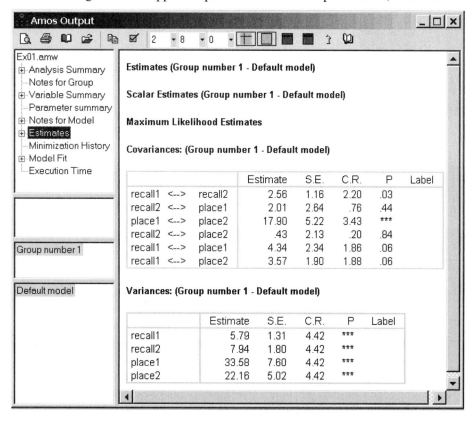

The first estimate displayed is of the covariance between *recall1* and *recall2*. The covariance is estimated to be 2.56. Right next to that estimate, in the *S.E.* column, is an estimate of the standard error of the covariance, 1.16. The estimate 2.56 is an observation on an approximately normally distributed random variable centered around the population covariance with a standard deviation of about 1.16, that is, if the assumptions in the section "Distribution Assumptions for Amos Models" on p. 39 are met. For example, you can use these figures to construct a 95% confidence interval on the population covariance by computing $2.56 \pm 1.96 \times 1.160 = 2.56 \pm 1.96$. Later, you will see that you can use Amos to estimate many kinds of population parameters besides covariances and can follow the same procedure to set a confidence interval on any one of them.

Next to the standard error, in the *C.R.* column, is the critical ratio obtained by dividing the covariance estimate by its standard error $(2.20 = 2.56 / 1.16)$. This ratio is relevant to the null hypothesis that, in the population from which Attig's 40 subjects came, the covariance between *recall1* and *recall2* is 0. If this hypothesis is true, and still under the assumptions in the section "Distribution Assumptions for Amos Models" on p. 39, the critical ratio is an observation on a random variable that has an approximate standard normal distribution. Thus, using a significance level of 0.05, any critical ratio that exceeds 1.96 in magnitude would be called significant. In this example, since 2.20 is greater than 1.96, you would say that the covariance between *recall1* and *recall2* is significantly different from 0 at the 0.05 level.

The *P* column, to the right of *C.R.*, gives an approximate two-tailed *p* value for testing the null hypothesis that the parameter value is 0 in the population. The table shows that the covariance between *recall1* and *recall2* is significantly different from 0 with $p = 0.03$. The calculation of *P* assumes that parameter estimates are normally distributed, and it is correct only in large samples. See Appendix A for more information.

The assertion that the parameter estimates are normally distributed is only an approximation. Moreover, the standard errors reported in the *S.E.* column are only approximations and may not be the best available. Consequently, the confidence interval and the hypothesis test just discussed are also only approximate. This is because the theory on which these results are based is **asymptotic**. Asymptotic means that it can be made to apply with any desired degree of accuracy, but only by using a sufficiently large sample. We will not discuss whether the approximation is satisfactory with the present sample size because there would be no way to generalize the conclusions to the many other kinds of analyses that you can do with Amos. However, you may want to re-examine the null hypothesis that *recall1* and *recall2* are uncorrelated, just to see what is meant by an approximate test. We previously concluded that the covariance is significantly different from 0 because 2.20 exceeds 1.96. The *p* value associated with a standard normal deviate of 2.20 is 0.028 (two-tailed), which, of course, is less than 0.05. By contrast, the conventional *t* statistic (for example, Runyon and Haber, 1980, p. 226) is 2.509 with 38 degrees of freedom ($p = 0.016$). In this example, both *p* values are less than 0.05, so both tests agree in rejecting the null hypothesis at the 0.05 level. However, in other situations, the two *p* values might lie on *opposite* sides of 0.05. You might or might not regard this as especially serious—at any rate, the two tests can give different results. There should be no doubt about which test is better. The *t* test is exact under the assumptions of normality and independence of observations, no matter what the sample size. In Amos, the test based on critical ratio depends on the same assumptions; however, with a finite sample, the test is only approximate.

Note: For many interesting applications of Amos, there is no exact test or exact standard error or exact confidence interval available.

On the bright side, when fitting a model for which conventional estimates exist, maximum likelihood point estimates (for example, the numbers in the *Estimate* column) are generally identical to the conventional estimates.

▶ Now click Notes for Model in the upper left pane of the Amos Output window.

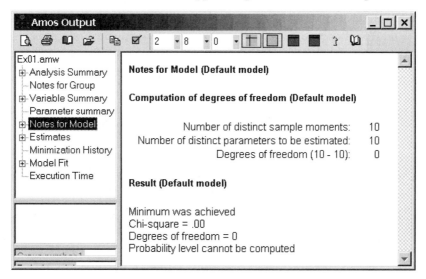

The following table plays an important role in every Amos analysis:

Number of distinct sample moments:	10
Number of distinct parameters to be estimated:	10
Degrees of freedom (10 – 10):	0

The *Number of distinct sample moments* referred to are sample means, variances, and covariances. In most analyses, including the present one, Amos ignores means, so that the sample moments are the sample variances of the four variables, *recall1*, *recall2*, *place1*, and *place2*, and their sample covariances. There are four sample variances and six sample covariances, for a total of 10 sample moments.

The *Number of distinct parameters to be estimated* are the corresponding population variances and covariances. There are, of course, four population variances and six population covariances, which makes 10 parameters to be estimated.

The *Degrees of freedom* is the amount by which the number of sample moments exceeds the number of parameters to be estimated. In this example, there is a one-to-one correspondence between the sample moments and the parameters to be estimated, so it is no accident that there are zero degrees of freedom.

As we will see beginning with Example 2, any nontrivial null hypothesis about the parameters reduces the number of parameters that have to be estimated. The result will be positive degrees of freedom. For now, there is no null hypothesis being tested. Without a null hypothesis to test, the following table is not very interesting:

```
Chi-square = 0.00
Degrees of freedom = 0
Probability level cannot be computed
```

If there *had* been a hypothesis under test in this example, the chi-square value would have been a measure of the extent to which the data were incompatible with the hypothesis. A chi-square value of 0 would ordinarily indicate no departure from the null hypothesis. But in the present example, the 0 value for degrees of freedom and the 0 chi-square value merely reflect the fact that there was no null hypothesis in the first place.

```
Minimum was achieved
```

This line indicates that Amos successfully estimated the variances and covariances. Sometimes structural modeling programs like Amos fail to find estimates. Usually, when Amos fails, it is because you have posed a problem that has no solution, or no unique solution. For example, if you attempt maximum likelihood estimation with observed variables that are linearly dependent, Amos will fail because such an analysis cannot be done in principle. Problems that have no unique solution are discussed elsewhere in this user's guide under the subject of identifiability. Less commonly, Amos can fail because an estimation problem is just too difficult. The possibility of such failures is generic to programs for analysis of moment structures. Although the computational method used by Amos is highly effective, no computer program that does the kind of analysis that Amos does can promise success in every case.

Optional Output

So far, we have discussed output that Amos generates by default. You can also request additional output.

Calculating Standardized Estimates

You may be surprised to learn that Amos displays estimates of covariances rather than correlations. When the scale of measurement is arbitrary or of no substantive interest, correlations have more descriptive meaning than covariances. Nevertheless, Amos and similar programs insist on estimating covariances. Also, as will soon be seen, Amos provides a simple method for testing hypotheses about covariances but not about correlations. This is mainly because it is easier to write programs that way. On the other hand, it is not hard to derive correlation estimates after the relevant variances and covariances have been estimated. To calculate standardized estimates:

▶ From the menus, choose View → Analysis Properties.

▶ In the Analysis Properties dialog box, click the Output tab.

▶ Select the Standardized estimates check box.

Example 1

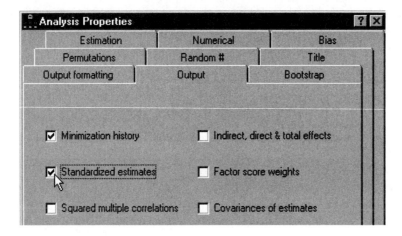

▶ Close the Analysis Properties dialog box.

Rerunning the Analysis

Because you have changed the options in the Analysis Properties dialog box, you must rerun the analysis.

▶ From the menus, choose Analyze → Calculate Estimates.

▶ Click the Show the output path diagram button.

▶ In the Parameter Formats pane to the left of the drawing area, click Standardized estimates.

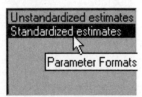

Viewing Correlation Estimates as Text Output

▶ From the menus, choose View → Text Output.

▶ In the tree diagram in the upper left pane of the Amos Output window, expand Estimates, Scalars, and then click Correlations.

Distribution Assumptions for Amos Models

Hypothesis testing procedures, confidence intervals, and claims for efficiency in maximum likelihood or generalized least-squares estimation depend on certain assumptions. First, observations must be independent. For example, the 40 young people in the Attig study have to be picked independently from the population of young people. Second, the observed variables must meet some distributional requirements. If the observed variables have a multivariate normal distribution, that will suffice. Multivariate normality of all observed variables is a standard distribution assumption in many structural equation modeling and factor analysis applications.

There is another, more general, situation under which maximum likelihood estimation can be carried out. If some exogenous variables are fixed (that is, they are either known beforehand or measured without error), their distributions may have any shape, provided that:

■ For any value pattern of the fixed variables, the remaining (random) variables have a (conditional) normal distribution.

■ The (conditional) variance-covariance matrix of the random variables is the same for every pattern of the fixed variables.

■ The (conditional) expected values of the random variables depend linearly on the values of the fixed variables.

A typical example of a fixed variable would be an experimental treatment, classifying respondents into a study group and a control group, respectively. It is all right that treatment is non-normally distributed, as long as the other exogenous variables are normally distributed for study and control cases alike, and with the same conditional variance-covariance matrix. Predictor variables in regression analysis (see Example 4) are often regarded as fixed variables.

Many people are accustomed to the requirements for normality and independent observations, since these are the usual requirements for many conventional procedures. However, with Amos, you have to remember that meeting these requirements leads only to asymptotic conclusions (that is, conclusions that are approximately true for large samples).

Modeling in VB.NET

It is possible to specify and fit a model by writing a program in VB.NET or in C#. Writing programs is an alternative to using Amos Graphics to specify a model by drawing its path diagram. This section shows how to write a VB.NET program to perform the analysis of Example 1. A later section explains how to do the same thing in C#.

Amos comes with its own built-in editor for VB.NET and C# programs. It is accessible from the Windows Start menu. To begin Example 1 using the built-in editor:

▶ From the Windows Start menu, choose Program Files → Amos 7 → Program Editor.

▶ In the Program Editor window, choose File → New VB Program.

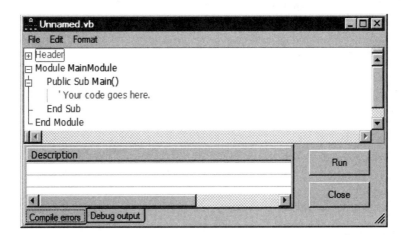

▶ Enter the VB.NET code for specifying and fitting the model in place of the 'Your code goes here comment. The following figure shows the program editor after the complete program has been entered.

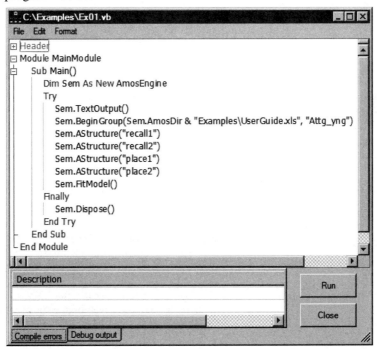

Note: The *Examples* directory contains all of the pre-written examples.

To open the VB.NET file for the present example:

▶ From the Program Editor menus, choose File → Open.

▶ Select the file *Ex01.vb* in the *Amos 7\Examples* directory.

The following table provides a line-by-line description of the program.

Program Statement	Description
Dim Sem As New AmosEngine	Declares Sem as an object of type AmosEngine. The methods and properties of the Sem object are used to specify and fit the model.
Sem.TextOutput	Creates an output file containing the results of the analysis. At the end of the analysis, the contents of the output file are displayed in a separate window.
Sem.BeginGroup ...	Begins the model specification for a single group (that is, a single population). This line also specifies that the *Attg_yng* worksheet in the Excel workbook *UserGuide.xls* contains the input data. Sem.AmosDir() is the location of the Amos program directory.
Sem.AStructure("recall1") Sem.AStructure("recall2") Sem.AStructure("place1") Sem.AStructure("place2")	Specifies the model. The four AStructure statements declare the variances of *recall1*, *recall2*, *place1*, and *place2* to be free parameters. The other eight variables in the *Attg_yng* data file are left out of this analysis. In an Amos program (but not in Amos Graphics), observed exogenous variables are assumed by default to be correlated, so that Amos will estimate the six covariances among the four variables.
Sem.FitModel()	Fits the model.
Sem.Dispose()	Releases resources used by the Sem object. It is particularly important for your program to use an AmosEngine object's Dispose method before creating another AmosEngine object. A process is allowed only one instance of an AmosEngine object at a time.
Try/Finally/End Try	The Try block guarantees that the Dispose method will be called even if an error occurs during program execution.

▶ To perform the analysis, from the menus, choose File → Run.

Generating Additional Output

Some AmosEngine methods generate additional output. For example, the Standardized method displays standardized estimates. The following figure shows the use of the Standardized method:

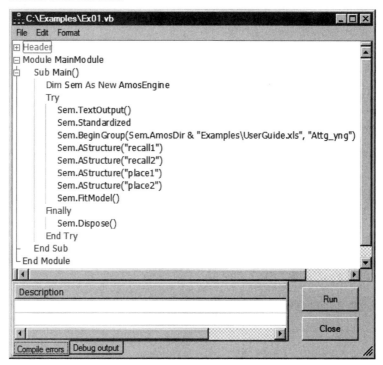

Modeling in C#

Writing an Amos program in C# is similar to writing one in VB.NET. To start a new C# program, in the built-in program editor of Amos:

▶   Choose File → New C# Program (rather than File → New VB Program).

▶   Choose File → Open to open *Ex01.cs*, which is a C# version of the VB.NET program *Ex01.vb*.

Other Program Development Tools

The built-in program editor in Amos is used throughout this user's guide for writing and executing Amos programs. However, you can use the development tool of your choice. The *Examples* folder contains a *VisualStudio* subfolder where you can find Visual Studio VB.NET and C# solutions for Example 1.

Example

2

Testing Hypotheses

Introduction

This example demonstrates how you can use Amos to test simple hypotheses about variances and covariances. It also introduces the chi-square test for goodness of fit and elaborates on the concept of degrees of freedom.

About the Data

We will use Attig's (1983) spatial memory data, which were described in Example 1. We will also begin with the same path diagram as in Example 1. To demonstrate the ability of Amos to use different data formats, this example uses an SPSS data file instead of an Excel file.

Parameters Constraints

The following is the path diagram from Example 1. We can think of the variable objects as having small boxes nearby (representing the variances) that are filled in once Amos has estimated the parameters.

Example 2

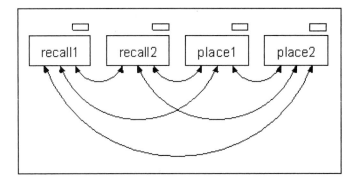

You can fill these boxes yourself instead of letting Amos fill them.

Constraining Variances

Suppose you want to set the variance of *recall1* to 6 and the variance of *recall2* to 8.

▶ In the drawing area, right-click *recall1* and choose Object Properties from the pop-up menu.

▶ Click the Parameters tab.

▶ In the Variance text box, type 6.

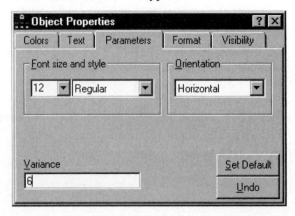

▶ With the Object Properties dialog box still open, click *recall2* and set its variance to 8.

▶ Close the dialog box.

The path diagram displays the parameter values you just specified.

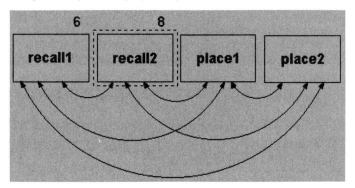

This is not a very realistic example because the numbers 6 and 8 were just picked out of the air. Meaningful parameter constraints must have some underlying rationale, perhaps being based on theory or on previous analyses of similar data.

Specifying Equal Parameters

Sometimes you will be interested in testing whether two parameters are equal in the population. You might, for example, think that the variances of *recall1* and *recall2* might be equal without having a particular value for the variances in mind. To investigate this possibility, do the following:

▶ In the drawing area, right-click *recall1* and choose Object Properties from the pop-up menu.

▶ Click the Parameters tab.

▶ In the Variance text box, type v_recall.

▶ Click *recall2* and label its variance as v_recall.

▶ Use the same method to label the *place1* and *place2* variances as v_place.

It doesn't matter what label you use. The important thing is to enter the same label for each variance you want to force to be equal. The effect of using the same label is to require both of the variances to have the same value without specifying ahead of time what that value is.

Benefits of Specifying Equal Parameters

Before adding any further constraints on the model parameters, let's examine why we might want to specify that two parameters, like the variances of *recall1* and *recall2* or *place1* and *place2*, are equal. Here are two benefits:

- If you specify that two parameters are equal in the population and if you are correct in this specification, then you will get more accurate estimates, not only of the parameters that are equal but usually of the others as well. This is the only benefit if you happen to know that the parameters are equal.

- If the equality of two parameters is a mere hypothesis, requiring their estimates to be equal will result in a test of that hypothesis.

Constraining Covariances

Your model may also include restrictions on parameters other than variances. For example, you may hypothesize that the covariance between *recall1* and *place1* is equal to the covariance between *recall2* and *place2*. To impose this constraint:

▶ In the drawing area, right-click the double-headed arrow that connects *recall1* and *place1*, and choose Object Properties from the pop-up menu.

▶ Click the Parameters tab.

▶ In the Covariance text box, type a non-numeric string such as cov_rp.

▶ Use the same method to set the covariance between *recall2* and *place2* to cov_rp.

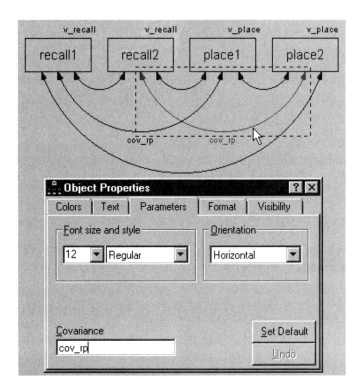

Moving and Formatting Objects

While a horizontal layout is fine for small examples, it is not practical for analyses that are more complex. The following is a different layout of the path diagram on which we've been working:

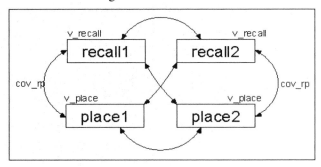

Example 2

You can use the following tools to rearrange your path diagram until it looks like the one above:

- To move objects, choose Edit → Move from the menus, and then drag the object to its new location. You can also use the Move button to drag the endpoints of arrows.

- To copy formatting from one object to another, choose Edit → Drag Properties from the menus, select the properties you wish to apply, and then drag from one object to another.

For more information about the Drag Properties feature, refer to online Help.

Data Input

This example uses an SPSS data file. If you have SPSS installed, you can view the data as you load it. Even if you don't have SPSS installed, Amos will still read the data.

▶ From the menus, choose File → Data Files.

▶ In the Data Files dialog box, click File Name.

▶ Browse to the *Examples* folder. If you performed a typical installation, the path is *C:\Program Files\Amos 7\Examples*.

▶ In the Files of type list, select *SPSS* (*.sav*), click *Attg_yng*, and then click Open.

▶ If you have SPSS installed, click the View Data button in the Data Files dialog box. An SPSS window opens and displays the data.

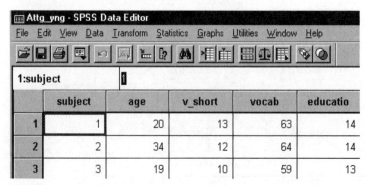

▶ Review the data and close the data view.

▶ In the Data Files dialog box, click OK.

Performing the Analysis

▶ From the menus, choose Analyze → Calculate Estimates.

▶ In the Save As dialog box, enter a name for the file and click Save.

Amos calculates the model estimates.

Viewing Text Output

▶ From the menus, choose View → Text Output.

▶ To view the parameter estimates, click Estimates in the tree diagram in the upper left pane of the Amos Output window.

Scalar Estimates (Group number 1 - Default model)

Maximum Likelihood Estimates

Covariances: (Group number 1 - Default model)

			Estimate	S.E.	C.R.	P	Label
recall2	<-->	recall1	2.87	1.21	2.38	.02	
recall2	<-->	place2	2.71	1.82	1.49	.14	cov_rp
place2	<-->	place1	17.15	5.15	3.33	***	
recall1	<-->	place1	2.71	1.82	1.49	.14	cov_rp
recall1	<-->	place2	4.61	2.17	2.13	.03	
recall2	<-->	place1	2.22	2.22	1.00	.32	

Variances: (Group number 1 - Default model)

		Estimate	S.E.	C.R.	P	Label
recall1		7.05	1.22	5.80	***	v_recall
recall2		7.05	1.22	5.80	***	v_recall
place2		27.53	5.18	5.32	***	v_place
place1		27.53	5.18	5.32	***	v_place

You can see that the parameters that were specified to be equal do have equal estimates. The standard errors here are generally smaller than the standard errors obtained in Example 1. Also, because of the constraints on the parameters, there are now positive degrees of freedom.

▶ Now click Notes for Model in the upper left pane of the Amos Output window.

Computation of degrees of freedom (Default model)	
Number of distinct sample moments:	10
Number of distinct parameters to be estimated:	7
Degrees of freedom (10 - 7):	3

While there are still 10 sample variances and covariances, the number of parameters to be estimated is only seven. Here is how the number seven is arrived at: The variances of *recall1* and *recall2*, labeled *v_recall*, are constrained to be equal, and thus count as a single parameter. The variances of *place1* and *place2* (labeled *v_place*) count as another single parameter. A third parameter corresponds to the equal covariances *recall1 <> place1* and *recall2 <> place2* (labeled *cov_rp*). These three parameters, plus the four unlabeled, unrestricted covariances, add up to seven parameters that have to be estimated.

The degrees of freedom (10 − 7 = 3) may also be thought of as the number of constraints placed on the original 10 variances and covariances.

Optional Output

The output we just discussed is all generated by default. You can also request additional output:

▶ From the menus, choose View → Analysis Properties.

▶ Click the Output tab.

▶ Ensure that the following check boxes are selected: Minimization history, Standardized estimates, Sample moments, Implied moments, and Residual moments.

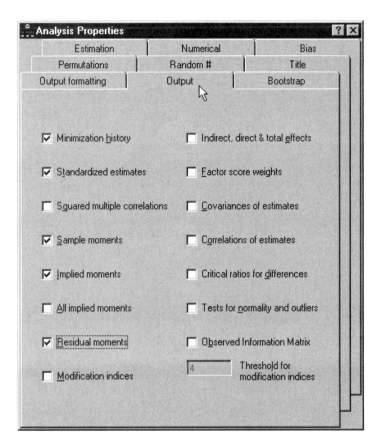

▶ From the menus, choose Analyze → Calculate Estimates.

Amos recalculates the model estimates.

Covariance Matrix Estimates

▶ To see the sample variances and covariances collected into a matrix, choose View → Text Output from the menus.

▶ Click Sample Moments in the tree diagram in the upper left corner of the Amos Output window.

The following is the sample covariance matrix:

Sample Covariances (Group number 1)

	place1	place2	recall1	recall2
place1	33.58			
place2	17.90	22.16		
recall1	4.34	3.57	5.79	
recall2	2.01	.43	2.56	7.94

▶ In the tree diagram, expand Estimates and then click Matrices.

The following is the matrix of implied covariances:

Implied Covariances (Group number 1 - Default model)

	place1	place2	recall1	recall2
place1	27.53			
place2	17.15	27.53		
recall1	2.71	4.61	7.05	
recall2	2.22	2.71	2.87	7.05

Note the differences between the sample and implied covariance matrices. Because the model imposes three constraints on the covariance structure, the implied variances and covariances are different from the sample values. For example, the sample variance of *place1* is 33.58, but the implied variance is 27.53. To obtain a matrix of residual covariances (sample covariances minus implied covariances), put a check mark next to Residual moments on the Output tab and repeat the analysis.

The following is the matrix of residual covariances:

Residual Covariances (Group number 1 - Default model)

	place1	place2	recall1	recall2
place1	6.05			
place2	.76	-5.37		
recall1	1.63	-1.03	-1.27	
recall2	-.21	-2.28	-.32	.89

Displaying Covariance and Variance Estimates on the Path Diagram

As in Example 1, you can display the covariance and variance estimates on the path diagram.

▶ Click the Show the output path diagram button.

▶ In the Parameter Formats pane to the left of the drawing area, click Unstandardized estimates. Alternatively, you can request correlation estimates in the path diagram by clicking Standardized estimates.

The following is the path diagram showing correlations:

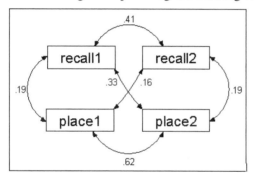

Labeling Output

It may be difficult to remember whether the displayed values are covariances or correlations. To avoid this problem, you can use Amos to label the output.

▶ Open the file *Ex02.amw*.

▶ Right-click the caption at the bottom of the path diagram, and choose Object Properties from the pop-up menu.

▶ Click the Text tab.

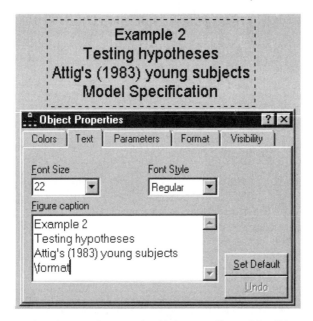

Notice the word \format in the bottom line of the figure caption. Words that begin with a backward slash, like \format, are called **text macros**. Amos replaces text macros with information about the currently displayed model. The text macro \format will be replaced by the heading *Model Specification*, *Unstandardized estimates*, or *Standardized estimates*, depending on which version of the path diagram is displayed.

Hypothesis Testing

The implied covariances are the best estimates of the population variances and covariances under the null hypothesis. (The null hypothesis is that the parameters required to have equal estimates are truly equal in the population.) As we know from Example 1, the sample covariances are the best estimates obtained without making any assumptions about the population values. A comparison of these two matrices is relevant to the question of whether the null hypothesis is correct. If the null hypothesis is correct, both the implied and sample covariances are maximum likelihood estimates of the corresponding population values (although the implied covariances are better estimates). Consequently, you would expect the two matrices to resemble each other. On the other hand, if the null hypothesis is wrong, only the sample covariances are maximum likelihood estimates, and there is no reason to expect them to resemble the implied covariances.

The chi-square statistic is an overall measure of how much the implied covariances differ from the sample covariances.

Chi-square = 6.276
Degrees of freedom = 3
Probability level = 0.099

In general, the more the implied covariances differ from the sample covariances, the bigger the chi-square statistic will be. If the implied covariances had been identical to the sample covariances, as they were in Example 1, the chi-square statistic would have been 0. You can use the chi-square statistic to test the null hypothesis that the parameters required to have equal estimates are really equal in the population. However, it is not simply a matter of checking to see if the chi-square statistic is 0. Since the implied covariances and the sample covariances are merely estimates, you can't expect them to be identical (even if they are both estimates of the same population covariances). Actually, you would expect them to differ enough to produce a chi-square in the neighborhood of the degrees of freedom, even if the null hypothesis is true. In other words, a chi-square value of 3 would not be out of the ordinary here, even with a true null hypothesis. You can say more than that: If the null hypothesis is true, the chi-square value (6.276) is a single observation on a random variable that has an approximate chi-square distribution with three degrees of freedom. The probability is about 0.099 that such an observation would be as large as 6.276. Consequently, the evidence against the null hypothesis is not significant at the 0.05 level.

Displaying Chi-Square Statistics on the Path Diagram

You can get the chi-square statistic and its degrees of freedom to appear in a figure caption on the path diagram using the text macros \cmin and \df. Amos replaces these text macros with the numeric values of the chi-square statistic and its degrees of freedom. You can use the text macro \p to display the corresponding right-tail probability under the chi-square distribution.

▶ From the menus, choose Diagram → Figure Caption.

▶ Click the location on the path diagram where you want the figure caption to appear.

The Figure Caption dialog box appears.

▶ In the Figure Caption dialog box, enter a caption that includes the \cmin, \df, and \p text macros, as follows:

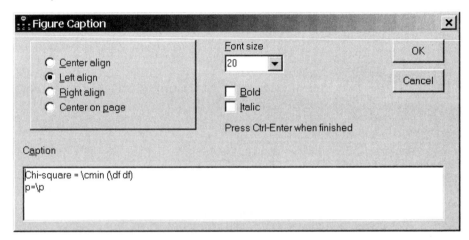

When Amos displays the path diagram containing this caption, it appears as follows:

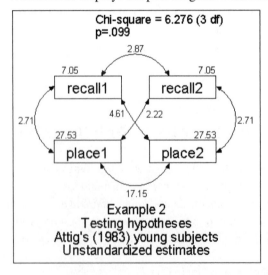

Modeling in VB.NET

The following program fits the constrained model of Example 2:

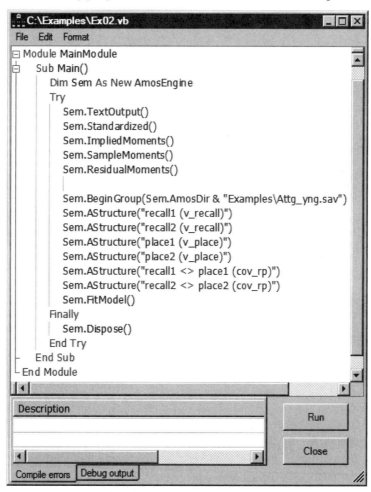

```
Module MainModule
    Sub Main()
        Dim Sem As New AmosEngine
        Try
            Sem.TextOutput()
            Sem.Standardized()
            Sem.ImpliedMoments()
            Sem.SampleMoments()
            Sem.ResidualMoments()

            Sem.BeginGroup(Sem.AmosDir & "Examples\Attg_yng.sav")
            Sem.AStructure("recall1 (v_recall)")
            Sem.AStructure("recall2 (v_recall)")
            Sem.AStructure("place1 (v_place)")
            Sem.AStructure("place2 (v_place)")
            Sem.AStructure("recall1 <> place1 (cov_rp)")
            Sem.AStructure("recall2 <> place2 (cov_rp)")
            Sem.FitModel()
        Finally
            Sem.Dispose()
        End Try
    End Sub
End Module
```

Example 2

This table provides a line-by-line description of the program:

Program Statement	Description
Dim Sem As New AmosEngine	Declares Sem as an object of type AmosEngine. The methods and properties of the Sem object are used to specify and fit the model.
Sem.TextOutput	Creates an output file containing the results of the analysis. At the end of the analysis, the contents of the output file are displayed in a separate window.
Sem.Standardized() Sem.ImpliedMoments() Sem.SampleMoments() Sem.ResidualMoments()	Displays standardized estimates, implied covariances, sample covariances, and residual covariances.
Sem.BeginGroup ...	Begins the model specification for a single group (that is, a single population). This line also specifies that the SPSS file *Attg_yng.sav* contains the input data. Sem.AmosDir() is the location of the Amos program directory.
Sem.AStructure("recall1 (v_recall)") Sem.AStructure("recall2 (v_recall)") Sem.AStructure("place1 (v_place)") Sem.AStructure("place2 (v_place)") Sem.AStructure("recall1 <> place1 (cov_rp)") Sem.AStructure("recall2 <> place2 (cov_rp)")	Specifies the model. The first four AStructure statements constrain the variances of the observed variables through the use of parameter names in parentheses. *Recall1* and *recall2* are required to have the same variance because both variances are labeled *v_recall*. The variances of *place1* and *place2* are similarly constrained to be equal. Each of the last two AStructure lines represents a covariance. The two covariances are both named *cov_rp*. Consequently, those covariances are constrained to be equal.
Sem.FitModel()	Fits the model.
Sem.Dispose()	Releases resources used by the Sem object. It is particularly important for your program to use an AmosEngine object's Dispose method before creating another AmosEngine object. A process is allowed to have only one instance of an AmosEngine object at a time.
Try/Finally/End Try	This Try block guarantees that the Dispose method will be called even if an error occurs during program execution.

▶ To perform the analysis, from the menus, choose File → Run.

Timing Is Everything

The AStructure lines must appear *after* BeginGroup; otherwise, Amos will not recognize that the variables named in the AStructure lines are observed variables in the *attg_yng.sav* dataset.

In general, the order of statements matters in an Amos program. In organizing an Amos program, AmosEngine methods can be divided into three general groups[1].

Group 1 — Declarative Methods

This group contains methods that tell Amos what results to compute and display. TextOutput is a Group 1 method, as are Standardized, ImpliedMoments, SampleMoments, and ResidualMoments. Many other Group 1 methods that are not used in this example are documented in the *Amos 7.0 Programming Reference Guide*.

Group 2 — Data and Model Specification Methods

This group consists of data description and model specification commands. BeginGroup and AStructure are Group 2 methods. Others are documented in the *Amos 7.0 Programming Reference Guide*.

Group 3 — Methods for Retrieving Results

These are commands to…well, retrieve results. So far, we have not used any Group 3 methods. Examples using Group 3 methods are given in the *Amos 7.0 Programming Reference Guide*.

Tip: When you write an Amos program, it is important to pay close attention to the order in which you call the Amos engine methods. The rule is that groups must appear in order: Group 1, then Group 2, and finally Group 3.

For more detailed information about timing rules and a complete listing of methods and their group membership, see the *Amos 7.0 Programming Reference Guide*.

---

1 There is also a fourth *special* group, consisting of only the Initialize Method. If the optional Initialize Method is used, it must come *before* the Group 1 methods.

Example

3

More Hypothesis Testing

Introduction

This example demonstrates how to test the null hypothesis that two variables are uncorrelated, reinforces the concept of degrees of freedom, and demonstrates, in a concrete way, what is meant by an asymptotically correct test.

About the Data

For this example, we use the group of older subjects from Attig's (1983) spatial memory study and the two variables *age* and *vocabulary*. We will use data formatted as a tab-delimited text file.

Bringing In the Data

▶ From the menus, choose File → New.

▶ From the menus, choose File → Data Files.

▶ In the Data Files dialog box, select File Name.

▶ Browse to the *Examples* folder. If you performed a typical installation, the path is *C:\Program Files\Amos 7\Examples*.

▶ In the Files of type list, select *Text (*.txt)*, select *Attg_old.txt*, and then click Open.

▶ In the Data Files dialog box, click OK.

Testing a Hypothesis That Two Variables Are Uncorrelated

Among Attig's 40 old subjects, the sample correlation between *age* and *vocabulary* is –0.09 (not very far from 0). Is this correlation nevertheless significant? To find out, we will test the null hypothesis that, in the population from which these 40 subjects came, the correlation between *age* and *vocabulary* is 0. We will do this by estimating the variance-covariance matrix under the constraint that *age* and *vocabulary* are uncorrelated.

Specifying the Model

Begin by drawing and naming the two observed variables, *age* and *vocabulary*, in the path diagram, using the methods you learned in Example 1.

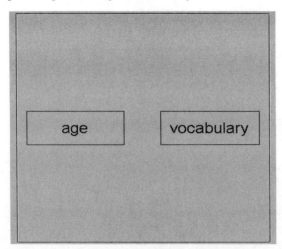

Amos provides two ways to specify that the covariance between *age* and *vocabulary* is 0. The most obvious way is simply to *not draw* a double-headed arrow connecting the two variables. The absence of a double-headed arrow connecting two exogenous variables implies that they are uncorrelated. So, without drawing anything more, the model specified by the simple path diagram above specifies that the covariance (and thus the correlation) between *age* and *vocabulary* is 0.

The second method of constraining a covariance parameter is the more general procedure introduced in Example 1 and Example 2.

▶ From the menus, choose Diagram → Draw Covariances.

▶ Click and drag to draw an arrow that connects *vocabulary* and *age*.

▶ Right-click the arrow and choose Object Properties from the pop-up menu.

▶ Click the Parameters tab.

▶ Type 0 in the Covariance text box.

▶ Close the Object Properties dialog box.

Your path diagram now looks like this:

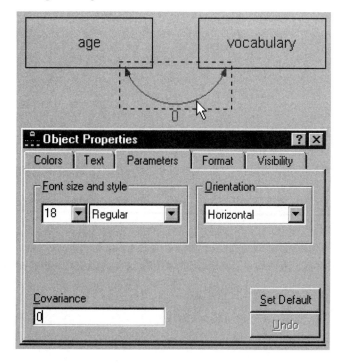

Example 3

▶ From the menus, choose Analyze → Calculate Estimates.

The Save As dialog box appears.

▶ Enter a name for the file and click Save.

Amos calculates the model estimates.

Viewing Text Output

▶ From the menus, choose View → Text Output.

▶ In the tree diagram in the upper left pane of the Amos Output window, click Estimates.

Although the parameter estimates are not of primary interest in this analysis, they are as follows:

Covariances: (Group number 1 - Default model)

	Estimate	S.E.	C.R.	P	Label
age <--> vocabulary	.00				

Correlations: (Group number 1 - Default model)

	Estimate
age <--> vocabulary	.00

Variances: (Group number 1 - Default model)

	Estimate	S.E.	C.R.	P	Label
age	21.57	4.89	4.42	***	
vocabulary	131.29	29.73	4.42	***	

In this analysis, there is one degree of freedom, corresponding to the single constraint that *age* and *vocabulary* be uncorrelated. The degrees of freedom can also be arrived at by the computation shown in the following text. To display this computation:

▶ Click Notes for Model in the upper left pane of the Amos Output window.

Computation of degrees of freedom (Default model)
Number of distinct sample moments: 3
Number of distinct parameters to be estimated: 2
Degrees of freedom (3 - 2): 1

The three sample moments are the variances of *age* and *vocabulary* and their covariance. The two distinct parameters to be estimated are the two population variances. The covariance is fixed at 0 in the model, not estimated from the sample information.

Viewing Graphics Output

▶ Click the Show the output path diagram button.

▶ In the Parameter Formats pane to the left of the drawing area, click Unstandardized estimates.

The following is the path diagram output of the unstandardized estimates, along with the test of the null hypothesis that *age* and *vocabulary* are uncorrelated:

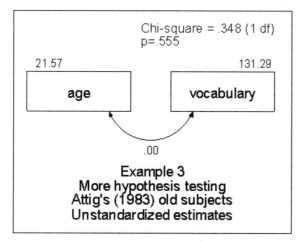

The probability of accidentally getting a departure this large from the null hypothesis is 0.555. The null hypothesis would not be rejected at any conventional significance level.

The usual *t* statistic for testing this null hypothesis is 0.59 ($df = 38$, $p = 0.56$ two-sided). The probability level associated with the *t* statistic is exact. The probability level of 0.555 of the chi-square statistic is *off*, owing to the fact that it does not have an exact chi-square distribution in finite samples. Even so, the probability level of 0.555 is not bad.

Here is an interesting question: If you use the probability level displayed by Amos to test the null hypothesis at either the 0.05 or 0.01 level, then what is the *actual* probability of rejecting a true null hypothesis? In the case of the present null hypothesis, this question has an answer, although the answer depends on the sample size. The second column in the next table shows, for several sample sizes, the real probability of a Type I error when using Amos to test the null hypothesis of *zero correlation* at the 0.05 level. The third column shows the real probability of a Type I error if you use a significance level of 0.01. The table shows that the bigger the sample size, the closer the true significance level is to what it is supposed to be. It's too bad that such a table cannot be constructed for every hypothesis that Amos can be used to test. However, this much can be said about any such table: Moving from top to bottom, the numbers in the 0.05 column would approach 0.05, and the numbers in the 0.01 column would approach 0.01. This is what is meant when it is said that hypothesis tests based on maximum likelihood theory are **asymptotically** correct.

The following table shows the actual probability of a Type I error when using Amos to test the hypothesis that two variables are uncorrelated:

Sample Size	Nominal Significance Level	
	0.05	**0.01**
3	0.250	0.122
4	0.150	0.056
5	0.115	0.038
10	0.073	0.018
20	0.060	0.013
30	0.056	0.012
40	0.055	0.012
50	0.054	0.011
100	0.052	0.011
150	0.051	0.010
200	0.051	0.010
≥500	0.050	0.010

Modeling in VB.NET

Here is a program for performing the analysis of this example:

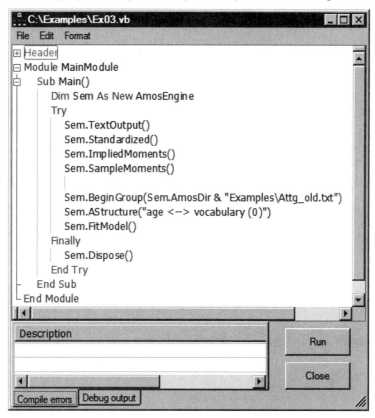

The AStructure method constrains the covariance, fixing it at a constant 0. The program does not refer explicitly to the variances of *age* and *vocabulary*. The default behavior of Amos is to estimate those variances without constraints. Amos treats the variance of every exogenous variable as a free parameter except for variances that are explicitly constrained by the program.

Example

4

Conventional Linear Regression

Introduction

This example demonstrates a conventional regression analysis, predicting a single observed variable as a linear combination of three other observed variables. It also introduces the concept of **identifiability**.

About the Data

Warren, White, and Fuller (1974) studied 98 managers of farm cooperatives. We will use the following four measurements:

Test	Description
performance	A 24-item test of performance related to "planning, organization, controlling, coordinating, and directing"
knowledge	A 26-item test of knowledge of "economic phases of management directed toward profit-making...and product knowledge"
value	A 30-item test of "tendency to rationally evaluate means to an economic end"
satisfaction	An 11-item test of "gratification obtained...from performing the managerial role"

A fifth measure, *past training*, was also reported, but we will not use it.

In this example, you will use the Excel worksheet *Warren5v* in the file *UserGuide.xls*, which is located in the *Examples* folder. If you performed a typical installation, the path is *C:\Program Files\Amos 7\Examples*.

Here are the sample variances and covariances:

rowtype_	varname_	performance	knowledge	value	satisfaction	past_training
n		98	98	98	98	98
cov	performance	0.0209				
cov	knowledge	0.0177	0.052			
cov	value	0.0245	0.028	0.1212		
cov	satisfaction	0.0046	0.0044	-0.0063	0.0901	
cov	past_training	0.0187	0.0192	0.0353	-0.0066	0.0946
mean		0.0589	1.3796	2.8773	2.4613	2.1174

Warren5v also contains the sample means. Raw data are not available, but they are not needed by Amos for most analyses, as long as the sample moments (that is, means, variances, and covariances) are provided. In fact, only sample variances and covariances are required in this example. We will not need the sample means in *Warren5v* for the time being, and Amos will ignore them.

Analysis of the Data

Suppose you want to use scores on *knowledge*, *value*, and *satisfaction* to predict *performance*. More specifically, suppose you think that *performance* scores can be approximated by a linear combination of *knowledge*, *value*, and *satisfaction*. The prediction will not be perfect, however, and the model should thus include an *error* variable.

Here is the initial path diagram for this relationship:

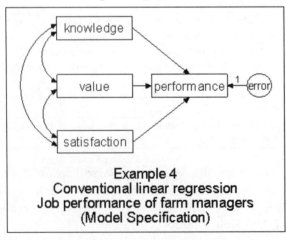

Example 4
Conventional linear regression
Job performance of farm managers
(Model Specification)

The single-headed arrows represent linear dependencies. For example, the arrow leading from *knowledge* to *performance* indicates that performance scores depend, in part, on knowledge. The variable *error* is enclosed in a circle because it is not directly observed. Error represents much more than random fluctuations in performance scores due to measurement error. Error also represents a composite of age, socioeconomic status, verbal ability, and anything else on which performance may depend but which was not measured in this study. This variable is essential because the path diagram is supposed to show *all* variables that affect performance scores. Without the circle, the path diagram would make the implausible claim that performance is an *exact* linear combination of knowledge, value, and satisfaction.

The double-headed arrows in the path diagram connect variables that may be correlated with each other. The absence of a double-headed arrow connecting *error* with any other variable indicates that *error* is assumed to be uncorrelated with every other predictor variable—a fundamental assumption in linear regression. *Performance* is also not connected to any other variable by a double-headed arrow, but this is for a different reason. Since performance depends on the other variables, it goes without saying that it might be correlated with them.

Specifying the Model

Using what you learned in the first three examples, do the following:

▶ Start a new path diagram.

▶ Specify that the dataset to be analyzed is in the Excel worksheet *Warren5v* in the file *UserGuide.xls*.

▶ Draw four rectangles and label them knowledge, value, satisfaction, and performance.

▶ Draw an ellipse for the *error* variable.

▶ Draw single-headed arrows that point from the **exogenous**, or predictor, variables (*knowledge, value, satisfaction,* and *error*) to the **endogenous**, or response, variable (*performance*).

Note: Endogenous variables have at least one single-headed path pointing toward them. Exogenous variables, in contrast, send out only single-headed paths but do not receive any.

▶ Draw three double-headed arrows that connect the observed exogenous variables (*knowledge*, *satisfaction*, and *value*).

Your path diagram should look like this:

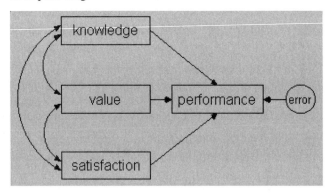

Identification

In this example, it is impossible to estimate the regression weight for the regression of *performance* on *error*, and, at the same time, estimate the variance of *error*. It is like having someone tell you, "I bought $5 worth of widgets," and attempting to infer both the price of each widget and the number of widgets purchased. There is just not enough information.

You can solve this *identification* problem by fixing either the regression weight applied to *error* in predicting *performance*, or the variance of the *error* variable itself, at an arbitrary, nonzero value. Let's fix the regression weight at 1. This will yield the same estimates as conventional linear regression.

Fixing Regression Weights

▶ Right-click the arrow that points from error to performance and choose Object Properties from the pop-up menu.

▶ Click the Parameters tab.

▶ Type 1 in the Regression weight box.

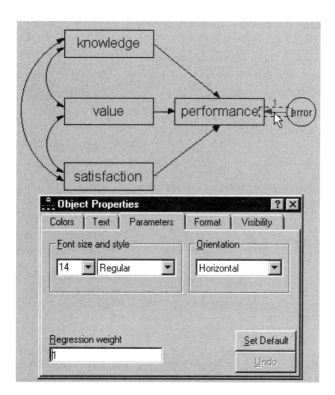

Setting a regression weight equal to 1 for every *error* variable can be tedious. Fortunately, Amos Graphics provides a default solution that works well in most cases.

▶ Click the Add a unique variable to an existing variable button.

▶ Click an endogenous variable.

Amos automatically attaches an error variable to it, complete with a fixed regression weight of 1. Clicking the endogenous variable repeatedly changes the position of the error variable.

Example 4

Viewing the Text Output

Here are the maximum likelihood estimates:

Regression Weights: (Group number 1 - Default model)

	Estimate	S.E.	C.R.	P	Label
performance<---knowledge	.26	.05	4.82	***	
performance<---value	.15	.04	4.14	***	
performance<---satisfaction	.05	.04	1.27	.20	

Covariances: (Group number 1 - Default model)

	Estimate	S.E.	C.R.	P	Label
knowledge <--> satisfaction	.00	.01	.63	.53	
value <--> satisfaction	-.01	.01	-.59	.55	
knowledge <--> value	.03	.01	3.28	.00	

Variances: (Group number 1 - Default model)

	Estimate	S.E.	C.R.	P	Label
knowledge	.05	.01	6.96	***	
value	.12	.02	6.96	***	
satisfaction	.09	.01	6.96	***	
error	.01	.00	6.96	***	

Amos does not display the path *performance <— error* because its value is fixed at the default value of 1. You may wonder how much the other estimates would be affected if a different constant had been chosen. It turns out that only the variance estimate for *error* is affected by such a change.

The following table shows the variance estimate that results from various choices for the *performance <— error* regression weight.

Fixed regression weight	Estimated variance of error
0.5	0.050
0.707	0.025
1.0	0.0125
1.414	0.00625
2.0	0.00313

Suppose you fixed the path coefficient at 2 instead of 1. Then the variance estimate would be divided by a factor of 4. You can extrapolate the rule that multiplying the path coefficient by a fixed factor goes along with dividing the error variance by the square of the same factor. Extending this, the product of the squared regression weight and the error variance is always a constant. This is what we mean when we say the regression weight (together with the error variance) is **unidentified**. If you assign a value to one of them, the other can be estimated, but they cannot both be estimated at the same time.

The identifiability problem just discussed arises from the fact that the variance of a variable, and any regression weights associated with it, depends on the units in which the variable is measured. Since *error* is an unobserved variable, there is no natural way to specify a measurement unit for it. Assigning an arbitrary value to a regression weight associated with *error* can be thought of as a way of indirectly choosing a unit of measurement for *error*. Every unobserved variable presents this identifiability problem, which must be resolved by imposing some constraint that determines its unit of measurement.

Changing the scale unit of the unobserved *error* variable does not change the overall model fit. In all the analyses, you get:

```
Chi-square = 0.00
Degrees of freedom = 0
Probability level cannot be computed
```

There are four sample variances and six sample covariances, for a total of 10 sample moments. There are three regression paths, four model variances, and three model covariances, for a total of 10 parameters that must be estimated. Hence, the model has zero degrees of freedom. Such a model is often called **saturated** or **just-identified**.

The standardized coefficient estimates are as follows:

Standardized Regression Weights: (Group number 1 - Default model)

		Estimate
performance<---	knowledge	.41
performance<---	value	.35
performance<---	satisfaction	.10

Correlations: (Group number 1 - Default model)

		Estimate
knowledge <-->	satisfaction	.06
value <-->	satisfaction	-.06
knowledge <-->	value	.35

The standardized regression weights and the correlations are independent of the units in which all variables are measured; therefore, they are not affected by the choice of identification constraints.

Squared multiple correlations are also independent of units of measurement. Amos displays a squared multiple correlation for each endogenous variable.

Squared Multiple Correlations: (Group number 1 - Default model)	
	Estimate
performance	.40

Note: The squared multiple correlation of a variable is the proportion of its variance that is accounted for by its predictors. In the present example, *knowledge*, *value*, and *satisfaction* account for 40% of the variance of *performance*.

Viewing Graphics Output

The following path diagram output shows unstandardized values:

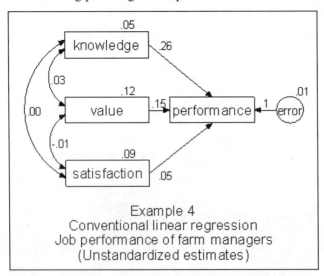

Example 4
Conventional linear regression
Job performance of farm managers
(Unstandardized estimates)

Here is the standardized solution:

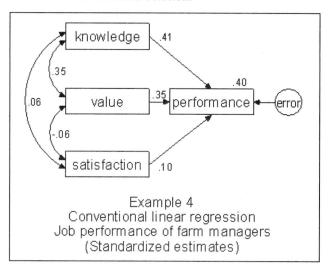

Example 4
Conventional linear regression
Job performance of farm managers
(Standardized estimates)

Viewing Additional Text Output

▶ In the tree diagram in the upper left pane of the Amos Output window, click Variable Summary.

Example 4

> **Variable Summary (Group number 1)**
>
> **Your model contains the following variables (Group number 1)**
>
> Observed, endogenous variables
>
>> performance
>
> Observed, exogenous variables
>
>> knowledge
>> value
>> satisfaction
>
> Unobserved, exogenous variables
>
>> error
>
> **Variable counts (Group number 1)**
>
> | | |
> |---|---|
> | Number of variables in your model: | 5 |
> | Number of observed variables: | 4 |
> | Number of unobserved variables: | 1 |
> | Number of exogenous variables: | 4 |
> | Number of endogenous variables: | 1 |

Endogenous variables are those that have single-headed arrows pointing to them; they depend on other variables. **Exogenous** variables are those that do not have single-headed arrows pointing to them; they do not depend on other variables.

Inspecting the preceding list will help you catch the most common (and insidious) errors in an input file: typing errors. If you try to type performance twice but unintentionally misspell it as preformance one of those times, both versions will appear on the list.

▶ Now click Notes for Model in the upper left pane of the Amos Output window.

The following output indicates that there are no feedback loops in the path diagram:

> Notes for Group (Group number 1)
> The model is recursive.

Later you will see path diagrams where you can pick a variable and, by tracing along the single-headed arrows, follow a path that leads back to the same variable.

Note: Path diagrams that have feedback loops are called **nonrecursive**. Those that do not are called **recursive**.

Modeling in VB.NET

The model in this example consists of a single regression equation. Each single-headed arrow in the path diagram represents a regression weight. Here is a program for estimating those regression weights:

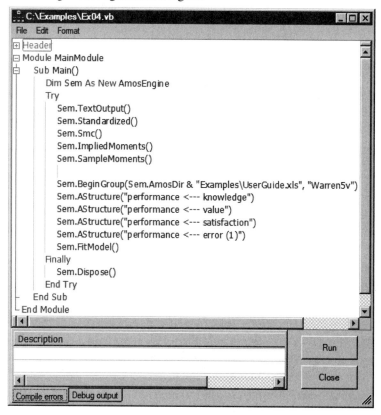

```
C:\Examples\Ex04.vb
File  Edit  Format

⊞ Header
⊟ Module MainModule
┤   Sub Main()
        Dim Sem As New AmosEngine
        Try
            Sem.TextOutput()
            Sem.Standardized()
            Sem.Smc()
            Sem.ImpliedMoments()
            Sem.SampleMoments()

            Sem.BeginGroup(Sem.AmosDir & "Examples\UserGuide.xls", "Warren5v")
            Sem.AStructure("performance <--- knowledge")
            Sem.AStructure("performance <--- value")
            Sem.AStructure("performance <--- satisfaction")
            Sem.AStructure("performance <--- error (1)")
            Sem.FitModel()
        Finally
            Sem.Dispose()
        End Try
    End Sub
 End Module
```

Description

Run

Close

Compile errors   Debug output

The four lines that come after Sem.BeginGroup correspond to the single-headed arrows in the Amos Graphics path diagram. The (1) in the last AStructure line fixes the error regression weight at a constant 1.

Assumptions about Correlations among Exogenous Variables

When executing a program, Amos makes assumptions about the correlations among exogenous variables that are not made in Amos Graphics. These assumptions simplify the specification of many models, especially models that have parameters. The differences between specifying a model in Amos Graphics and specifying one programmatically are as follows:

- Amos Graphics is entirely WYSIWYG (What You See Is What You Get). If you draw a two-headed arrow (without constraints) between two exogenous variables, Amos Graphics will estimate their covariance. If two exogenous variables are not connected by a double-headed arrow, Amos Graphics will assume that the variables are uncorrelated.

The default assumptions in an Amos program are:

- **Unique** variables (unobserved, exogenous variables that affect only one other variable) are assumed to be uncorrelated with each other and with all other exogenous variables.

- **Exogenous** variables other than unique variables are assumed to be correlated among themselves.

In Amos programs, these defaults reflect standard assumptions of conventional linear regression analysis. Thus, in this example, the program assumes that the predictors, *knowledge*, *value*, and *satisfaction*, are correlated and that *error* is uncorrelated with the predictors.

Equation Format for the AStructure Method

The AStructure method permits model specification in equation format. For instance, the single Sem.AStructure statement in the following program describes the same model as the program on p. 81 but in a single line. This program is saved under the name *Ex04-eq.vb* in the *Examples* directory.

Note that in the AStructure line above, each predictor variable (on the right side of the equation) is associated with a regression weight to be estimated. We could make these regression weights explicit through the use of empty parentheses as follows:

```
Sem.AStructure("performance = ()knowledge + ()value + ()satisfaction + error(1)")
```

The empty parentheses are optional. By default, Amos will automatically estimate a regression weight for each predictor.

Example

5

Unobserved Variables

Introduction

This example demonstrates a regression analysis with unobserved variables.

About the Data

The variables in the previous example were surely unreliable to some degree. The fact that the reliability of *performance* is unknown presents a minor problem when it comes to interpreting the fact that the predictors account for only 39.9% of the variance of *performance*. If the test were extremely unreliable, that fact in itself would explain why the performance score could not be predicted accurately. Unreliability of the predictors, on the other hand, presents a more serious problem because it can lead to biased estimates of regression weights.

The present example, based on Rock, et al. (1977), will assess the reliabilities of the four tests included in the previous analysis. It will also obtain estimates of regression weights for perfectly reliable, hypothetical versions of the four tests. Rock, et al. re-examined the data of Warren, White, and Fuller (1974) that were discussed in the previous example. This time, each test was randomly split into two halves, and each half was scored separately.

Here is a list of the input variables:

Variable name	Description
1performance	12-item subtest of Role Performance
2performance	12-item subtest of Role Performance
1knowledge	13-item subtest of Knowledge
2knowledge	13-item subtest of Knowledge
1value	15-item subtest of Value Orientation
2value	15-item subtest of Value Orientation
1satisfaction	5-item subtest of Role Satisfaction
2satisfaction	6-item subtest of Role Satisfaction
past_training	degree of formal education

For this example, we will use a Lotus data file, *Warren9v.wk1*, to obtain the sample variances and covariances of these subtests. The sample means that appear in the file will not be used in this example. Statistics on formal education (*past_training*) are present in the file, but they also will not enter into the present analysis. The following is a portion of the dataset:

warren9v.wk1				
File Format Help				
warren9v	rowtype_	varname_	1performance	2performance
	n		98	98
	cov	1performance	0.0271	
	cov	2performance	0.0172	0.0222
	cov	1knowledge	0.0219	0.0193
	cov	2knowledge	0.0164	0.013
	cov	1value	0.0284	0.0294
	cov	2value	0.0217	0.0185

Model A

The following path diagram presents a model for the eight subtests:

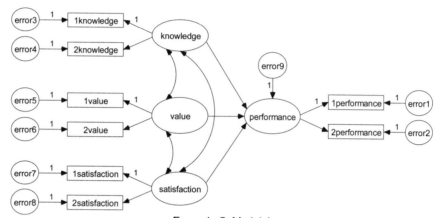

Example 5: Model A
Regression with unobserved variables
Job performance of farm managers
Warren, White and Fuller (1974)
Standardized estimates

Four ellipses in the figure are labeled *knowledge*, *value*, *satisfaction*, and *performance*. They represent unobserved variables that are indirectly measured by the eight split-half tests.

Measurement Model

The portion of the model that specifies how the observed variables depend on the unobserved, or latent, variables is sometimes called the **measurement model**. The current model has four distinct measurement submodels.

Example 5

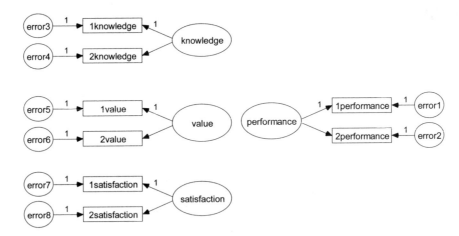

Consider, for instance, the *knowledge* submodel: The scores of the two split-half subtests, *1knowledge* and *2knowledge*, are hypothesized to depend on the single underlying, but not directly observed variable, *knowledge*. According to the model, scores on the two subtests may still disagree, owing to the influence of *error3* and *error4*, which represent errors of measurement in the two subtests. *1knowledge* and *2knowledge* are called **indicators** of the latent variable *knowledge*. The measurement model for *knowledge* forms a pattern that is repeated three more times in the path diagram shown above.

Structural Model

The portion of the model that specifies how the latent variables are related to each other is sometimes called the **structural model**.

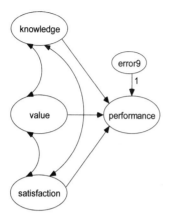

The structural part of the current model is the same as the one in Example 4. It is only in the measurement model that this example differs from the one in Example 4.

Identification

With 13 unobserved variables in this model, it is certainly not identified. It will be necessary to fix the unit of measurement of each unobserved variable by suitable constraints on the parameters. This can be done by repeating 13 times the trick that was used for the single unobserved variable in Example 4: Find a single-headed arrow leading away from each unobserved variable in the path diagram, and fix the corresponding regression weight to an arbitrary value such as 1. If there is more than one single-headed arrow leading away from an unobserved variable, any one of them will do. The path diagram for "Model A" on p. 87 shows one satisfactory choice of identifiability constraints.

Specifying the Model

Because the path diagram is wider than it is tall, you may want to change the shape of the drawing area so that it fits the path diagram better. By default, the drawing area in Amos is taller than it is wide so that it is suitable for printing in portrait mode.

Example 5

Changing the Orientation of the Drawing Area

▶ From the menus, choose View → Interface Properties.

▶ In the Interface Properties dialog box, click the Page Layout tab.

▶ In the Orientation group, click Landscape.

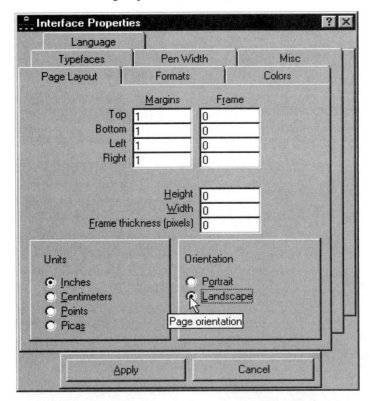

▶ Click Apply.

Creating the Path Diagram

Now you are ready to draw the model as shown in the path diagram on page 87. There are a number of ways to do this. One is to start by drawing the measurement model first. Here, we draw the measurement model for one of the latent variables, *knowledge*, and then use it as a pattern for the other three.

▶ Draw an ellipse for the unobserved variable *knowledge*.

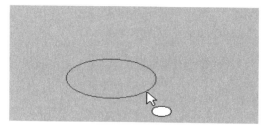

▶ From the menus, choose Diagram → Draw Indicator Variable.

▶ Click twice inside the ellipse.

Each click creates one indicator variable for *knowledge*:

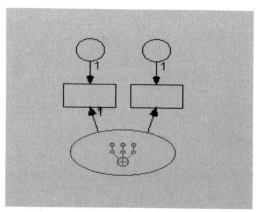

As you can see, with the Draw indicator variable button enabled, you can click multiple times on an unobserved variable to create multiple indicators, complete with unique or error variables. Amos Graphics maintains suitable spacing among the indicators and inserts identification constraints automatically.

Example 5

Rotating Indicators

The indicators appear by default above the *knowledge* ellipse, but you can change their location.

▶ From the menus, choose Edit → Rotate.

▶ Click the *knowledge* ellipse.

Each time you click the *knowledge* ellipse, its indicators rotate 90° clockwise. If you click the ellipse three times, its indicators will look like this:

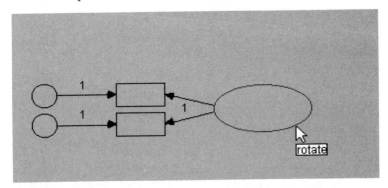

Duplicating Measurement Models

The next step is to create measurement models for *value* and *satisfaction*.

▶ From the menus, choose Edit → Select All.

The measurement model turns blue.

▶ From the menus, choose Edit → Duplicate.

▶ Click any part of the measurement model, and drag a copy to beneath the original.

▶ Repeat to create a third measurement model above the original.

Your path diagram should now look like this:

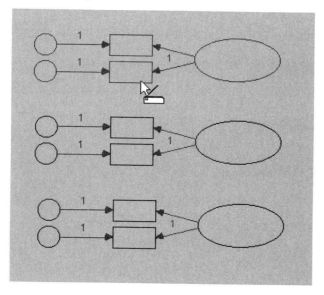

▶ Create a fourth copy for *performance*, and position it to the right of the original.

▶ From the menus, choose Edit → Reflect.

This repositions the two indicators of *performance* as follows:

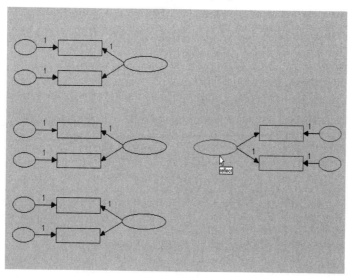

Entering Variable Names

▶ Right-click each object and select Object Properties from the pop-up menu

▶ In the Object Properties dialog box, click the Text tab, and enter a name into the Variable Name text box.

Alternatively, you can choose View → Variables in Dataset from the menus and then drag variable names onto objects in the path diagram.

Completing the Structural Model

There are only a few things left to do to complete the structural model.

▶ Draw the three covariance paths connecting *knowledge*, *value*, and *satisfaction*.

▶ Draw a single-headed arrow from each of the latent predictors, *knowledge*, *value*, and *satisfaction*, to the latent dependent variable, *performance*.

▶ Add the unobserved variable *error9* as a predictor of *performance* (from the menus, choose Diagram → Draw Unique Variable).

Your path diagram should now look like the one on p. 87. The Amos Graphics input file that contains this path diagram is *Ex05-a.amw*.

Results for Model A

As an exercise, you might want to confirm the following degrees of freedom calculation:

Computation of degrees of freedom (Default model)	
Number of distinct sample moments:	36
Number of distinct parameters to be estimated:	22
Degrees of freedom (36 - 22):	14

The hypothesis that Model A is correct is accepted.

> Chi-square = 10.335
> Degrees of freedom = 14
> Probability level = 0.737

The parameter estimates are affected by the identification constraints.

Regression Weights: (Group number 1 - Default model)

			Estimate	S.E.	C.R.	P	Label
performance	<---	knowledge	.337	.125	2.697	.007	
performance	<---	satisfaction	.061	.054	1.127	.260	
performance	<---	value	.176	.079	2.225	.026	
2satisfaction	<---	satisfaction	.792	.438	1.806	.071	
1satisfaction	<---	satisfaction	1.000				
2value	<---	value	.763	.185	4.128	***	
1value	<---	value	1.000				
2knowledge	<---	knowledge	.683	.161	4.252	***	
1knowledge	<---	knowledge	1.000				
1performance	<---	performance	1.000				
2performance	<---	performance	.867	.116	7.450	***	

Covariances: (Group number 1 - Default model)

			Estimate	S.E.	C.R.	P	Label
value	<-->	knowledge	.037	.012	3.036	.002	
satisfaction	<-->	value	-.008	.013	-.610	.542	
satisfaction	<-->	knowledge	.004	.009	.462	.644	

Variances: (Group number 1 - Default model)

	Estimate	S.E.	C.R.	P	Label
satisfaction	.090	.052	1.745	.081	
value	.100	.032	3.147	.002	
knowledge	.046	.015	3.138	.002	
error9	.007	.003	2.577	.010	
error3	.041	.011	3.611	***	
error4	.035	.007	5.167	***	
error5	.080	.025	3.249	.001	
error6	.087	.018	4.891	***	
error7	.022	.049	.451	.652	
error8	.045	.032	1.420	.156	
error1	.007	.002	3.110	.002	
error2	.007	.002	3.871	***	

Example 5

Standardized estimates, on the other hand, are not affected by the identification constraints. To calculate standardized estimates:

▶ From the menus, choose View → Analysis Properties.

▶ In the Analysis Properties dialog box, click the Output tab.

▶ Enable the Standardized estimates check box.

Standardized Regression Weights: (Group number 1 - Default model)

			Estimate
performance	<---	knowledge	.516
performance	<---	satisfaction	.130
performance	<---	value	.398
2satisfaction	<---	satisfaction	.747
1satisfaction	<---	satisfaction	.896
2value	<---	value	.633
1value	<---	value	.745
2knowledge	<---	knowledge	.618
1knowledge	<---	knowledge	.728
1performance	<---	performance	.856
2performance	<---	performance	.819

Correlations: (Group number 1 - Default model)

			Estimate
value	<-->	knowledge	.542
satisfaction	<-->	value	-.084
satisfaction	<-->	knowledge	.064

Viewing the Graphics Output

The path diagram with standardized parameter estimates displayed is as follows:

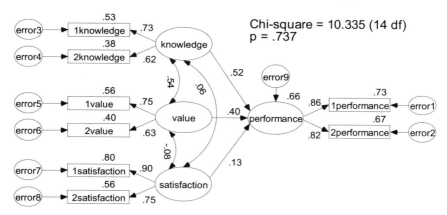

Example 5: Model A
Regression with unobserved variables
Job performance of farm managers
Warren, White and Fuller (1974)
Standardized estimates

The value above *performance* indicates that *pure knowledge, value,* and *satisfaction* account for 66% of the variance of *performance*. The values displayed above the observed variables are reliability estimates for the eight individual subtests. A formula for the reliability of the original tests (before they were split in half) can be found in Rock et al. (1977) or any book on mental test theory.

Model B

Assuming that Model A is correct (and there is no evidence to the contrary), consider the additional hypothesis that *1knowledge* and *2knowledge* are parallel tests. Under the parallel tests hypothesis, the regression of *1knowledge* on *knowledge* should be the same as the regression of *2knowledge* on *knowledge*. Furthermore, the *error* variables associated with *1knowledge* and *2knowledge* should have identical variances. Similar consequences flow from the assumption that *1value* and *2value* are parallel tests, as well as *1performance* and *2performance.* But it is not altogether reasonable to assume that *1satisfaction* and *2satisfaction* are parallel. One of the subtests is slightly longer than the other because the original test had an odd number of items and could not be

Example 5

split exactly in half. As a result, *2satisfaction* is 20% longer than *1satisfaction*. Assuming that the tests differ only in length leads to the following conclusions:

- The regression weight for regressing *2satisfaction* on *satisfaction* should be 1.2 times the weight for regressing *1satisfaction* on *satisfaction*.

- Given equal variances for *error7* and *error8*, the regression weight for *error8* should be $\sqrt{1.2} = 1.095445$ times as large as the regression weight for *error7*.

You do not need to redraw the path diagram from scratch in order to impose these parameter constraints. You can take the path diagram that you created for Model A as a starting point and then change the values of two regression weights. Here is the path diagram after those changes:

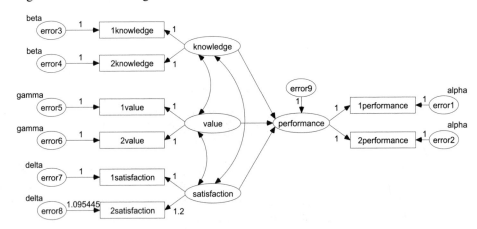

Example 5: Model B
Parallel tests regression
Job performance of farm managers
Warren, White and Fuller (1974)
Model Specification

Results for Model B

The additional parameter constraints of Model B result in increased degrees of freedom:

Computation of degrees of freedom (Default model)	
Number of distinct sample moments:	36
Number of distinct parameters to be estimated:	14
Degrees of freedom (36 - 14):	22

The chi-square statistic has also increased but not by much. It indicates no significant departure of the data from Model B.

Chi-square = 26.967
Degrees of freedom = 22
Probability level = 0.212

If Model B is indeed correct, the associated parameter estimates are to be preferred over those obtained under Model A. The raw parameter estimates will not be presented here because they are affected too much by the choice of identification constraints. However, here are the standardized estimates and the squared multiple correlations:

Standardized Regression Weights: (Group number 1 - Default model)

			Estimate
performance	<---	knowledge	.529
performance	<---	satisfaction	.114
performance	<---	value	.382
2satisfaction	<---	error8	.578
2satisfaction	<---	satisfaction	.816
1satisfaction	<---	satisfaction	.790
2value	<---	value	.685
1value	<---	value	.685
2knowledge	<---	knowledge	.663
1knowledge	<---	knowledge	.663
1performance	<---	performance	.835
2performance	<---	performance	.835

Correlations: (Group number 1 - Default model)

			Estimate
satisfaction	<-->	value	-.085
value	<-->	knowledge	.565
satisfaction	<-->	knowledge	.094

Squared Multiple Correlations: (Group number 1 - Default model)

	Estimate
performance	.671
2performance	.698
1performance	.698
2satisfaction	.666
1satisfaction	.625
2value	.469
1value	.469
2knowledge	.439
1knowledge	.439

Here are the standardized estimates and squared multiple correlations displayed on the path diagram:

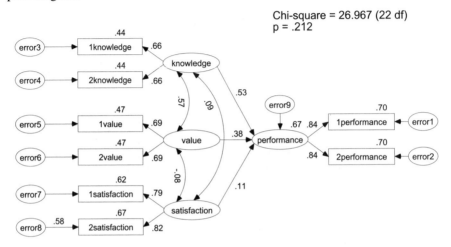

Chi-square = 26.967 (22 df)
p = .212

Example 5: Model B
Parallel tests regression
Job performance of farm managers
Warren, White and Fuller (1974)
Standardized estimates

Testing Model B against Model A

Sometimes you may have two alternative models for the same set of data, and you would like to know which model fits the data better. You can perform a direct comparison whenever one of the models can be obtained by placing additional constraints on the parameters of the other. We have such a case here. We obtained Model B by imposing *eight* additional constraints on the parameters of Model A. Let us say that Model B is the stronger of the two models, in the sense that it represents the stronger hypothesis about the population parameters. (Model A would then be the weaker model). The stronger model will have greater degrees of freedom. The chi-square statistic for the stronger model will be at least as large as the chi-square statistic for the weaker model.

A test of the stronger model (Model B) against the weaker one (Model A) can be obtained by subtracting the smaller chi-square statistic from the larger one. In this example, the new statistic is 16.632 (that is, 26.967 – 10.335). If the stronger model (Model B) is correctly specified, this statistic will have an approximate chi-square distribution with degrees of freedom equal to the difference between the degrees of freedom of the competing models. In this example, the difference in degrees of freedom is 8 (that is, 22 – 14). Model B imposes all of the parameter constraints of Model A, plus an additional 8.

In summary, if Model B is correct, the value 16.632 comes from a chi-square distribution with eight degrees of freedom. If only the weaker model (Model A) is correct, and not the stronger model (Model B), the new statistic will tend to be large. Hence, the stronger model (Model B) is to be rejected in favor of the weaker model (Model A) when the new chi-square statistic is unusually large. With eight degrees of freedom, chi-square values greater than 15.507 are significant at the 0.05 level. Based on this test, we reject Model B.

What about the earlier conclusion, based on the chi-square value of 26.967 with 22 degrees of freedom, that Model B is correct? The disagreement between the two conclusions can be explained by noting that the two tests differ in their assumptions. The test based on eight degrees of freedom assumes that Model A is correct when testing Model B. The test based on 22 degrees of freedom makes no such assumption about Model A. If you are quite sure that Model A is correct, you should use the test comparing Model B against Model A (the one based here on eight degrees of freedom); otherwise, you should use the test based on 22 degrees of freedom.

Example 5

Modeling in VB.NET

Model A

The following program fits Model A:

```
Sub Main()
   Dim Sem As New AmosEngine
   Try
      Sem.TextOutput()
      Sem.Standardized()
      Sem.Smc()

      Sem.BeginGroup(Sem.AmosDir & "Examples\Warren9v.wk1")
      Sem.AStructure("1performance <--- performance (1)")
      Sem.AStructure("2performance <--- performance")
      Sem.AStructure("1knowledge <--- knowledge (1)")
      Sem.AStructure("2knowledge <--- knowledge")
      Sem.AStructure("1value <--- value (1)")
      Sem.AStructure("2value <--- value")
      Sem.AStructure("1satisfaction <--- satisfaction (1)")
      Sem.AStructure("2satisfaction <--- satisfaction")

      Sem.AStructure("1performance <--- error1 (1)")
      Sem.AStructure("2performance <--- error2 (1)")
      Sem.AStructure("1knowledge <--- error3 (1)")
      Sem.AStructure("2knowledge <--- error4 (1)")
      Sem.AStructure("1value <--- error5 (1)")
      Sem.AStructure("2value <--- error6 (1)")
      Sem.AStructure("1satisfaction <--- error7 (1)")
      Sem.AStructure("2satisfaction <--- error8 (1)")

      Sem.AStructure("performance <--- knowledge")
      Sem.AStructure("performance <--- satisfaction")
      Sem.AStructure("performance <--- value")
      Sem.AStructure("performance <--- error9 (1)")
      Sem.FitModel()
   Finally
      Sem.Dispose()
   End Try
End Sub
```

Because of the assumptions that Amos makes about correlations among exogenous variables (discussed in Example 4), the program does not need to indicate that *knowledge*, *value*, and *satisfaction* are allowed to be correlated. It is also not necessary to specify that *error1*, *error2*, ... , *error9* are uncorrelated among themselves and with every other exogenous variable.

Model B

The following program fits Model B:

```
Sub Main()
   Dim Sem As New AmosEngine

   Try
      Sem.TextOutput()
      Sem.Standardized()
      Sem.Smc()

      Sem.BeginGroup(Sem.AmosDir & "Examples\Warren9v.wk1")
      Sem.AStructure("1performance <--- performance (1)")
      Sem.AStructure("2performance <--- performance (1)")
      Sem.AStructure("1knowledge <--- knowledge (1)")
      Sem.AStructure("2knowledge <--- knowledge (1)")
      Sem.AStructure("1value <--- value (1)")
      Sem.AStructure("2value <--- value (1)")
      Sem.AStructure("1satisfaction <--- satisfaction (1)")

      Sem.AStructure("2satisfaction <--- satisfaction (" & CStr(1.2) & ")")

      Sem.AStructure("performance <--- knowledge")
      Sem.AStructure("performance <--- value")
      Sem.AStructure("performance <--- satisfaction")
      Sem.AStructure("performance <--- error9 (1)")

      Sem.AStructure("1performance <--- error1 (1)")
      Sem.AStructure("2performance <--- error2 (1)")
      Sem.AStructure("1knowledge <--- error3 (1)")
      Sem.AStructure("2knowledge <--- error4 (1)")
      Sem.AStructure("1value <--- error5 (1)")
      Sem.AStructure("2value <--- error6 (1)")
      Sem.AStructure("1satisfaction <--- error7 (1)")

      Sem.AStructure("2satisfaction <--- error8 (" & CStr(1.095445) & ")")

      Sem.AStructure("error1 (alpha)")
      Sem.AStructure("error2 (alpha)")
      Sem.AStructure("error8 (delta)")
      Sem.AStructure("error7 (delta)")
      Sem.AStructure("error6 (gamma)")
      Sem.AStructure("error5 (gamma)")
      Sem.AStructure("error4 (beta)")
      Sem.AStructure("error3 (beta)")
      Sem.FitModel()
   Finally
      Sem.Dispose()
   End Try
End Sub
```

Example

6

Exploratory Analysis

Introduction

This example demonstrates structural modeling with time-related latent variables, the use of modification indices and critical ratios in exploratory analyses, how to compare multiple models in a single analysis, and computation of implied moments, factor score weights, total effects, and indirect effects.

About the Data

Wheaton et al. (1977) reported a longitudinal study of 932 persons over the period from 1966 to 1971. Jöreskog and Sörbom (1984), and others since, have used the Wheaton data to demonstrate analysis of moment structures. Six of Wheaton's measures will be used for this example.

Measure	Description
anomia67	1967 score on the *anomia* scale
anomia71	1971 *anomia* score
powles67	1967 score on the *powerlessness* scale
powles71	1971 *powerlessness* score
education	Years of schooling recorded in 1966
SEI	Duncan's Socioeconomic Index administered in 1966

Take a look at the sample means, standard deviations, and correlations for these six measures. You will find the following table in the SPSS file, *Wheaton.sav*. After reading the data, Amos converts the standard deviations and correlations into

variances and covariances, as needed for the analysis. We will not use the sample
means in the analysis.

	rowtype_	varname_	anomia67	powles67	anomia71	powles71	educatio	sei
1	n		932.00	932.00	932.00	932.00	932.00	932.00
2	corr	anomia67	1.00	.	.	.	.	.
3	corr	powles67	.66	1.00	.	.	.	.
4	corr	anomia71	.56	.47	1.00	.	.	.
5	corr	powles71	.44	.52	.67	1.00	.	.
6	corr	educatio	-.36	-.41	-.35	-.37	1.00	.
7	corr	sei	-.30	-.29	-.29	-.28	.54	1.00
8	stddev		3.44	3.06	3.54	3.16	3.10	21.22
9	mean		13.61	14.76	14.13	14.90	10.90	37.49

Model A for the Wheaton Data

Jöreskog and Sörbom (1984) proposed the model shown on p. 107 for the Wheaton
data, referring to it as their Model A. The model asserts that all of the observed
variables depend on underlying, unobserved variables. For example, *anomia67* and
powles67 both depend on the unobserved variable *67_alienation*, a hypothetical
variable that Jöreskog and Sörbom referred to as alienation. The unobserved variables
eps1 and *eps2* appear to play the same role as the variables *error1* and *error2* did in
Example 5. However, their interpretation here is different. In Example 5, *error1* and
error2 had a natural interpretation as errors of measurement. In the present example,
since the anomia and powerlessness scales were not designed to measure the same
thing, it seems reasonable to believe that differences between them will be due to more
than just measurement error. So in this case, *eps1* and *eps2* should be thought of as
representing not only errors of measurement in *anomia67* and *powles67* but in every
other variable that might affect scores on the two tests besides *67_alienation* (the one
variable that affects them both).

Specifying the Model

To specify Model A in Amos Graphics, draw the path diagram shown next, or open the
example file *Ex06–a.amw*. Notice that the eight unique variables (*delta1*, *delta2*, *zeta1*,
zeta2, and *eps1* through *eps4*) are uncorrelated among themselves and with the three
latent variables: *ses*, *67_alienation*, and *71_alienation*.

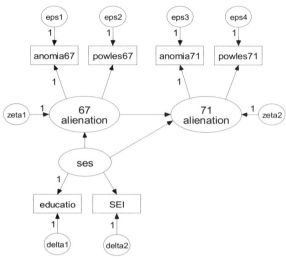

Example 6: Model A
Exploratory analysis
Wheaton (1977)
Model Specification

Identification

Model A is identified except for the usual problem that the measurement scale of each unobserved variable is indeterminate. The measurement scale of each unobserved variable may be fixed arbitrarily by setting a regression weight to unity (1) for one of the paths that points away from it. The path diagram shows 11 regression weights fixed at unity (1), that is, one constraint for each unobserved variable. These constraints are sufficient to make the model identified.

Results of the Analysis

The model has 15 parameters to be estimated (6 regression weights and 9 variances). There are 21 sample moments (6 sample variances and 15 covariances). This leaves 6 degrees of freedom.

<table>
<tr><td colspan="2">Computation of degrees of freedom (Default model)</td></tr>
<tr><td>Number of distinct sample moments:</td><td>21</td></tr>
<tr><td>Number of distinct parameters to be estimated:</td><td>15</td></tr>
<tr><td>Degrees of freedom (21 - 15):</td><td>6</td></tr>
</table>

The Wheaton data depart significantly from Model A.

Chi-square = 71.544
Degrees of freedom = 6
Probability level = 0.000

Dealing with Rejection

You have several options when a proposed model has to be rejected on statistical grounds:

- You can point out that statistical hypothesis testing can be a poor tool for choosing a model. Jöreskog (1967) discussed this issue in the context of factor analysis. It is a widely accepted view that a model can be only an approximation at best, and that, fortunately, a model can be useful without being true. In this view, any model is bound to be rejected on statistical grounds if it is tested with a big enough sample. From this point of view, rejection of a model on purely statistical grounds (particularly with a large sample) is not necessarily a condemnation.

- You can start from scratch to devise another model to substitute for the rejected one.

- You can try to modify the rejected model in small ways so that it fits the data better.

It is the last tactic that will be demonstrated in this example. The most natural way of modifying a model to make it fit better is to relax some of its assumptions. For example, Model A assumes that *eps1* and *eps3* are uncorrelated. You could relax this restriction by connecting *eps1* and *eps3* with a double-headed arrow. The model also specifies that *anomia67* does not depend directly on *ses*. You could remove this assumption by drawing a single-headed arrow from *ses* to *anomia67*. Model A does not happen to constrain any parameters to be equal to other parameters, but if such constraints were present, you might consider removing them in hopes of getting a better fit. Of course, you have to be careful when relaxing the assumptions of a model that you do not turn an identified model into an unidentified one.

Modification Indices

You can test various modifications of a model by carrying out a separate analysis for each potential modification, but this approach is time-consuming. **Modification indices** allow you to evaluate many potential modifications in a single analysis. They provide suggestions for model modifications that are likely to pay off in smaller chi-square values.

Using Modification Indices

▶ From the menus, choose View → Analysis Properties.

▶ In the Analysis Properties dialog box, click the Output tab.

▶ Enable the Modification Indices check box. For this example, leave the Threshold for modification indices set at 4.

The following are the modification indices for Model A:

Covariances: (Group number 1 - Default model)

	M.I.	Par Change
eps2 <--> delta1	5.905	-.424
eps2 <--> eps4	26.545	.825
eps2 <--> eps3	32.071	-.988
eps1 <--> delta1	4.609	.421
eps1 <--> eps4	35.367	-1.069
eps1 <--> eps3	40.911	1.253

Variances: (Group number 1 - Default model)

M.I.   Par Change

Regression Weights: (Group number 1 - Default model)

	M.I.	Par Change
powles71 <--- powles67	5.457	.057
powles71 <--- anomia67	9.006	-.065
anomia71 <--- powles67	6.775	-.069
anomia71 <--- anomia67	10.352	.076
powles67 <--- powles71	5.612	.054
powles67 <--- anomia71	7.278	-.054
anomia67 <--- powles71	7.706	-.070
anomia67 <--- anomia71	9.065	.068

The column heading *M.I.* in this table is short for *Modification Index*. The modification indices produced are those described by Jöreskog and Sörbom (1984). The first modification index listed (*5.905*) is a conservative estimate of the decrease in chi-square that will occur if *eps2* and *delta1* are allowed to be correlated. The new chi-square statistic would have 5 (= 6 − 1) degrees of freedom and would be no greater than 65.639 (71.544 − 5.905). The actual decrease of the chi-square statistic might be much larger than 5.905. The column labeled *Par Change* gives approximate estimates of how much each parameter would change if it were estimated rather than fixed at 0. Amos estimates that the covariance between *eps2* and *delta1* would be −0.424. Based on the small modification index, it does not look as though much would be gained by allowing *eps2* and *delta1* to be correlated. Besides, it would be hard to justify this particular modification on theoretical grounds even if it did produce an acceptable fit.

Changing the Modification Index Threshold

By default, Amos displays only modification indices that are greater than 4, but you can change this threshold.

▶ From the menus, choose View → Analysis Properties.

▶ In the Analysis Properties dialog box, click the Output tab.

▶ Enter a value in the Threshold for modification indices text box. A very small threshold will result in the display of a lot of modification indices that are too small to be of interest.

The largest modification index in Model A is 40.911. It indicates that allowing *eps1* and *eps3* to be correlated will decrease the chi-square statistic by at least 40.911. This is a modification well worth considering because it is quite plausible that these two variables should be correlated. *Eps1* represents variability in *anomia67* that is not due to variation in *67_alienation*. Similarly, *eps3* represents variability in *anomia71* that is not due to variation in *71_alienation*. *Anomia67* and *anomia71* are scale scores on the same instrument (at different times). If the anomia scale measures something other than alienation, you would expect to find a nonzero correlation between *eps1* and *eps3*. In fact, you would expect the correlation to be positive, which is consistent with the fact that the number in the *Par Change* column is positive.

The theoretical reasons for suspecting that *eps1* and *eps3* might be correlated apply to *eps2* and *eps4* as well. The modification indices also suggest allowing *eps2* and *eps4* to be correlated. However, we will ignore this potential modification and proceed immediately to look at the results of modifying Model A by allowing *eps1* and *eps3* to be correlated. The new model is Jöreskog and Sörbom's Model B.

Model B for the Wheaton Data

You can obtain Model B by starting with the path diagram for Model A and drawing a double-headed arrow between *eps1* and *eps3*. If the new double-headed arrow extends beyond the bounds of the print area, you can use the Shape button to adjust the curvature of the double-headed arrow. You can also use the Move button to reposition the end points of the double-headed arrow.

The path diagram for Model B is contained in the file *Ex06-b.amw*.

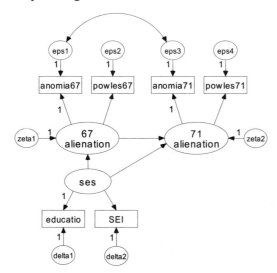

Example 6: Model B
Exploratory analysis
Wheaton (1977)
Model Specification

Example 6

Text Output

The added covariance between *eps1* and *eps3* decreases the degrees of freedom by 1.

Number of distinct sample moments:	21
Number of distinct parameters to be estimated:	16
Degrees of freedom (21 - 16):	5

The chi-square statistic is reduced by substantially more than the promised 40.911.

Chi-square = 6.383
Degrees of freedom = 5
Probability level = 0.271

Model B cannot be rejected. Since the fit of Model B is so good, we will not pursue the possibility, mentioned earlier, of allowing *eps2* and *eps4* to be correlated. (An argument could be made that a nonzero correlation between *eps2* and *eps4* should be allowed in order to achieve a symmetry that is lacking in the Model B.)

The raw parameter estimates must be interpreted cautiously since they would have been different if different identification constraints had been imposed.

Regression Weights: (Group number 1 - Default model)

			Estimate	S.E.	C.R.	P	Label
67_alienation	<---	ses	-.550	.053	-10.294	***	
71_alienation	<---	67_alienation	.617	.050	12.421	***	
71_alienation	<---	ses	-.212	.049	-4.294	***	
powles71	<---	71_alienation	.971	.049	19.650	***	
anomia71	<---	71_alienation	1.000				
powles67	<---	67_alienation	1.027	.053	19.322	***	
anomia67	<---	67_alienation	1.000				
educatio	<---	ses	1.000				
SEI	<---	ses	5.164	.421	12.255	***	

Covariances: (Group number 1 - Default model)

			Estimate	S.E.	C.R.	P	Label
eps1	<-->	eps3	1.886	.240	7.866	***	

Variances: (Group number 1 - Default model)

	Estimate	S.E.	C.R.	P	Label
ses	6.872	.657	10.458	***	
zeta1	4.700	.433	10.864	***	
zeta2	3.862	.343	11.257	***	
eps1	5.059	.371	13.650	***	
eps2	2.211	.317	6.968	***	
eps3	4.806	.395	12.173	***	
eps4	2.681	.329	8.137	***	
delta1	2.728	.516	5.292	***	
delta2	266.567	18.173	14.668	***	

Note the large critical ratio associated with the new covariance path. The covariance between *eps1* and *eps3* is clearly different from 0. This explains the poor fit of Model A, in which that covariance was fixed at 0.

Graphics Output for Model B

The following path diagram displays the standardized estimates and the squared multiple correlations:

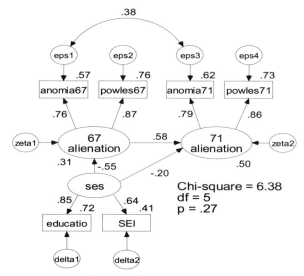

Example 6: Model B
Exploratory analysis
Wheaton (1977)
Standardized estimates

Because the error variables in the model represent more than just measurement error, the squared multiple correlations cannot be interpreted as estimates of reliabilities. Rather, each squared multiple correlation is an estimate of a lower bound on the corresponding reliability. Take *education*, for example. *Ses* accounts for 72% of its variance. Because of this, you would estimate its reliability to be at least 0.72. Considering that *education* is measured in years of schooling, it seems likely that its reliability is much greater.

Example 6

Misuse of Modification Indices

In trying to improve upon a model, you should not be guided exclusively by modification indices. A modification should be considered only if it makes theoretical or common sense.

A slavish reliance on modification indices without such a limitation amounts to sorting through a very large number of potential modifications in search of one that provides a big improvement in fit. Such a strategy is prone, through capitalization on chance, to producing an incorrect (and absurd) model that has an acceptable chi-square value. This issue is discussed by MacCallum (1986) and by MacCallum, Roznowski, and Necowitz (1992).

Improving a Model by Adding New Constraints

Modification indices suggest ways of improving a model by increasing the number of parameters in such a way that the chi-square statistic falls faster than its degrees of freedom. This device can be misused, but it has a legitimate place in exploratory studies. There is also another trick that can be used to produce a model with a more acceptable chi-square value. This technique introduces additional constraints in such a way as to produce a relatively large increase in degrees of freedom, coupled with a relatively small increase in the chi-square statistic. Many such modifications can be roughly evaluated by looking at the critical ratios in the *C.R.* column. We have already seen (in Example 1) how a single critical ratio can be used to test the hypothesis that a single population parameter equals 0. However, the critical ratio also has another interpretation. The square of the critical ratio of a parameter is, approximately, the amount by which the chi-square statistic will increase if the analysis is repeated with that parameter fixed at 0.

Calculating Critical Ratios

If two parameter estimates turn out to be nearly equal, you might be able to improve the chi-square test of fit by postulating a new model where those two parameters are specified to be exactly equal. To assist in locating pairs of parameters that do not differ significantly from each other, Amos provides a critical ratio for every pair of parameters.

▶ From the menus, choose View → Analysis Properties.

▶ In the Analysis Properties dialog box, click the Output tab.

▶ Enable the Critical ratios for differences check box.

When Amos calculates critical ratios for parameter differences, it generates names for any parameters that you did not name during model specification. The names are displayed in the text output next to the parameter estimates.

Here are the parameter estimates for Model B. The parameter names generated by Amos are in the *Label* column.

Regression Weights: (Group number 1 - Default model)

			Estimate	S.E.	C.R.	P	Label
67_alienation	<---	ses	-.550	.053	-10.294	***	par_6
71_alienation	<---	67_alienation	.617	.050	12.421	***	par_4
71_alienation	<---	ses	-.212	.049	-4.294	***	par_5
powles71	<---	71_alienation	.971	.049	19.650	***	par_1
anomia71	<---	71_alienation	1.000				
powles67	<---	67_alienation	1.027	.053	19.322	***	par_2
anomia67	<---	67_alienation	1.000				
educatio	<---	ses	1.000				
SEI	<---	ses	5.164	.421	12.255	***	par_3

Covariances: (Group number 1 - Default model)

	Estimate	S.E.	C.R.	P	Label
eps1 <--> eps3	1.886	.240	7.866	***	par_7

Variances: (Group number 1 - Default model)

	Estimate	S.E.	C.R.	P	Label
ses	6.872	.657	10.458	***	par_8
zeta1	4.700	.433	10.864	***	par_9
zeta2	3.862	.343	11.257	***	par_10
eps1	5.059	.371	13.650	***	par_11
eps2	2.211	.317	6.968	***	par_12
eps3	4.806	.395	12.173	***	par_13
eps4	2.681	.329	8.137	***	par_14
delta1	2.728	.516	5.292	***	par_15
delta2	266.567	18.173	14.668	***	par_16

Example 6

The parameter names are needed for interpreting the critical ratios in the following table:

Critical Ratios for Differences between Parameters (Default model)					
	par_1	par_2	par_3	par_4	par_5	par_6
par_1	.000					
par_2	.877	.000				
par_3	9.883	9.741	.000			
par_4	-4.429	-5.931	-10.579	.000		
par_5	-17.943	-16.634	-12.284	-18.098	.000	
par_6	-22.343	-26.471	-12.661	-17.300	-5.115	.000
par_7	3.903	3.689	-6.762	5.056	8.490	10.124
par_8	8.955	8.866	1.707	9.576	10.995	11.797
par_9	8.364	7.872	-.714	9.256	11.311	12.047
par_10	7.781	8.040	-2.362	9.470	11.683	12.629
par_11	11.106	11.705	-.186	11.969	14.039	15.431
par_12	3.826	3.336	-5.599	4.998	7.698	8.253
par_13	10.425	9.659	-.621	10.306	12.713	13.575
par_14	4.697	4.906	-4.642	6.353	8.554	9.602
par_15	3.393	3.283	-7.280	4.019	5.508	5.975
par_16	14.615	14.612	14.192	14.637	14.687	14.712

Critical Ratios for Differences between Parameters (Default model)					
	par_7	par_8	par_9	par_10	par_11	par_12
par_7	.000					
par_8	7.128	.000				
par_9	5.388	-2.996	.000			
par_10	4.668	-4.112	-1.624	.000		
par_11	9.773	-2.402	.548	2.308	.000	
par_12	.740	-6.387	-5.254	-3.507	-4.728	.000
par_13	8.318	-2.695	.169	1.554	-.507	5.042
par_14	1.798	-5.701	-3.909	-2.790	-4.735	.999
par_15	1.482	-3.787	-2.667	-1.799	-3.672	.855
par_16	14.563	14.506	14.439	14.458	14.387	14.544

Critical Ratios for Differences between Parameters (Default model)			
	par_13	par_14	par_15	par_16
par_13	.000			
par_14	-3.322	.000		
par_15	-3.199	.077	.000	
par_16	14.400	14.518	14.293	.000

Ignoring the 0's down the main diagonal, the table of critical ratios contains 120 entries, one for each pair of parameters. Take the number *0.877* near the upper left corner of the table. This critical ratio is the difference between the parameters labeled *par_1* and *par_2* divided by the estimated standard error of this difference. These two parameters are the regression weights for *powles71 <– 71_alienation* and *powles67 <– 67_alienation*.

Under the distribution assumptions stated on p. 39, the critical ratio statistic can be evaluated using a table of the standard normal distribution to test whether the two parameters are equal in the population. Since 0.877 is less in magnitude than 1.96, you would not reject, at the 0.05 level, the hypothesis that the two regression weights are equal in the population.

The square of the critical ratio for differences between parameters is approximately the amount by which the chi-square statistic would increase if the two parameters were set equal to each other. Since the square of 0.877 is 0.769, modifying Model B to require that the two regression weights have equal estimates would yield a chi-square value of about $6.383 + 0.769 = 7.172$. The degrees of freedom for the new model would be 6 instead of 5. This would be an improved fit ($p = 0.307$ versus $p = 0.275$ for Model B), but we can do much better than that.

Let's look for the smallest critical ratio. The smallest critical ratio in the table is *0.077*, for the parameters labeled *par_14* and *par_15*. These two parameters are the variances of *eps4* and *delta1*. The square of 0.077 is about 0.006. A modification of Model B that assumes *eps4* and *delta1* to have equal variances will result in a chi-square value that exceeds 6.383 by about 0.006, but with 6 degrees of freedom instead of 5. The associated probability level would be about 0.381. The only problem with this modification is that there does not appear to be any justification for it; that is, there does not appear to be any *a priori* reason for expecting *eps4* and *delta1* to have equal variances.

We have just been discussing a misuse of the table of critical ratios for differences. However, the table does have a legitimate use in the quick examination of a small number of hypotheses. As an example of the proper use of the table, consider the fact that observations on *anomia67* and *anomia71* were obtained by using the same instrument on two occasions. The same goes for *powles67* and *powles71*. It is plausible that the tests would behave the same way on the two occasions. The critical ratios for differences are consistent with this hypothesis. The variances of *eps1* and *eps3* (*par_11* and *par_13*) differ with a critical ratio of –0.51. The variances of *eps2* and *eps4* (*par_12* and *par_14*) differ with a critical ratio of 1.00. The weights for the regression of *powerlessness* on *alienation* (*par_1* and *par_2*) differ with a critical ratio of 0.88. None of these differences, taken individually, is significant at any conventional significance level. This suggests that it may be worthwhile to investigate more carefully a model in which all three differences are constrained to be 0. We will call this new model **Model C**.

Example 6

Model C for the Wheaton Data

Here is the path diagram for Model C from the file *Ex06–c.amw*:

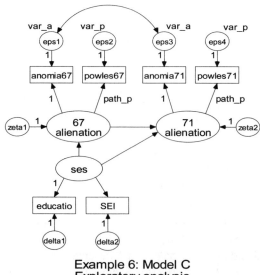

Example 6: Model C
Exploratory analysis
Wheaton (1977)
Model Specification

The label *path_p* requires the regression weight for predicting *powerlessness* from *alienation* to be the same in 1971 as it is in 1967. The label *var_a* is used to specify that *eps1* and *eps3* have the same variance. The label *var_p* is used to specify that *eps2* and *eps4* have the same variance.

Results for Model C

Model C has three more degrees of freedom than Model B:

Computation of degrees of freedom (Default model)	
Number of distinct sample moments:	21
Number of distinct parameters to be estimated:	13
Degrees of freedom (21 - 13):	8

Testing Model C

As expected, Model C has an acceptable fit, with a higher probability level than Model B:

Chi-square = 7.501
Degrees of freedom = 8
Probability level = 0.484

You can test Model C against Model B by examining the difference in chi-square values ($7.501 - 6.383 = 1.118$) and the difference in degrees of freedom ($8 - 5 = 3$). A chi-square value of 1.118 with 3 degrees of freedom is not significant.

Parameter Estimates for Model C

The standardized estimates for Model C are as follows:

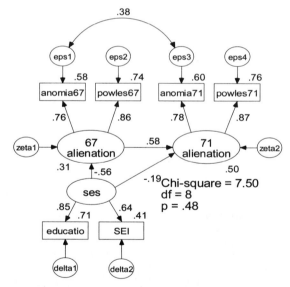

Example 6: Model C
Exploratory analysis
Wheaton (1977)
Standardized estimates

Multiple Models in a Single Analysis

Amos allows for the fitting of multiple models in a single analysis. This allows Amos to summarize the results for all models in a single table. It also allows Amos to perform a chi-square test for nested model comparisons. In this example, Models A, B, and C can be fitted in a single analysis by noting that Models A and C can each be obtained by constraining the parameters of Model B.

In the following path diagram from the file *Ex06-all.amw*, parameters of Model B that need to be constrained to yield Model A or Model C have been assigned names:

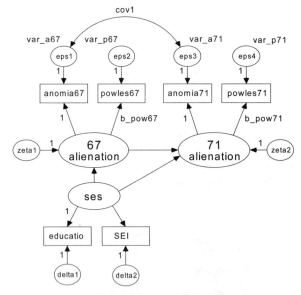

Example 6: Most General Model
Exploratory Analysis
Wheaton (1977)
Model Specification

Seven parameters in this path diagram are named: *var_a67*, *var_p67*, *var_a71*, *var_p71*, *b_pow67*, *b_pow71*, and *cov1*. The naming of the parameters does not constrain any of the parameters to be equal to each other because no two parameters were given the same name. However, having names for the variables allows constraining them in various ways, as will now be demonstrated.

Using the parameter names just introduced, Model A can be obtained from the most general model (Model B) by requiring *cov1 = 0.*

▶ In the Models panel to the left of the path diagram, double-click Default Model.

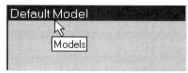

The Manage Models dialog box appears.

▶ In the Model Name text box, type Model A: No Autocorrelation.

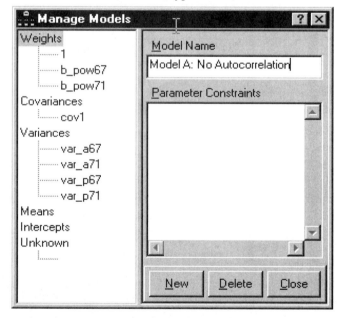

▶ Double-click cov1 in the left panel.

Notice that cov1 appears in the Parameter Constraints box.

▶ Type cov1 =0 in the Parameter Constraints box.

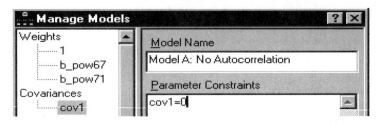

This completes the specification of Model A.

▶ In the Manage Models dialog box, click New.

▶ In the Model Name text box, type Model B: Most General.

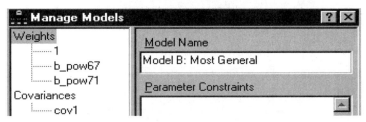

Model B has no constraints other than those in the path diagram, so you can proceed immediately to Model C.

▶ Click New.

▶ In the Model Name text box, type Model C: Time-Invariance.

▶ In the Parameter Constraints box, type:

    b_pow67 = b_pow71
    var_a67 = var_a71
    var_p67 = var_p71

For the sake of completeness, a fourth model (Model D) will be introduced, combining the single constraint of Model A with the three constraints of Model C. Model D can be specified without retyping the constraints.

▶ Click New.

▶ In the Model Name text box, type Model D: A and C Combined.

▶ In the Parameter Constraints box, type:
> Model A: No Autocorrelation
>
> Model C: Time-Invariance

These lines tell Amos that Model D incorporates the constraints of both Model A and Model C.

Now that we have set up the parameter constraints for all four models, the final step is to perform the analysis and view the output.

Output from Multiple Models

Viewing Graphics Output for Individual Models

When you are fitting multiple models, use the Models panel to display the diagrams from different models. The Models panel is just to the left of the path diagram. To display a model, click its name.

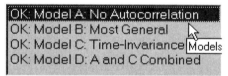

Viewing Fit Statistics for All Four Models

▶ From the menus, choose View → Text Output.

▶ In the tree diagram in the upper left pane of the Amos Output window, click Model Fit.

The following is the portion of the output that shows the chi-square statistic:

CMIN					
Model	NPAR	CMIN	DF	P	CMIN/DF
Model A: No Autocorrelation	15	71.544	6	.000	11.924
Model B: Most General	16	6.383	5	.271	1.277
Model C: Time-Invariance	13	7.501	8	.484	.938
Model D: A and C Combined	12	73.077	9	.000	8.120
Saturated model	21	.000	0		
Independence model	6	2131.790	15	.000	142.119

The *CMIN* column contains the minimum discrepancy for each model. In the case of maximum likelihood estimation (the default), the *CMIN* column contains the chi-square statistic. The *p* column contains the corresponding upper-tail probability for testing each model.

For nested pairs of models, Amos provides tables of model comparisons, complete with chi-square difference tests and their associated *p* values.

▶ In the tree diagram in the upper left pane of the Amos Output window, click Model Comparison.

Nested Model Comparisons

Assuming model Model A: No Autocorrelation to be correct:

Model	DF	CMIN	P	NFI Delta-1	IFI Delta-2	RFI rho-1	TLI rho2
Model D: A and C Combined	3	1.533	.675	.001	.001	-.027	-.027

Assuming model Model B: Most General to be correct:

Model	DF	CMIN	P	NFI Delta-1	IFI Delta-2	RFI rho-1	TLI rho2
Model A: No Autocorrelation	1	65.160	.000	.031	.031	.075	.075
Model C: Time-Invariance	3	1.117	.773	.001	.001	-.002	-.002
Model D: A and C Combined	4	66.693	.000	.031	.031	.048	.048

Assuming model Model C: Time-Invariance to be correct:

Model	DF	CMIN	P	NFI Delta-1	IFI Delta-2	RFI rho-1	TLI rho2
Model D: A and C Combined	1	65.576	.000	.031	.031	.051	.051

This table shows, for example, that Model C does not fit significantly worse than Model B ($p = 0.773$). In other words, assuming that Model B is correct, you would accept the hypothesis of time invariance.

On the other hand, the table shows that Model A fits significantly worse than Model B ($p = 0.000$). In other words, assuming that Model B is correct, you would reject the hypothesis that *eps1* and *eps3* are uncorrelated.

Obtaining Optional Output

The variances and covariances among the observed variables can be estimated under the assumption that Model C is correct.

▶ From the menus, choose View → Analysis Properties.

▶ In the Analysis Properties dialog box, click the Output tab.

▶ Select Implied moments (a check mark appears next to it).

▶ To obtain the implied variances and covariances for all the variables in the model except error variables, select All implied moments.

For Model C, selecting All implied moments gives the following output:

Implied (for all variables) Covariances

	ses	67_alienation	71_alienation	SEI	educatio
ses	6.858				
67_alienation	-3.838	6.914			
71_alienation	-3.720	4.977	7.565		
SEI	35.484	-19.858	-19.246	449.805	
educatio	6.858	-3.838	-3.720	35.484	9.600
powles71	-3.717	4.973	7.559	-19.231	-3.717
anomia71	-3.720	4.977	7.565	-19.246	-3.720
powles67	-3.835	6.909	4.973	-19.842	-3.835
anomia67	-3.838	6.914	4.977	-19.858	-3.838

	powles71	anomia71	powles67	anomia67
powles71	9.989			
anomia71	7.559	12.515		
powles67	4.969	4.973	9.339	
anomia67	4.973	6.865	6.909	11.864

The implied variances and covariances for the observed variables are not the same as the sample variances and covariances. As estimates of the corresponding population values, the implied variances and covariances are superior to the sample variances and covariances (assuming that Model C is correct).

If you enable both the Standardized estimates and All implied moments check boxes in the Analysis Properties dialog box, Amos will give you the implied *correlation* matrix of all variables as well as the implied covariance matrix.

Example 6

The matrix of implied covariances for all variables in the model can be used to carry out a regression of the unobserved variables on the observed variables. The resulting regression weight estimates can be obtained from Amos by enabling the Factor score weights check box. Here are the estimated factor score weights for Model C:

Factor Score Weights

	SEI	educatio	powles71	anomia71	powles67	anomia67
ses	.029	.542	-.055	-.016	-.069	-.028
67_alienation	-.003	-.061	.134	-.027	.471	.242
71_alienation	-.003	-.049	.491	.253	.134	-.031

The table of factor score weights has a separate row for each unobserved variable, and a separate column for each observed variable. Suppose you wanted to estimate the *ses* score of an individual. You would compute a weighted sum of the individual's six observed scores using the six weights in the *ses* row of the table.

Obtaining Tables of Indirect, Direct, and Total Effects

The coefficients associated with the single-headed arrows in a path diagram are sometimes called **direct effects**. In Model C, for example, *ses* has a direct effect on *71_alienation*. In turn, *71_alienation* has a direct effect on *powles71*. *Ses* is then said to have an **indirect effect** (through the intermediary of *71_alienation*) on *powles71*.

▶ From the menus, choose View → Analysis Properties.

▶ In the Analysis Properties dialog box, click the Output tab.

▶ Enable the Indirect, direct & total effects check box.

For Model C, the output includes the following table of total effects:

Total Effects (Group number 1 - Model C: Time-Invariance)

	ses	67_alienation	71_alienation
67_alienation	-.560	.000	.000
71_alienation	-.542	.607	.000
SEI	5.174	.000	.000
educatio	1.000	.000	.000
powles71	-.542	.607	.999
anomia71	-.542	.607	1.000
powles67	-.559	.999	.000
anomia67	-.560	1.000	.000

The first row of the table indicates that *67_alienation* depends, directly or indirectly, on *ses* only. The *total effect* of *ses* on *67_alienation* is –0.56. The fact that the effect is negative means that, all other things being equal, relatively high *ses* scores are associated with relatively low *67_alienation* scores. Looking in the fifth row of the table, *powles71* depends, directly or indirectly, on *ses*, *67_alienation*, and *71_alienation*. Low scores on *ses*, high scores on *67_alienation*, and high scores on *71_alienation* are associated with high scores on *powles71*. See Fox (1980) for more help in interpreting direct, indirect, and total effects.

Modeling in VB.NET

Model A

The following program fits Model A. It is saved as *Ex06–a.vb*.

```
Sub Main()
    Dim Sem As New AmosEngine
    Try
        Sem.TextOutput()
        Sem.Mods(4)
        Sem.BeginGroup(Sem.AmosDir & "Examples\Wheaton.sav")
        Sem.AStructure("anomia67 <--- 67_alienation (1)")
        Sem.AStructure("anomia67 <--- eps1 (1)")
        Sem.AStructure("powles67 <--- 67_alienation")
        Sem.AStructure("powles67 <--- eps2 (1)")
        Sem.AStructure("anomia71 <--- 71_alienation (1)")
        Sem.AStructure("anomia71 <--- eps3 (1)")
        Sem.AStructure("powles71 <--- 71_alienation")
        Sem.AStructure("powles71 <--- eps4 (1)")

        Sem.AStructure("67_alienation <--- ses")
        Sem.AStructure("67_alienation <--- zeta1 (1)")

        Sem.AStructure("71_alienation <--- 67_alienation")
        Sem.AStructure("71_alienation <--- ses")
        Sem.AStructure("71_alienation <--- zeta2 (1)")

        Sem.AStructure("educatio <--- ses (1)")
        Sem.AStructure("educatio <--- delta1 (1)")
        Sem.AStructure("SEI <--- ses")
        Sem.AStructure("SEI <--- delta2 (1)")
        Sem.FitModel()
    Finally
        Sem.Dispose()
    End Try
End Sub
```

Model B

The following program fits Model B. It is saved as *Ex06–b.vb*.

```vb
Sub Main()
    Dim Sem As New AmosEngine
    Try
        Sem.TextOutput()
        Sem.Standardized()
        Sem.Smc()
        Sem.Crdiff()
        Sem.BeginGroup(Sem.AmosDir & "Examples\Wheaton.sav")
        Sem.AStructure("anomia67 <--- 67_alienation (1)")
        Sem.AStructure("anomia67 <--- eps1 (1)")
        Sem.AStructure("powles67 <--- 67_alienation")
        Sem.AStructure("powles67 <--- eps2 (1)")
        Sem.AStructure("anomia71 <--- 71_alienation (1)")
        Sem.AStructure("anomia71 <--- eps3 (1)")
        Sem.AStructure("powles71 <--- 71_alienation")
        Sem.AStructure("powles71 <--- eps4 (1)")
        Sem.AStructure("67_alienation <--- ses")
        Sem.AStructure("67_alienation <--- zeta1 (1)")
        Sem.AStructure("71_alienation <--- 67_alienation")
        Sem.AStructure("71_alienation <--- ses")
        Sem.AStructure("71_alienation <--- zeta2 (1)")
        Sem.AStructure("educatio <--- ses (1)")
        Sem.AStructure("educatio <--- delta1 (1)")
        Sem.AStructure("SEI <--- ses")
        Sem.AStructure("SEI <--- delta2 (1)")
        Sem.AStructure("eps1 <---> eps3")      ' Autocorrelated residual
        Sem.FitModel()
    Finally
        Sem.Dispose()
    End Try
End Sub
```

Model C

The following program fits Model C. It is saved as *Ex06–c.vb*.

```
Sub Main()
    Dim Sem As New AmosEngine
    Try
        Sem.TextOutput()
        Sem.Standardized()
        Sem.Smc()
        Sem.AllImpliedMoments()
        Sem.FactorScoreWeights()
        Sem.TotalEffects()

        Sem.BeginGroup(Sem.AmosDir & "Examples\Wheaton.sav")
        Sem.AStructure("anomia67 <--- 67_alienation (1)")
        Sem.AStructure("anomia67 <--- eps1 (1)")
        Sem.AStructure("powles67 <--- 67_alienation (path_p)")
        Sem.AStructure("powles67 <--- eps2 (1)")
        Sem.AStructure("anomia71 <--- 71_alienation (1)")
        Sem.AStructure("anomia71 <--- eps3 (1)")
        Sem.AStructure("powles71 <--- 71_alienation (path_p)")
        Sem.AStructure("powles71 <--- eps4 (1)")
        Sem.AStructure("67_alienation <--- ses")
        Sem.AStructure("67_alienation <--- zeta1 (1)")
        Sem.AStructure("71_alienation <--- 67_alienation")
        Sem.AStructure("71_alienation <--- ses")
        Sem.AStructure("71_alienation <--- zeta2 (1)")
        Sem.AStructure("educatio <--- ses (1)")
        Sem.AStructure("educatio <--- delta1 (1)")
        Sem.AStructure("SEI <--- ses")
        Sem.AStructure("SEI <--- delta2 (1)")
        Sem.AStructure("eps3 <--> eps1")
        Sem.AStructure("eps1 (var_a)")
        Sem.AStructure("eps2 (var_p)")
        Sem.AStructure("eps3 (var_a)")
        Sem.AStructure("eps4 (var_p)")
        Sem.FitModel()
    Finally
        Sem.Dispose()
    End Try
End Sub
```

Example 6

Fitting Multiple Models

To fit all three models, A, B, and C in a single analysis, start with the following program, which assigns unique names to some parameters:

```
Sub Main()
    Dim Sem As New AmosEngine
    Try
        Sem.TextOutput()
        Sem.Standardized()
        Sem.Smc()
        Sem.AllImpliedMoments()
        Sem.TotalEffects()
        Sem.FactorScoreWeights()
        Sem.Mods(4)
        Sem.Crdiff()

        Sem.BeginGroup(Sem.AmosDir & "Examples\Wheaton.sav")
        Sem.AStructure("anomia67 <--- 67_alienation (1)")
        Sem.AStructure("anomia67 <--- eps1 (1)")
        Sem.AStructure("powles67 <--- 67_alienation (b_pow67)")
        Sem.AStructure("powles67 <--- eps2 (1)")

        Sem.AStructure("anomia71 <--- 71_alienation (1)")
        Sem.AStructure("anomia71 <--- eps3 (1)")
        Sem.AStructure("powles71 <--- 71_alienation (b_pow71)")
        Sem.AStructure("powles71 <--- eps4 (1)")

        Sem.AStructure("67_alienation <--- ses")
        Sem.AStructure("67_alienation <--- zeta1 (1)")
        Sem.AStructure("71_alienation <--- 67_alienation")
        Sem.AStructure("71_alienation <--- ses")
        Sem.AStructure("71_alienation <--- zeta2 (1)")

        Sem.AStructure("educatio <--- ses (1)")
        Sem.AStructure("educatio <--- delta1 (1)")
        Sem.AStructure("SEI <--- ses")
        Sem.AStructure("SEI <--- delta2 (1)")

        Sem.AStructure("eps3 <--> eps1 (cov1)")

        Sem.AStructure("eps1 (var_a67)")
        Sem.AStructure("eps2 (var_p67)")
        Sem.AStructure("eps3 (var_a71)")
        Sem.AStructure("eps4 (var_p71)")
        Sem.FitModel()
    Finally
        Sem.Dispose()
    End Try
End Sub
```

Since the parameter names are unique, naming the parameters does not constrain them. However, naming the parameters does permit imposing constraints through the use of the Model method. Adding the following lines to the program, in place of the Sem.FitModel line, will fit the model four times, each time with a different set of parameter constraints:

```
Sem.Model("Model A: No Autocorrelation", "cov1 = 0")
Sem.Model("Model B: Most General", "")
Sem.Model("Model C: Time-Invariance", _
        "b_pow67 = b_pow71;var_a67 = var_a71;var_p67 = var_p71")
Sem.Model("Model D: A and C Combined", _
        "Model A: No Autocorrelation;Model C: Time-Invariance")
Sem.FitAllModels()
```

The first line defines a version of the model called Model A: No Autocorrelation in which the parameter called *cov1* is fixed at 0.

The second line defines a version of the model called Model B: Most General in which no additional constraints are imposed on the model parameters.

The third use of the Model method defines a version of the model called Model C: Time-Invariance that imposes the equality constraints:

b_pow67 = b_pow71

var_a67 = var_a71

var_p67 = var_p71

The fourth use of the Model method defines a version of the model called Model D: A and C Combined that combines the single constraint of Model A with the three constraints of Model C.

The last model specification (Model D) shows how earlier model specifications can be used in the definition of a new, more constrained model.

In order to fit all models at once, the FitAllModels method has to be used instead of FitModel. The FitModel method fits a single model only. By default, it fits the first model, which in this example is Model A. You could use FitModel(1) to fit the first model, or FitModel(2) to fit the second model. You could also use, say, FitModel("Model C: Time-Invariance") to fit Model C.

Ex06–all.vb contains a program that fits all four models.

Example

7

A Nonrecursive Model

Introduction

This example demonstrates structural equation modeling with a nonrecursive model.

About the Data

Felson and Bohrnstedt (1979) studied 209 girls from sixth through eighth grade. They made measurements on the following variables:

Variables	Description
academic	Perceived academic ability, a sociometric measure based on the item *Name who you think are your three smartest classmates*
athletic	Perceived athletic ability, a sociometric measure based on the item *Name three of your classmates who you think are best at sports*
attract	Perceived attractiveness, a sociometric measure based on the item *Name the three girls in the classroom who you think are the most good-looking (excluding yourself)*
GPA	Grade point average
height	Deviation of height from the mean height for a subject's grade and sex
weight	Weight, adjusted for height
rating	Ratings of physical attractiveness obtained by having children from another city rate photographs of the subjects

Sample correlations, means, and standard deviations for these six variables are contained in the SPSS file *Fels_fem.sav*. Here is the data file as it appears in the SPSS Data Editor:

	rowtype_	varname_	academic	athletic	attract	gpa	height	weight	rating
1	n		209.00	209.00	209.0	209.0	209.0	209.0	209.0
2	corr	academic	1.00	.	.	.	.	.	.
3	corr	athletic	.43	1.00	.	.	.	.	.
4	corr	attract	.50	.48	1.00	.	.	.	.
5	corr	GPA	.49	.22	.32	1.00	.	.	.
6	corr	height	.10	-.04	-.03	.18	1.00	.	.
7	corr	weight	.04	.02	-.16	-.10	.34	1.00	.
8	corr	rating	.09	.14	.43	.15	-.16	-.27	1.00
9	stddev		.16	.07	.49	3.49	2.91	19.32	1.01
10	mean		.12	.05	.42	10.34	.00	94.13	2.65

The sample means are not used in this example.

Felson and Bohrnstedt's Model

Felson and Bohrnstedt proposed the following model for six of their seven measured variables:

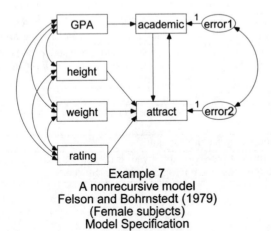

Example 7
A nonrecursive model
Felson and Bohrnstedt (1979)
(Female subjects)
Model Specification

Perceived *academic* performance is modeled as a function of *GPA* and perceived attractiveness (*attract*). Perceived attractiveness, in turn, is modeled as a function of perceived *academic* performance, *height*, *weight*, and the *rating* of attractiveness by children from another city. Particularly noteworthy in this model is that perceived academic ability depends on perceived attractiveness, and vice versa. A model with these feedback loops is called **nonrecursive** (the terms **recursive** and **nonrecursive** were defined earlier in Example 4). The current model is nonrecursive because it is possible to trace a path from *attract* to *academic* and back. This path diagram is saved in the file *Ex07.amw*.

Model Identification

We need to establish measurement units for the two unobserved variables, *error1* and *error2*, for identification purposes. The preceding path diagram shows two regression weights fixed at 1. These two constraints are enough to make the model identified.

Results of the Analysis

Text Output

The model has two degrees of freedom, and there is no significant evidence that the model is wrong.

Chi-square = 2.761
Degrees of freedom = 2
Probability level = 0.251

There is, however, some evidence that the model is unnecessarily complicated, as indicated by some exceptionally small critical ratios in the text output.

Example 7

Regression Weights: (Group number 1 - Default model)

	Estimate	S.E.	C.R.	P	Label
academic <--- GPA	.023	.004	6.241	***	
attract <--- height	.000	.010	.050	.960	
attract <--- weight	-.002	.001	-1.321	.186	
attract <--- rating	.176	.027	6.444	***	
attract <--- academic	1.607	.349	4.599	***	
academic <--- attract	-.002	.051	-.039	.969	

Covariances: (Group number 1 - Default model)

	Estimate	S.E.	C.R.	P	Label
GPA <--> rating	.526	.246	2.139	.032	
height <--> rating	-.468	.205	-2.279	.023	
GPA <--> weight	-6.710	4.676	-1.435	.151	
GPA <--> height	1.819	.712	2.555	.011	
height <--> weight	19.024	4.098	4.643	***	
weight <--> rating	-5.243	1.395	-3.759	***	
error1 <--> error2	-.004	.010	-.382	.702	

Variances: (Group number 1 - Default model)

	Estimate	S.E.	C.R.	P	Label
GPA	12.122	1.189	10.198	***	
height	8.428	.826	10.198	***	
weight	371.476	36.426	10.198	***	
rating	1.015	.100	10.198	***	
error1	.019	.003	5.747	***	
error2	.143	.014	9.974	***	

Judging by the critical ratios, you see that each of these three null hypotheses would be accepted at conventional significance levels:

■ Perceived attractiveness does not depend on height (critical ratio = 0.050).

■ Perceived academic ability does not depend on perceived attractiveness (critical ratio = –0.039).

■ The residual variables *error1* and *error2* are uncorrelated (critical ratio = –0.382).

Strictly speaking, you cannot use the critical ratios to test all three hypotheses at once. Instead, you would have to construct a model that incorporates all three constraints simultaneously. This idea will not be pursued here.

The raw parameter estimates reported above are not affected by the identification constraints (except for the variances of *error1* and *error2*). They are, of course, affected by the units in which the observed variables are measured. By contrast, the standardized estimates are independent of all units of measurement.

Obtaining Standardized Estimates

Before you perform the analysis, do the following:

▶ From the menus, choose View → Analysis Properties.

▶ In the Analysis Properties dialog box, click the Output tab.

▶ Select Standardized estimates (a check mark appears next to it).

▶ Close the dialog box.

Standardized Regression Weights: (Group number 1 - Default model)

			Estimate
academic	<---	GPA	.492
attract	<---	height	.003
attract	<---	weight	-.078
attract	<---	rating	.363
attract	<---	academic	.525
academic	<---	attract	-.006

Correlations: (Group number 1 - Default model)

			Estimate
GPA	<-->	rating	.150
height	<-->	rating	-.160
GPA	<-->	weight	-.100
GPA	<-->	height	.180
height	<-->	weight	.340
weight	<-->	rating	-.270
error1	<-->	error2	-.076

Here it can be seen that the regression weights and the correlation that we discovered earlier to be statistically insignificant are also, speaking descriptively, small.

Obtaining Squared Multiple Correlations

The squared multiple correlations, like the standardized estimates, are independent of units of measurement. To obtain squared multiple correlations, do the following before you perform the analysis:

▶ From the menus, choose View → Analysis Properties.

▶ In the Analysis Properties dialog box, click the Output tab.

▶ Select Squared multiple correlations (a check mark appears next to it).

▶ Close the dialog box.

Squared Multiple Correlations: (Group number 1 - Default model)	
	Estimate
attract	.402
academic	.236

The squared multiple correlations show that the two endogenous variables in this model are not predicted very accurately by the other variables in the model. This goes to show that the chi-square test of fit is not a measure of accuracy of prediction.

Graphics Output

Here is the path diagram output displaying standardized estimates and squared multiple correlations:

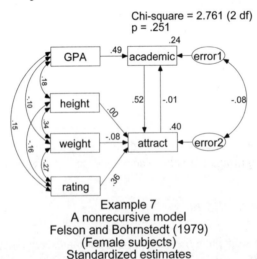

Example 7
A nonrecursive model
Felson and Bohrnstedt (1979)
(Female subjects)
Standardized estimates

Stability Index

The existence of feedback loops in a nonrecursive model permits certain problems to arise that cannot occur in recursive models. In the present model, attractiveness depends on perceived academic ability, which in turn depends on attractiveness, which depends on perceived academic ability, and so on. This appears to be an infinite regress, and it is. One wonders whether this infinite sequence of linear dependencies can actually result in well-defined relationships among attractiveness, academic ability, and the other variables of the model. The answer is that they might, and then again they might not. It all depends on the regression weights. For some values of the regression weights, the infinite sequence of linear dependencies will converge to a set of well-defined relationships. In this case, the system of linear dependencies is called **stable**; otherwise, it is called **unstable**.

Note: You cannot tell whether a linear system is stable by looking at the path diagram. You need to know the regression weights.

Amos cannot know what the regression weights are in the population, but it estimates them and, from the estimates, it computes a **stability index** (Fox 1980; Bentler and Freeman 1983).

If the stability index falls between −1 and +1, the system is stable; otherwise, it is unstable. In the present example, the system is stable.

Stability index for the following variables is 0.003:
attract
academic

To view the stability index for a nonrecursive model:

▶ Click Notes for Group/Model in the tree diagram in the upper left pane of the Amos Output window.

An unstable system (with a stability index equal to or greater than 1) is *impossible*, in the same sense that, for example, a negative variance is impossible. If you do obtain a stability index of 1 (or greater than 1), this implies that your model is wrong or that your sample size is too small to provide accurate estimates of the regression weights. If there are several loops in a path diagram, Amos computes a stability index for each one. If any one of the stability indices equals or exceeds 1, the linear system is unstable.

Example 7

Modeling in VB.NET

The following program fits the model of this example. It is saved in the file *Ex07.vb*.

```
Sub Main()
    Dim Sem As New AmosEngine
    Try
        Sem.TextOutput()
        Sem.Standardized()
        Sem.Smc()
        Sem.BeginGroup(Sem.AmosDir & "Examples\Fels_fem.sav")
        Sem.AStructure("academic <--- GPA")
        Sem.AStructure("academic <--- attract")
        Sem.AStructure("academic <--- error1 (1)")

        Sem.AStructure("attract <--- height")
        Sem.AStructure("attract <--- weight")
        Sem.AStructure("attract <--- rating")
        Sem.AStructure("attract <--- academic")
        Sem.AStructure("attract <--- error2 (1)")

        Sem.AStructure("error2 <--> error1")
        Sem.FitModel()
    Finally
        Sem.Dispose()
    End Try
End Sub
```

The final AStructure line is essential to Felson and Bohrnstedt's model. Without it, Amos would assume that *error1* and *error2* are uncorrelated.

You can specify the same model in an equation-like format as follows:

```
Sub Main()
    Dim Sem As New AmosEngine

    Try
        Sem.TextOutput()
        Sem.Standardized()
        Sem.Smc()
        Sem.BeginGroup(Sem.AmosDir & "Examples\Fels_fem.sav")
        Sem.AStructure("academic = GPA + attract + error1 (1)")
        Sem.AStructure("attract  = height + weight + rating + " _
            & "academic + error2 (1)")
        Sem.AStructure("error2 <--> error1")
        Sem.FitModel()
    Finally
        Sem.Dispose()
    End Try
End Sub
```

Example

8

Factor Analysis

Introduction

This example demonstrates confirmatory common factor analysis.

About the Data

Holzinger and Swineford (1939) administered 26 psychological tests to 301 seventh-
and eighth-grade students in two Chicago schools. In the present example, we use
scores obtained by the 73 girls from a single school (the Grant-White school). Here is
a summary of the six tests used in this example:

Test	Description
visperc	Visual perception scores
cubes	Test of spatial visualization
lozenges	Test of spatial orientation
paragraph	Paragraph comprehension score
sentence	Sentence completion score
wordmean	Word meaning test score

The file *Grnt_fem.sav* contains the test scores:

	visperc	cubes	lozenges	paragrap	sentence	wordmean
1	33.00	22.00	17.00	8.00	17.00	10.00
2	30.00	25.00	20.00	10.00	23.00	18.00
3	36.00	33.00	36.00	17.00	25.00	41.00
4	28.00	25.00	9.00	10.00	18.00	11.00
5	30.00	25.00	11.00	11.00	21.00	8.00
6	20.00	25.00	6.00	9.00	21.00	16.00
7	17.00	21.00	6.00	5.00	10.00	10.00
8	33.00	31.00	30.00	11.00	23.00	18.00

A Common Factor Model

Consider the following model for the six tests:

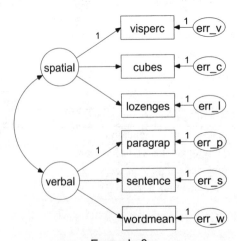

Example 8
Factor analysis: Girls' sample
Holzinger and Swineford (1939)
Model Specification

This model asserts that the first three tests depend on an unobserved variable called *spatial*. *Spatial* can be interpreted as an underlying ability (spatial ability) that is not directly observed. According to the model, performance on the first three tests depends on this ability. In addition, performance on each of these tests may depend on something other than spatial ability. In the case of *visperc*, for example, the unique variable *err_v* is also involved. *Err_v* represents any and all influences on *visperc* that are not shown elsewhere in the path diagram. *Err_v* represents error of measurement in *visperc*, certainly, but also socioeconomic status, age, physical stamina, vocabulary, and every other trait or ability that might affect scores on *visperc* but do not appear elsewhere in the model.

The model presented here is a common factor analysis model. In the lingo of common factor analysis, the unobserved variable *spatial* is called a **common factor**, and the three unobserved variables, *err_v*, *err_c*, and *err_l*, are called **unique factors**. The path diagram shows another common factor, *verbal*, on which the last three tests depend. The path diagram also shows three more unique factors, *err_p*, *err_s*, and *err_w*. The two common factors, *spatial* and *verbal*, are allowed to be correlated. On the other hand, the unique factors are assumed to be uncorrelated with each other and with the common factors. The path coefficients leading from the common factors to the observed variables are sometimes called **factor loadings**.

Identification

This model is identified except that, as usual, the measurement scale of each unobserved variable is indeterminate. The measurement scale of each unobserved variable can be established arbitrarily by setting its regression weight to a constant, such as 1, in some regression equation. The preceding path diagram shows how to do this. In that path diagram, eight regression weights are fixed at 1, which is one fixed regression weight for each unobserved variable. These constraints are sufficient to make the model identified.

The proposed model is a particularly simple common factor analysis model, in that each observed variable depends on just one common factor. In other applications of common factor analysis, an observed variable can depend on any number of common factors at the same time. In the general case, it can be very difficult to decide whether a common factor analysis model is identified or not (Davis 1993; Jöreskog 1969, 1979). The discussion of identifiability given in this and earlier examples make the issue appear simpler than it actually is, giving the impression that the lack of a natural unit of measurement for unobserved variables is the sole cause of non-identification. It is true that the lack of a unit of measurement for unobserved variables is an ever-present cause of non-identification. Fortunately, it is one that is easy to cure, as we have done repeatedly.

But other kinds of underidentification can occur for which there is no simple remedy. Conditions for identifiability have to be established separately for individual models. Jöreskog and Sörbom (1984) show how to achieve identification of many models by imposing equality constraints on their parameters. In the case of the factor analysis model (and many others), figuring out what must be done to make the model identified requires a pretty deep understanding of the model. If you are unable to tell whether a model is identified, you can try fitting the model in order to see whether Amos reports that it is unidentified. In practice, this empirical approach works quite well, although there are objections to it in principle (McDonald and Krane 1979), and it is no substitute for an *a priori* understanding of the identification status of a model. Bollen (1989) discusses causes and treatments of many types of non-identification in his excellent textbook.

Specifying the Model

Amos analyzes the model directly from the path diagram shown on p. 142. Notice that the model can conceptually be separated into *spatial* and *verbal* branches. You can use the structural similarity of the two branches to accelerate drawing the model.

Drawing the Model

After you have drawn the first branch:

▶ From the menus, choose Edit → Select All to highlight the entire branch.

▶ To create a copy of the entire branch, from the menus, choose Edit → Duplicate and drag one of the objects in the branch to another location in the path diagram.

Be sure to draw a double-headed arrow connecting *spatial* and *verbal*. If you leave out the double-headed arrow, Amos will assume that the two common factors are uncorrelated. The input file for this example is *Ex08.amw*.

Results of the Analysis

Here are the unstandardized results of the analysis. As shown at the upper right corner of the figure, the model fits the data quite well.

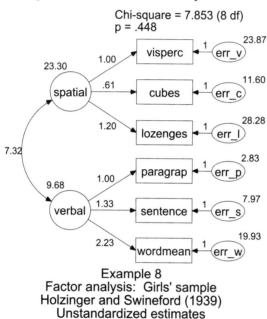

Chi-square = 7.853 (8 df)
p = .448

Example 8
Factor analysis: Girls' sample
Holzinger and Swineford (1939)
Unstandardized estimates

As an exercise, you may wish to confirm the computation of degrees of freedom.

Computation of degrees of freedom: (Default model)	
Number of distinct sample moments:	21
Number of distinct parameters to be estimated:	13
Degrees of freedom (21 – 13):	8

The parameter estimates, both standardized and unstandardized, are shown next. As you would expect, the regression weights are positive, as is the correlation between spatial ability and verbal ability.

Example 8

Regression Weights: (Group number 1 - Default model)

			Estimate	S.E.	C.R.	P	Label
visperc	<---	spatial	1.000				
cubes	<---	spatial	.610	.143	4.250	***	
lozenges	<---	spatial	1.198	.272	4.405	***	
paragrap	<---	verbal	1.000				
sentence	<---	verbal	1.334	.160	8.322	***	
wordmean	<---	verbal	2.234	.263	8.482	***	

Standardized Regression Weights: (Group number 1 - Default model)

			Estimate
visperc	<---	spatial	.703
cubes	<---	spatial	.654
lozenges	<---	spatial	.736
paragrap	<---	verbal	.880
sentence	<---	verbal	.827
wordmean	<---	verbal	.841

Covariances: (Group number 1 - Default model)

	Estimate	S.E.	C.R.	P	Label
spatial <--> verbal	7.315	2.571	2.846	.004	

Correlations: (Group number 1 - Default model)

	Estimate
spatial <--> verbal	.487

Variances: (Group number 1 - Default model)

	Estimate	S.E.	C.R.	P	Label
spatial	23.302	8.123	2.868	.004	
verbal	9.682	2.159	4.485	***	
err_v	23.873	5.986	3.988	***	
err_c	11.602	2.584	4.490	***	
err_l	28.275	7.892	3.583	***	
err_p	2.834	.868	3.263	.001	
err_s	7.967	1.869	4.263	***	
err_w	19.925	4.951	4.024	***	

Obtaining Standardized Estimates

To get the standardized estimates shown above, do the following before you perform the analysis:

▶ From the menus, choose View → Analysis Properties.

▶ In the Analysis Properties dialog box, click the Output tab.

▶ Select Standardized estimates (a check mark appears next to it).

▶ Also select Squared multiple correlations if you want squared multiple correlations for each endogenous variable, as shown in the next graphic.

▶ Close the dialog box.

Squared Multiple Correlations: (Group number 1 - Default model)

	Estimate
wordmean	.708
sentence	.684
paragrap	.774
lozenges	.542
cubes	.428
visperc	.494

Viewing Standardized Estimates

▶ In the Amos Graphics window, click the Show the output path diagram button.

▶ Select Standardized estimates in the Parameter Formats panel at the left of the path diagram.

Here is the path diagram with standardized estimates displayed:

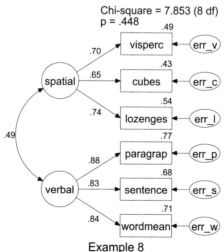

Example 8
Factor analysis: Girls' sample
Holzinger and Swineford (1939)
Standardized estimates

The squared multiple correlations can be interpreted as follows: To take *wordmean* as an example, 71% of its variance is accounted for by verbal ability. The remaining 29% of its variance is accounted for by the unique factor *err_w*. If *err_w* represented measurement error only, we could say that the estimated reliability of *wordmean* is 0.71. As it is, 0.71 is an estimate of a lower bound on the reliability of *wordmean*.

The Holzinger and Swineford data have been analyzed repeatedly in textbooks and in demonstrations of new factor analytic techniques. The six tests used in this example are taken from a larger subset of nine tests used in a similar example by Jöreskog and Sörbom (1984). The factor analysis model employed here is also adapted from theirs. In view of the long history of exploration of the Holzinger and Swineford data in the factor analysis literature, it is no accident that the present model fits very well. Even more than usual, the results presented here require confirmation on a fresh set of data.

Modeling in VB.NET

The following program specifies the factor model for Holzinger and Swineford's data. It is saved in the file *Ex08.vb*.

```
Sub Main()
    Dim Sem As New AmosEngine
    Try
        Sem.TextOutput()
        Sem.Standardized()
        Sem.Smc()

        Sem.BeginGroup(Sem.AmosDir & "Examples\Grnt_fem.sav")
        Sem.AStructure("visperc  = (1) spatial + (1) err_v")
        Sem.AStructure("cubes    =     spatial + (1) err_c")
        Sem.AStructure("lozenges =     spatial + (1) err_l")

        Sem.AStructure("paragrap = (1) verbal  + (1) err_p")
        Sem.AStructure("sentence =     verbal  + (1) err_s")
        Sem.AStructure("wordmean =     verbal  + (1) err_w")
        Sem.FitModel()
    Finally
        Sem.Dispose()
    End Try
End Sub
```

You do not need to explicitly allow the factors (*spatial* and *verbal*) to be correlated. Nor is it necessary to specify that the unique factors be uncorrelated with each other and with the two common factors. These are default assumptions in an Amos program (but not in Amos Graphics).

Example

9

An Alternative to Analysis of Covariance

Introduction

This example demonstrates a simple alternative to an analysis of covariance that does not require perfectly reliable covariates. A better, but more complicated, alternative will be demonstrated in Example 16.

Analysis of Covariance and Its Alternative

Analysis of covariance is a technique that is frequently used in experimental and quasi-experimental studies to reduce the effect of preexisting differences among treatment groups. Even when random assignment to treatment groups has eliminated the possibility of systematic pretreatment differences among groups, analysis of covariance can pay off in increased precision in evaluating treatment effects.

The usefulness of analysis of covariance is compromised by the assumption that each covariate be measured without error. The method makes other assumptions as well, but the assumption of perfectly reliable covariates has received particular attention (for example, Cook and Campbell 1979). In part, this is because the effects of violating the assumption can be so bad. Using unreliable covariates can lead to the erroneous conclusion that a treatment has an effect when it doesn't or that a treatment has no effect when it really does. Unreliable covariates can even make a treatment look like it does harm when it is actually beneficial. At the same time, unfortunately, the assumption of perfectly reliable covariates is typically impossible to meet.

The present example demonstrates an alternative to analysis of covariance in which no variable has to be measured without error. The method to be demonstrated

149

here has been employed by Bentler and Woodward (1979) and others. Another approach, by Sörbom (1978), is demonstrated in Example 16. The Sörbom method is more general. It allows testing other assumptions of analysis of covariance and permits relaxing some of them as well. The Sörbom approach is comparatively complicated because of its generality. By contrast, the method demonstrated in this example makes the usual assumptions of analysis of covariance, except for the assumption that covariates are measured without error. The virtue of the method is its comparative simplicity.

The present example employs two treatment groups and a single covariate. It may be generalized to any number of treatment groups and any number of covariates. Sörbom (1978) used the data that we will be using in this example and Example 16. The analysis closely follows Sörbom's example.

About the Data

Olsson (1973) administered a battery of eight tests to 213 eleven-year-old students on two occasions. We will employ two of the eight tests, *Synonyms* and *Opposites*, in this example. Between the two administrations of the test battery, 108 of the students (the experimental group) received training that was intended to improve performance on the tests. The other 105 students (the control group) did not receive any special training. As a result of taking two tests on two occasions, each of the 213 students obtained four test scores. A fifth, dichotomous variable was created to indicate membership in the experimental or control group. Altogether, the following variables are used in this example:

Variable	Description
pre_syn	Pretest scores on the Synonyms test.
pre_opp	Pretest scores on the Opposites test.
post_syn	Posttest scores on the Synonyms test.
post_opp	Posttest scores on the Opposites test.
treatment	A dichotomous variable taking on the value 1 for students who received the special training, and 0 for those who did not. This variable was created especially for the analyses in this example.

Correlations and standard deviations for the five measures are contained in the Microsoft Excel workbook *UserGuide.xls*, in the *Olss_all* worksheet. Here is the dataset:

rowtype_	varname_	pre_syn	pre_opp	post_syn	post_opp	treatment
n		213	213	213	213	213
corr	pre_syn	1				
corr	pre_opp	0.78255618	1			
corr	post_syn	0.78207295	0.69286541	1		
corr	post_opp	0.70438031	0.77390019	0.77567354	1	
corr	treatment	0.16261758	0.07784579	0.37887943	0.32533034	1
stddev		6.68680566	6.49938562	6.95007062	6.95685347	0.4999504

There are positive correlations between *treatment* and each of the posttests, which indicates that the trained students did better on the posttests than the untrained students. The correlations between *treatment* and each of the pretests are positive but relatively small. This indicates that the control and experimental groups did about equally well on the pretests. You would expect this, since students were randomly assigned to the control and experimental groups.

Analysis of Covariance

To evaluate the effect of training on performance, one might consider carrying out an analysis of covariance with one of the posttests as the criterion variable, and the two pretests as covariates. In order for that analysis to be appropriate, both the synonyms pretest and the opposites pretest would have to be perfectly reliable.

Model A for the Olsson Data

Consider the model for the Olsson data shown in the next path diagram. The model asserts that *pre_syn* and *pre_opp* are both imperfect measures of an unobserved ability called *pre_verbal* that might be thought of as verbal ability at the time of the pretest. The unique variables *eps1* and *eps2* represent errors of measurement in *pre_syn* and *pre_opp*, as well as any other influences on the two tests not represented elsewhere in the path diagram.

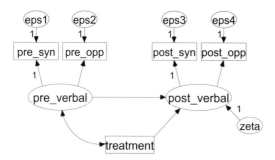

Example 9: Model A
Olsson (1973) test coaching study
Model Specification

Similarly, the model asserts that *post_syn* and *post_opp* are imperfect measures of an unobserved ability called *post_verbal*, which might be thought of as verbal ability at the time of the posttest. *Eps3* and *eps4* represent errors of measurement and other sources of variation not shown elsewhere in the path diagram.

The model shows two variables that may be useful in accounting for verbal ability at the time of the posttest. One such predictor is verbal ability at the time of the pretest. It would not be surprising to find that verbal ability at the time of the posttest depends on verbal ability at the time of the pretest. Because past performance is often an excellent predictor of future performance, the model uses the latent variable *pre_verbal* as a covariate. However, our primary interest lies in the second predictor, *treatment*. We are mostly interested in the regression weight associated with the arrow pointing from *treatment* to *post_verbal* and whether it is significantly different from 0. In other words, we will eventually want to know whether the model shown above could be accepted as correct under the additional hypothesis that that particular regression weight is 0. But first, we had better ask whether Model A can be accepted as it stands.

Identification

The units of measurement of the seven unobserved variables are indeterminate. This indeterminacy can be remedied by finding one single-headed arrow pointing away from each unobserved variable in the above figure and fixing the corresponding regression weight to unity (1). The seven 1's shown in the path diagram above indicate a satisfactory choice of identification constraints.

Specifying Model A

To specify Model A, draw a path diagram similar to the one on p. 152. The path diagram is saved as the file *Ex09-a.amw*.

Results for Model A

There is considerable empirical evidence against Model A:

Chi-square = 33.215
Degrees of freedom = 3
Probability level = 0.000

This is bad news. If we had been able to accept Model A, we could have taken the next step of repeating the analysis with the regression weight for regressing *post_verbal* on *treatment* fixed at 0. But there is no point in doing that now. We have to start with a model that we believe is correct in order to use it as the basis for testing a stronger *no treatment effect* version of the model.

Searching for a Better Model

Perhaps there is some way of modifying Model A so that it fits the data better. Some suggestions for suitable modifications can be obtained from *modification indices*.

Requesting Modification Indices

▶ From the menus, choose View → Analysis Properties.

▶ In the Analysis Properties dialog box, click the Output tab.

▶ Select Modification indices and enter a suitable threshold in the field to its right. For this example, the threshold will remain at its default value of 4.

Requesting modification indices with a threshold of 4 produces the following additional output:

Modification Indices (Group number 1 - Default model) Covariances: (Group number 1 - Default model)		
	M.I.	Par Change
eps2 <--> eps4	13.161	3.249
eps2 <--> eps3	10.813	-2.822
eps1 <--> eps4	11.968	-3.228
eps1 <--> eps3	9.788	2.798

According to the first modification index in the *M.I.* column, the chi-square statistic will decrease by at least 13.161 if the unique variables *eps2* and *eps4* are allowed to be correlated (the actual decrease may be greater). At the same time, of course, the number of degrees of freedom will drop by 1 because of the extra parameter that will have to be estimated. Since 13.161 is the largest modification index, we should consider it first and ask whether it is reasonable to think that *eps2* and *eps4* might be correlated.

Eps2 represents whatever *pre_opp* measures, other than verbal ability, that exist at the pretest. Similarly, *eps4* represents whatever *post_opp* measures, other than verbal ability, that exist at the posttest. It is plausible that some stable trait or ability other than verbal ability is measured on both administrations of the Opposites test. If so, then you would expect a positive correlation between *eps2* and *eps4*. In fact, the expected parameter change (the number in the *Par Change* column) associated with the covariance between *eps2* and *eps4* is positive, which indicates that the covariance will probably have a positive estimate if the covariance is not fixed at 0.

It might be added that the same reasoning that suggests allowing *eps2* and *eps4* to be correlated applies almost as well to *eps1* and *eps3*, whose covariance also has a fairly large modification index. For now, however, we will add only one parameter to Model A: the covariance between *eps2* and *eps4*. We call this new model **Model B**.

Model B for the Olsson Data

Below is the path diagram for Model B. It can be obtained by taking the path diagram for Model A and adding a double-headed arrow connecting *eps2* and *eps4*. This path diagram is saved in the file *Ex09-b.amw*.

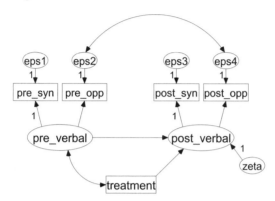

Example 9: Model B
Olsson (1973) test coaching study
Model Specification

You may find your error variables already positioned at the top of the path diagram, with no room to draw the double-headed arrow. To fix the problem:

▶ From the menus, choose Edit → Fit to Page.

Alternatively, you can:

▶ Draw the double-headed arrow and, if it is out of bounds, click the Resize (page with arrows) button. Amos will shrink your path diagram to fit within the page boundaries.

Results for Model B

Allowing *eps2* and *eps4* to be correlated results in a dramatic reduction of the chi-square statistic.

Chi-square = 2.684
Degrees of freedom = 2
Probability level = 0.261

You may recall from the results of Model A that the modification index for the covariance between *eps1* and *eps3* was 9.788. Clearly, freeing that covariance in addition to the covariance between *eps2* and *eps4* covariance would not have produced an additional drop in the chi-square statistic of 9.788, since this would imply a negative chi-square statistic. Thus, a modification index represents the minimal drop in the chi-square statistic that will occur if the corresponding constraint—and *only* that constraint—is removed.

The following raw parameter estimates are difficult to interpret because they would have been different if the identification constraints had been different:

Regression Weights: (Group number 1 - Default model)

	Estimate	S.E.	C.R.	P	Label
post_verbal <--- pre_verbal	.889	.053	16.900	***	
post_verbal <--- treatment	3.640	.477	7.625	***	
pre_syn <--- pre_verbal	1.000				
pre_opp <--- pre_verbal	.881	.053	16.606	***	
post_syn <--- post_verbal	1.000				
post_opp <--- post_verbal	.906	.053	16.948	***	

Covariances: (Group number 1 - Default model)

	Estimate	S.E.	C.R.	P	Label
pre_verbal <--> treatment	.467	.226	2.066	.039	
eps2 <--> eps4	6.797	1.344	5.059	***	

Variances: (Group number 1 - Default model)

	Estimate	S.E.	C.R.	P	Label
pre_verbal	38.491	4.501	8.552	***	
treatment	.249	.024	10.296	***	
zeta	4.824	1.331	3.625	***	
eps1	6.013	1.502	4.004	***	
eps2	12.255	1.603	7.646	***	
eps3	6.546	1.501	4.360	***	
eps4	14.685	1.812	8.102	***	

As expected, the covariance between *eps2* and *eps4* is positive. The most interesting result that appears along with the parameter estimates is the critical ratio for the effect of *treatment* on *post_verbal*. This critical ratio shows that *treatment* has a highly significant effect on *post_verbal*. We will shortly obtain a better test of the significance of this effect by modifying Model B so that this regression weight is fixed at 0. In the meantime, here are the standardized estimates and the squared multiple correlations as displayed by Amos Graphics:

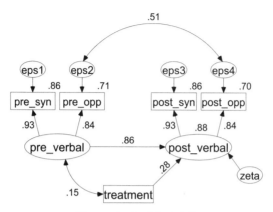

Example 9: Model B
Olsson (1973) test coaching study
Standardized estimates

In this example, we are primarily concerned with testing a particular hypothesis and not so much with parameter estimation. However, even when the parameter estimates themselves are not of primary interest, it is a good idea to look at them anyway to see if they are reasonable. Here, for instance, you may not care exactly what the correlation between *eps2* and *eps4* is, but you would expect it to be positive. Similarly, you would be surprised to find any negative estimates for regression weights in this model. In any model, you know that variables cannot have negative variances, so a negative variance estimate would always be an unreasonable estimate. If estimates cannot pass a gross sanity check, particularly with a reasonably large sample, you have to question the correctness of the model under which they were obtained, no matter how well the model fits the data.

Model C for the Olsson Data

Now that we have a model (Model B) that we can reasonably believe is correct, let's see how it fares if we add the constraint that *post_verbal* does not depend on *treatment*. In other words, we will test a new model (call it **Model C**) that is just like Model B except that Model C specifies that *post_verbal* has a regression weight of 0 on *treatment*.

Example 9

Drawing a Path Diagram for Model C

To draw the path diagram for Model C:

▶ Start with the path diagram for Model B.

▶ Right-click the arrow that points from *treatment* to *post_verbal* and choose Object Properties from the pop-up menu.

▶ In the Object Properties dialog box, click the Parameters tab and type 0 in the Regression weight text box.

The path diagram for Model C is saved in the file *Ex09-c.amw*.

Results for Model C

Model C has to be rejected at any conventional significance level.

Chi-square = 55.396
Degrees of freedom = 3
Probability level = 0.000

If you assume that Model B is correct and that only the correctness of Model C is in doubt, then a better test of Model C can be obtained as follows: In going from Model B to Model C, the chi-square statistic increased by 52.712 (that is, 55.396 – 2.684), while the number of degrees of freedom increased by 1 (that is, 3 – 2). If Model C is correct, 52.712 is an observation on a random variable that has an approximate chi-square distribution with one degree of freedom. The probability of such a random variable exceeding 52.712 is exceedingly small. Thus, Model C is rejected in favor of Model B. *Treatment* has a significant effect on *post_verbal*.

Fitting All Models At Once

The example file *Ex09-all.amw* fits all three models (A through C) in a single analysis. The procedure for fitting multiple models in a single analysis was demonstrated in Example 6.

Modeling in VB.NET

Model A

This program fits Model A. It is saved in the file *Ex09–a.vb*.

```
Sub Main()
    Dim Sem As New AmosEngine
    Try
        Sem.TextOutput()
        Sem.Mods(4)
        Sem.Standardized()
        Sem.Smc()

        Sem.BeginGroup(Sem.AmosDir & "Examples\UserGuide.xls", "Olss_all")
        Sem.AStructure("pre_syn    = (1) pre_verbal  + (1) eps1")
        Sem.AStructure("pre_opp    =     pre_verbal  + (1) eps2")

        Sem.AStructure("post_syn   = (1) post_verbal + (1) eps3")
        Sem.AStructure("post_opp   =     post_verbal + (1) eps4")

        Sem.AStructure("post_verbal = pre_verbal + treatment + (1) zeta")
        Sem.FitModel()
    Finally
        Sem.Dispose()
    End Try
End Sub
```

Model B

This program fits Model B. It is saved in the file *Ex09–b.vb*.

```
Sub Main()
    Dim Sem As New AmosEngine
    Try
        Sem.TextOutput()
        Sem.Standardized()
        Sem.Smc()

        Sem.BeginGroup(Sem.AmosDir & "Examples\UserGuide.xls", "Olss_all")
        Sem.AStructure("pre_syn    = (1) pre_verbal  + (1) eps1")
        Sem.AStructure("pre_opp    =     pre_verbal  + (1) eps2")
        Sem.AStructure("post_syn   = (1) post_verbal + (1) eps3")
        Sem.AStructure("post_opp   =     post_verbal + (1) eps4")

        Sem.AStructure("post_verbal = pre_verbal + treatment + (1) zeta")

        Sem.AStructure("eps2 <---> eps4")
        Sem.FitModel()
    Finally
        Sem.Dispose()
    End Try
End Sub
```

Example 9

Model C

This program fits Model C. It is saved in the file *Ex09–c.vb*.

```
Sub Main()
   Dim Sem As New AmosEngine
   Try
      Sem.TextOutput()
      Sem.Mods(4)
      Sem.Standardized()
      Sem.Smc()

      Sem.BeginGroup(Sem.AmosDir & "Examples\UserGuide.xls", "Olss_all")
      Sem.AStructure("pre_syn    = (1) pre_verbal  + (1) eps1")
      Sem.AStructure("pre_opp    =     pre_verbal  + (1) eps2")
      Sem.AStructure("post_syn   = (1) post_verbal + (1) eps3")
      Sem.AStructure("post_opp   =     post_verbal + (1) eps4")

      Sem.AStructure("post_verbal = pre_verbal + (0) treatment + (1) zeta")

      Sem.AStructure("eps2 <---> eps4")

      Sem.FitModel()
   Finally
      Sem.Dispose()
   End Try
End Sub
```

Fitting Multiple Models

This program *(Ex09-all.vb)* fits all three models (A through C).

```
Sub Main()
   Dim Sem As New AmosEngine
   Try
      Sem.TextOutput()
      Sem.Mods(4)
      Sem.Standardized()
      Sem.Smc()

      Sem.BeginGroup(Sem.AmosDir & "Examples\UserGuide.xls", "Olss_all")
      Sem.AStructure("pre_syn    = (1) pre_verbal  + (1) eps1")
      Sem.AStructure("pre_opp    =     pre_verbal  + (1) eps2")
      Sem.AStructure("post_syn   = (1) post_verbal + (1) eps3")
      Sem.AStructure("post_opp   =     post_verbal + (1) eps4")

      Sem.AStructure("post_verbal = pre_verbal + (effect) treatment + (1) zeta")

      Sem.AStructure("eps2 <---> eps4 (cov2_4)")

      Sem.Model("Model_A", "cov2_4 = 0")
      Sem.Model("Model_B")
      Sem.Model("Model_C", "effect = 0")
      Sem.FitAllModels()
   Finally
      Sem.Dispose()
   End Try
End Sub
```

Example
10

Simultaneous Analysis of Several Groups

Introduction

This example demonstrates how to fit a model to two sets of data at once. Amos is capable of modeling data from multiple groups (or samples) simultaneously. This multigroup facility allows for many additional types of analyses, as illustrated in the next several examples.

Analysis of Several Groups

We return once again to Attig's (1983) memory data from young and old subjects, which were used in Example 1 through Example 3. In this example, we will compare results from the two groups to see how similar they are. However, we will not compare the groups by performing separate analyses for old people and young people. Instead, we will perform a single analysis that estimates parameters and tests hypotheses about both groups at once. This method has two advantages over doing separate analyses for the young and old groups. First, it provides a test for the significance of any differences found between young and old people. Second, if there are no differences between young and old people or if the group differences concern only a few model parameters, the simultaneous analysis of both groups provides more accurate parameter estimates than would be obtained from two separate single-group analyses.

Example 10

About the Data

We will use Attig's memory data from both young and old subjects. Following is a partial listing of the old subjects' data found in the worksheet *Attg_old* located in the Microsoft Excel workbook *UserGuide.xls*:

subject	age	education	sex	recall1	recall2	cued1	cued2
1	65	16	1	5	11	5	11
2	68	18	0	12	16	14	16
3	64	17	1	11	11	10	11
4	77	16	0	3	3	3	4
5	72	12	0	8	9	11	9
6	75	12	1	10	9	10	10
7	69	12	0	8	7	10	8
8	74	12	0	7	6	8	9
9	66	12	0	8	12	9	13
10	77	12	0	8	11	10	13

The young subjects' data are in the *Attg_yng* worksheet. This example uses only the measures *recall1* and *cued1*.

Data for multigroup analysis can be organized in a variety of ways. One option is to separate the data into different files, with one file for each group (as we have done in this example). A second possibility is to keep all the data in one big file and include a group membership variable.

Model A

We will begin with a truly trivial model (Model A) for two variables: *recall1* and *cued1*. The model simply says that, for young subjects as well as old subjects, *recall1* and *cued1* are two variables that have some unspecified variances and some unspecified covariance. The variances and the covariance are allowed to be different for young and old people.

Conventions for Specifying Group Differences

The main purpose of a multigroup analysis is to find out the extent to which groups differ. Do the groups all have the same path diagram with the same parameter values? Do the groups have the same path diagram but with different parameter values for different groups? Does each group need a different path diagram? Amos Graphics has the following conventions for specifying group differences in a multigroup analysis:

- All groups have the same path diagram unless explicitly declared otherwise.

- Unnamed parameters are permitted to have different values in different groups. Thus, the default multigroup model under Amos Graphics uses the same path diagram for all groups but allows different parameter values for different groups.

- Parameters in different groups can be constrained to the same value by giving them the same label. (This will be demonstrated in Model B on p. 176.)

Specifying Model A

▶ From the menus, choose File → New to start a new path diagram.

▶ From the menus, choose File → Data Files.

Notice that the Data Files dialog box allows you to specify a data file for only a single group called Group number 1. We have not yet told the program that this is a multigroup analysis.

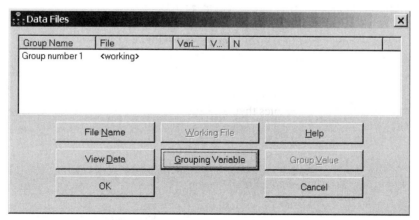

Example 10

▶ Click File Name, select the Excel workbook *UserGuide.xls* that is in the Amos *Examples* directory, and click Open.

▶ In the Select a Data Table dialog box, select the *Attg_yng* worksheet.

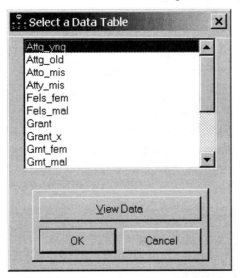

▶ Click OK to close the Select a Data Table dialog box.

▶ Click OK to close the Data Files dialog box.

▶ From the menus, choose View → Variables in Dataset.

▶ Drag observed variables *recall1* and *cued1* to the diagram.

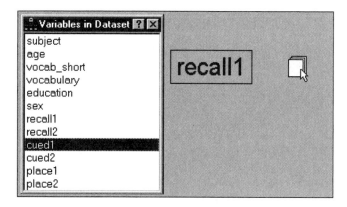

▶ Connect *recall1* and *cued1* with a double-headed arrow.

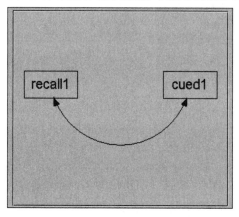

▶ To add a caption to the path diagram, from the menus, choose Diagram → Figure Caption and then click the path diagram at the spot where you want the caption to appear.

▶ In the Figure Caption dialog box, enter a title that contains the text macros \group and \format.

Example 10

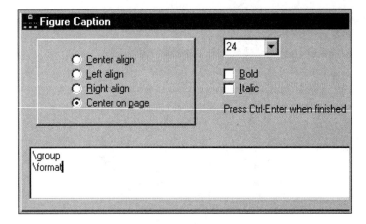

▶ Click OK to complete the model specification for the young group.

▶ To add a second group, from the menus, choose Analyze → Manage Groups.

▶ In the Manage Groups dialog box, change the name in the Group Name text box from Group number 1 to young subjects.

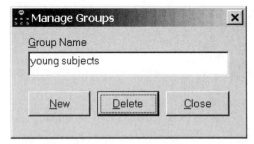

▶ Click New to create a second group.

▶ Change the name in the Group Name text box from Group number 2 to old subjects.

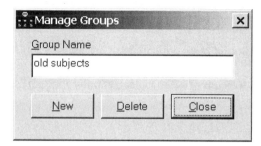

▶ Click Close.

▶ From the menus, choose File → Data Files.

The Data Files dialog box shows that there are two groups labeled *young subjects* and *old subjects*.

▶ To specify the dataset for the old subjects, in the Data Files dialog box, select old subjects.

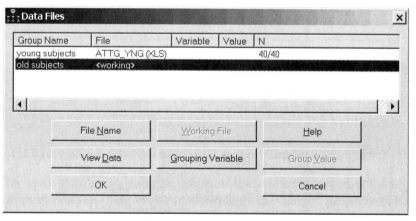

▶ Click File Name, select the Excel workbook *UserGuide.xls* that is in the Amos *Examples* directory, and click Open.

▶ In the Select a Data Table dialog box, select the *Attg_old* worksheet.

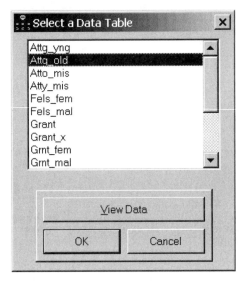

▶ Click OK.

Text Output

Model A has zero degrees of freedom.

Computation of degrees of freedom (Default model)	
Number of distinct sample moments:	6
Number of distinct parameters to be estimated:	6
Degrees of freedom (6 - 6):	0

Amos computed the number of distinct sample moments this way: The young subjects have two sample variances and one sample covariance, which makes three sample moments. The old subjects also have three sample moments, making a total of six sample moments. The parameters to be estimated are the population moments, and there are six of them as well. Since there are zero degrees of freedom, this model is untestable.

Chi-square = 0.000
Degrees of freedom = 0
Probability level cannot be computed

To view parameter estimates for the young people in the Amos Output window:

▶ Click Estimates in the tree diagram in the upper left pane.

▶ Click young subjects in the Groups panel at the left side of the window.

Covariances: (young subjects - Default model)

	Estimate	S.E.	C.R.	P	Label
recall1 <--> cued1	3.225	.944	3.416	***	

Variances: (young subjects - Default model)

	Estimate	S.E.	C.R.	P	Label
recall1	5.787	1.311	4.416	***	
cued1	4.210	.953	4.416	***	

To view the parameter estimates for the old subjects:

▶ Click old subjects in the Groups panel.

Covariances: (old subjects - Default model)

	Estimate	S.E.	C.R.	P	Label
recall1 <--> cued1	4.887	1.252	3.902	***	

Variances: (old subjects - Default model)

	Estimate	S.E.	C.R.	P	Label
recall1	5.569	1.261	4.416	***	
cued1	6.694	1.516	4.416	***	

Graphics Output

The following are the output path diagrams showing unstandardized estimates for the two groups:

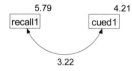

Example 10: Model A
Simultaneous analysis of several groups
Attig (1983) young subjects
Unstandardized estimates

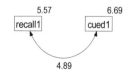

Example 10: Model A
Simultaneous analysis of several groups
Attig (1983) old subjects
Unstandardized estimates

The panels at the left of the Amos Graphics window provide a variety of viewing options.

- Click either the View Input or View Output button to see an input or output path diagram.

- Select either young subjects or old subjects in the Groups panel.

- Select either Unstandardized estimates or Standardized estimates in the Parameter Formats panel.

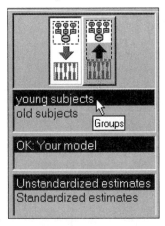

Model B

It is easy to see that the parameter estimates are different for the two groups. But are the differences significant? One way to find out is to repeat the analysis, but this time requiring that each parameter in the young population be equal to the corresponding parameter in the old population. The resulting model will be called Model B.

For Model B, it is necessary to name each parameter, using the same parameter names in the old group as in the young group.

▶ Start by clicking young subjects in the Groups panel at the left of the path diagram.

▶ Right-click the *recall1* rectangle in the path diagram.

▶ From the pop-up menu, choose Object Properties.

▶ In the Object Properties dialog box, click the Parameters tab.

▶ In the Variance text box, enter a name for the variance of *recall1*; for example, type var_rec.

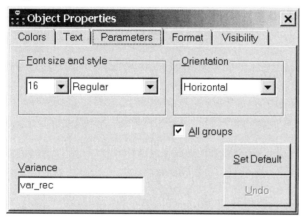

▶ Select All groups (a check mark will appear next to it).

The effect of the check mark is to assign the name *var_rec* to the variance of *recall1* in all groups. Without the check mark, *var_rec* would be the name of the variance for *recall1* for the young group only.

▶ While the Object Properties dialog box is open, click cued1 and type the name var_cue for its variance.

▶ Click the double-headed arrow and type the name cov_rc for the covariance. Always make sure that you select All groups.

The path diagram for each group should now look like this:

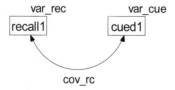

Example 10: Model B
Homogenous covariance structures
in two groups, Attig (1983) data.
Model Specification

Example 10

Text Output

Because of the constraints imposed in Model B, only three distinct parameters are estimated instead of six. As a result, the number of degrees of freedom has increased from 0 to 3.

Computation of degrees of freedom (Default model)	
Number of distinct sample moments:	6
Number of distinct parameters to be estimated:	3
Degrees of freedom (6 - 3):	3

Model B is acceptable at any conventional significance level.

Chi-square = 4.588
Degrees of freedom = 3
Probability level = 0.205

The following are the parameter estimates obtained under Model B for the young subjects. (The parameter estimates for the old subjects are the same.)

Covariances: (young subjects - Default model)

	Estimate	S.E.	C.R.	P	Label
recall1 <--> cued1	4.056	.780	5.202	***	cov_rc

Variances: (young subjects - Default model)

	Estimate	S.E.	C.R.	P	Label
recall1	5.678	.909	6.245	***	var_rec
cued1	5.452	.873	6.245	***	var_cue

You can see that the standard error estimates obtained under Model B are smaller (for the young subjects, 0.780, 0.909, and 0.873) than the corresponding estimates obtained under Model A (0.944, 1.311, and 0.953). The Model B estimates are to be preferred over the ones from Model A as long as you believe that Model B is correct.

Graphics Output

For Model B, the output path diagram is the same for both groups.

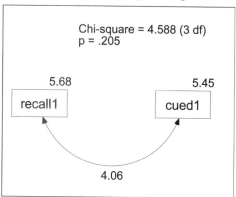

Chi-square = 4.588 (3 df)
p = .205

5.68   recall1   5.45   cued1

4.06

Modeling in VB.NET

Model A

Here is a program (*Ex10-a.vb*) for fitting Model A:

```
Sub Main()
   Dim Sem As New AmosEngine
   Try
      Sem.TextOutput()

      Sem.BeginGroup(Sem.AmosDir & "Examples\UserGuide.xls", "Attg_yng")
         Sem.GroupName("young subjects")
         Sem.AStructure("recall1")
         Sem.AStructure("cued1")

      Sem.BeginGroup(Sem.AmosDir & "Examples\UserGuide.xls", "Attg_old")
         Sem.GroupName("old subjects")
         Sem.AStructure("recall1")
         Sem.AStructure("cued1")
      Sem.FitModel()
   Finally
      Sem.Dispose()
   End Try
End Sub
```

The BeginGroup method is used twice in this two-group analysis. The first BeginGroup line specifies the *Attg_yng* dataset. The three lines that follow supply a name and a model for that group. The second BeginGroup line specifies the *Attg_old* dataset, and the following three lines supply a name and a model for that group. The model for each group simply says that *recall1* and *cued1* are two variables with unconstrained variances and an unspecified covariance. The GroupName method is optional, but it is useful in multiple-group analyses because it helps Amos to label the output in a meaningful way.

Model B

The following program for Model B is saved in *Ex10-b.vb*:

```
Sub Main()
    Dim Sem As New AmosEngine
    Try
        Dim dataFile As String = Sem.AmosDir & "Examples\UserGuide.xls"

        Sem.Standardized()
        Sem.TextOutput()

        Sem.BeginGroup(dataFile, "Attg_yng")
            Sem.GroupName("young subjects")
            Sem.AStructure("recall1      (var_rec)")
            Sem.AStructure("cued1         (var_cue)")
            Sem.AStructure("recall1 <> cued1  (cov_rc)")
        Sem.BeginGroup(dataFile, "Attg_old")
            Sem.GroupName("old subjects")
            Sem.AStructure("recall1      (var_rec)")
            Sem.AStructure("cued1         (var_cue)")
            Sem.AStructure("recall1 <> cued1  (cov_rc)")
        Sem.FitModel()
    Finally
        Sem.Dispose()
    End Try
End Sub
```

The parameter names *var_rec*, *var_cue*, and *cov_rc* (in parentheses) are used to require that some parameters have the same value for old people as for young people. Using the name *var_rec* twice requires *recall1* to have the same variance in both populations. Similarly, using the name *var_cue* twice requires *cued1* to have the same variance in both populations. Using the name *cov_rc* twice requires that *recall1* and *cued1* have the same covariance in both populations.

Multiple Model Input

Here is a program (*Ex10-all.vb*) for fitting both Models A and B.[1]

```
Sub Main()
   Dim Sem As New AmosEngine
   Try
      Sem.Standardized()
      Sem.TextOutput()

      Sem.BeginGroup(Sem.AmosDir & "Examples\UserGuide.xls", "Attg_yng")
         Sem.GroupName("young subjects")
         Sem.AStructure("recall1          (yng_rec)")
         Sem.AStructure("cued1          (yng_cue)")
         Sem.AStructure("recall1 <> cued1  (yng_rc)")

      Sem.BeginGroup(Sem.AmosDir & "Examples\UserGuide.xls", "Attg_old")
         Sem.GroupName("old subjects")
         Sem.AStructure("recall1          (old_rec)")
         Sem.AStructure("cued1          (old_cue)")
         Sem.AStructure("recall1 <> cued1  (old_rc)")

      Sem.Model("Model A")
      Sem.Model("Model B", "yng_rec=old_rec", "yng_cue=old_cue", _
         "yng_rc=old_rc")
      Sem.FitAllModels()
   Finally
      Sem.Dispose()
   End Try
End Sub
```

The Sem.Model statements should appear immediately after the AStructure specifications for the last group. It does not matter which Model statement goes first.

---

1 In Example 6 (*Ex06-all.vb*), multiple model constraints were written in a single string, within which individual constraints were separated by semicolons. In the present example, each constraint is in its own string, and the individual strings are separated by commas. Either syntax is acceptable.

Example

11

Felson and Bohrnstedt's Girls and Boys

Introduction

This example demonstrates how to fit a simultaneous equations model to two sets of data at once.

Felson and Bohrnstedt's Model

Example 7 tested Felson and Bohrnstedt's (1979) model for perceived attractiveness and perceived academic ability using a sample of 209 girls. Here, we take the same model and attempt to apply it simultaneously to the Example 7 data and to data from another sample of 207 boys. We will examine the question of whether the measured variables are related to each other in the same way for boys as for girls.

About the Data

The Felson and Bohrnstedt (1979) data for girls were described in Example 7. Here is a table of the boys' data from the SPSS file *Fels_mal.sav*:

	rowtype_	varname_	academic	athletic	attract	gpa	skills	height	weight	rating
1	n		207.00	207.00	207.00	207.00	207.00	207.00	207.00	207.00
2	corr	academic	1.00	.	.	.	.	.	.	.
3	corr	athletic	.47	1.00	.	.	.	.	.	.
4	corr	attract	.49	.72	1.00	.	.	.	.	.
5	corr	GPA	.58	.27	.30	1.00	.	.	.	.
6	corr	skills	.35	.65	.44	.35	1.00	.	.	.
7	corr	height	-.02	.15	.04	-.11	.12	1.00	.	.
8	corr	weight	-.11	-.01	-.19	-.16	-.05	.51	1.00	.
9	corr	rating	.11	.24	.28	.13	.38	.06	-.18	1.00
10	stddev		.16	.21	.49	4.04	.74	3.41	24.32	.97
11	mean		.10	.17	.44	8.63	2.93	.00	101.91	2.59

Notice that there are eight variables in the boys' data file but only seven in the girls' data file. The extra variable *skills* is not used in any model of this example, so its presence in the data file is ignored.

Specifying Model A for Girls and Boys

Consider extending the Felson and Bohrnstedt model of perceived attractiveness and academic ability to boys as well as girls. To do this, we will start with the girls-only model specification from Example 7 and modify it to accommodate two groups. If you have already drawn the path diagram for Example 7, you can use it as a starting point for this example. No additional drawing is needed.

Parameter estimates can be displayed on a path diagram for only one group at a time in a multigroup analysis. It is useful then to display a figure caption that tells which group the parameter estimates represent.

Specifying a Figure Caption

To create a figure caption that displays the group name, place the \group text macro in the caption.

▶ From the menus, choose Diagram → Figure Caption.

▶ Click the path diagram at the spot where you want the caption to appear.

▶ In the Figure Caption dialog box, enter a title that contains the text macro \group. For example:

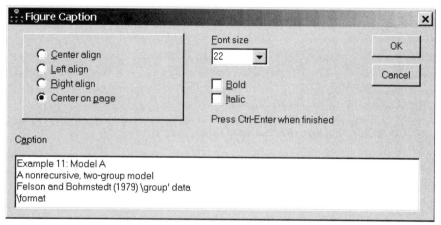

In Example 7, where there was only one group, the group's name didn't matter. Accepting the default name *Group number 1* was good enough. Now that there are two groups to keep track of, the groups should be given meaningful names.

▶ From the menus, choose Analyze → Manage Groups.

▶ In the Manage Groups dialog box, type girls for Group Name.

▶ While the Manage Groups dialog box is open, create a second group by clicking New.

▶ Type boys in the Group Name text box.

Example 11

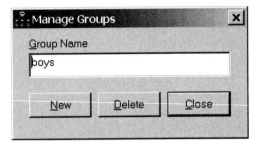

▶ Click Close to close the Manage Groups dialog box.

▶ From the menus, choose File → Data Files.

▶ In the Data Files dialog box, double-click girls and select the data file *Fels_fem.sav*.

▶ Then, double-click boys and select the data file *Fels_mal.sav*.

▶ Click OK to close the Data Files dialog box.

Your path diagram should look something like this for the boys' sample:

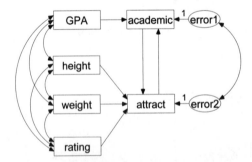

Example 11: Model A
A nonrecursive, two-group model
Felson and Bohrnstedt (1979) boys' data
Model Specification

Notice that, although girls and boys have the same path diagram, there is no requirement that the parameters have the same values in the two groups. This means that estimates of regression weights, covariances, and variances may be different for boys than for girls.

Text Output for Model A

With two groups instead of one (as in Example 7), there are twice as many sample moments and twice as many parameters to estimate. Therefore, you have twice as many degrees of freedom as there were in Example 7.

Computation of degrees of freedom (Default model)	
Number of distinct sample moments:	42
Number of distinct parameters to be estimated:	38
Degrees of freedom (42 - 38):	4

The model fits the data from both groups quite well.

Chi-square = 3.183
Degrees of freedom = 4
Probability level = 0.528

We accept the hypothesis that the Felson and Bohrnstedt model is correct for both boys and girls. The next thing to look at is the parameter estimates. We will be interested in how the girls' estimates compare to the boys' estimates. The following are the parameter estimates for the girls:

Regression Weights: (girls - Default model)

	Estimate	S.E.	C.R.	P	Label
academic <--- GPA	.023	.004	6.241	***	
attract <--- height	.000	.010	.050	.960	
attract <--- weight	-.002	.001	-1.321	.186	
attract <--- rating	.176	.027	6.444	***	
attract <--- academic	1.607	.350	4.599	***	
academic <--- attract	-.002	.051	-.039	.969	

Covariances: (girls - Default model)

	Estimate	S.E.	C.R.	P	Label
GPA <--> rating	.526	.246	2.139	.032	
height <--> rating	-.468	.205	-2.279	.023	
GPA <--> weight	-6.710	4.676	-1.435	.151	
GPA <--> height	1.819	.712	2.555	.011	
height <--> weight	19.024	4.098	4.642	***	
weight <--> rating	-5.243	1.395	-3.759	***	
error1 <--> error2	-.004	.010	-.382	.702	

Variances: (girls - Default model)

	Estimate	S.E.	C.R.	P	Label
GPA	12.122	1.189	10.198	***	
height	8.428	.826	10.198	***	
weight	371.476	36.427	10.198	***	
rating	1.015	.100	10.198	***	
error1	.019	.003	5.747	***	
error2	.143	.014	9.974	***	

Example 11

These parameter estimates are the same as in Example 7. Standard errors, critical ratios, and *p* values are also the same. The following are the unstandardized estimates for the boys:

Regression Weights: (boys - Default model)

	Estimate	S.E.	C.R.	P	Label
academic <--- GPA	.021	.003	6.927	***	
attract <--- height	.019	.010	1.967	.049	
attract <--- weight	-.003	.001	-2.484	.013	
attract <--- rating	.095	.030	3.150	.002	
attract <--- academic	1.386	.315	4.398	***	
academic <--- attract	.063	.059	1.071	.284	

Covariances: (boys - Default model)

	Estimate	S.E.	C.R.	P	Label
GPA <--> rating	.507	.274	1.850	.064	
height <--> rating	.198	.230	.860	.390	
GPA <--> weight	-15.645	6.899	-2.268	.023	
GPA <--> height	-1.508	.961	-1.569	.117	
height <--> weight	42.091	6.455	6.521	***	
weight <--> rating	-4.226	1.662	-2.543	.011	
error1 <--> error2	-.010	.011	-.898	.369	

Variances: (boys - Default model)

	Estimate	S.E.	C.R.	P	Label
GPA	16.243	1.600	10.149	***	
height	11.572	1.140	10.149	***	
weight	588.605	57.996	10.149	***	
rating	.936	.092	10.149	***	
error1	.015	.002	7.571	***	
error2	.164	.016	10.149	***	

Graphics Output for Model A

For girls, this is the path diagram with unstandardized estimates displayed:

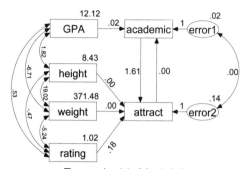

Example 11: Model A
A nonrecursive, two-group model
Felson and Bohrnstedt (1979) girls' data
Unstandardized estimates

The following is the path diagram with the estimates for the boys:

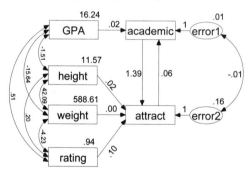

Example 11: Model A
A nonrecursive, two-group model
Felson and Bohrnstedt (1979) boys' data
Unstandardized estimates

You can visually inspect the girls' and boys' estimates in Model A, looking for sex differences. To find out if girls and boys differ significantly with respect to any single parameter, you could examine the table of critical ratios of differences among all pairs of free parameters.

Obtaining Critical Ratios for Parameter Differences

▶ From the menus, choose View → Analysis Properties.

▶ In the Analysis Properties dialog box, click the Output tab.

▶ Select Critical ratios for differences.

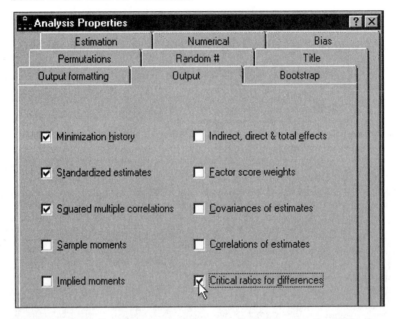

In this example, however, we will not use critical ratios for differences; instead, we will take an alternative approach to looking for group differences.

Model B for Girls and Boys

Suppose we are mainly interested in the regression weights, and we hypothesize (Model B) that girls and boys have the same regression weights. In this model, the variances and covariances of the exogenous variables are still allowed to differ from one group to another.

This model allows the distribution of variables such as *height* and *weight* to be different for boys than for girls while requiring the linear dependencies among variables to be group-invariant. For Model B, you need to constrain six regression weights in each group.

▶ First, display the girls' path diagram by clicking girls in the Groups panel at the left of the path diagram.

▶ Right-click one of the single-headed arrows and choose Object Properties from the pop-up menu.

▶ In the Object Properties dialog box, click the Parameters tab.

▶ Enter a name in the Regression weight text box.

▶ Select All groups. A check mark appears next to it. The effect of the check mark is to assign the same name to this regression weight in all groups.

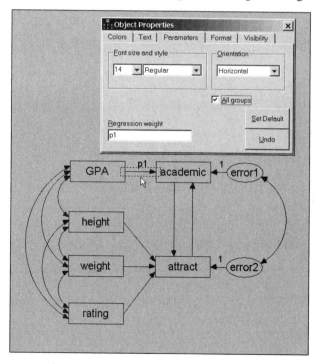

▶ Keeping the Object Properties dialog box open, click another single-headed arrow and enter another name in the Regression weight text box.

▶ Repeat this until you have named every regression weight. Always make sure to select (put a check mark next to) All groups.

After you have named all of the regression weights, the path diagram for each sample should look something like this:

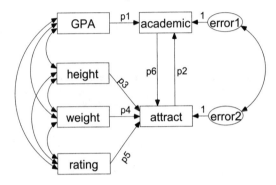

Results for Model B

Text Output

Model B fits the data very well.

Chi-square = 9.493
Degrees of freedom = 10
Probability level = 0.486

Comparing Model B against Model A gives a nonsignificant chi-square of 9.493 – 3.183 = 6.310 with 10 – 4 = 6 degrees of freedom. Assuming that Model B is indeed correct, the Model B estimates are preferable over the Model A estimates.

The unstandardized parameter estimates for the girls' sample are:

Regression Weights: (girls - Default model)

			Estimate	S.E.	C.R.	P	Label
academic	<---	GPA	.022	.002	9.475	***	p1
attract	<---	height	.008	.007	1.177	.239	p3
attract	<---	weight	-.003	.001	-2.453	.014	p4
attract	<---	rating	.145	.020	7.186	***	p5
attract	<---	academic	1.448	.232	6.234	***	p6
academic	<---	attract	.018	.039	.469	.639	p2

Covariances: (girls - Default model)

	Estimate	S.E.	C.R.	P	Label
GPA <--> rating	.526	.246	2.139	.032	
height <--> rating	-.468	.205	-2.279	.023	
GPA <--> weight	-6.710	4.676	-1.435	.151	
GPA <--> height	1.819	.712	2.555	.011	
height <--> weight	19.024	4.098	4.642	***	
weight <--> rating	-5.243	1.395	-3.759	***	
error1 <--> error2	-.004	.008	-.464	.643	

Variances: (girls - Default model)

	Estimate	S.E.	C.R.	P	Label
GPA	12.122	1.189	10.198	***	
height	8.428	.826	10.198	***	
weight	371.476	36.427	10.198	***	
rating	1.015	.100	10.198	***	
error1	.018	.003	7.111	***	
error2	.144	.014	10.191	***	

Example 11

The unstandardized parameter estimates for the boys are:

Regression Weights: (boys - Default model)

			Estimate	S.E.	C.R.	P	Label
academic	<---	GPA	.022	.002	9.475	***	p1
attract	<---	height	.008	.007	1.177	.239	p3
attract	<---	weight	-.003	.001	-2.453	.014	p4
attract	<---	rating	.145	.020	7.186	***	p5
attract	<---	academic	1.448	.232	6.234	***	p6
academic	<---	attract	.018	.039	.469	.639	p2

Covariances: (boys - Default model)

	Estimate	S.E.	C.R.	P	Label
GPA <--> rating	.507	.274	1.850	.064	
height <--> rating	.198	.230	.860	.390	
GPA <--> weight	-15.645	6.899	-2.268	.023	
GPA <--> height	-1.508	.961	-1.569	.117	
height <--> weight	42.091	6.455	6.521	***	
weight <--> rating	-4.226	1.662	-2.543	.011	
error1 <--> error2	-.004	.008	-.466	.641	

Variances: (boys - Default model)

	Estimate	S.E.	C.R.	P	Label
GPA	16.243	1.600	10.149	***	
height	11.572	1.140	10.149	***	
weight	588.605	57.996	10.149	***	
rating	.936	.092	10.149	***	
error1	.016	.002	7.220	***	
error2	.167	.016	10.146	***	

As Model B requires, the estimated regression weights for the boys are the same as those for the girls.

Graphics Output

The output path diagram for the girls is:

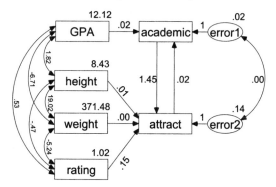

Example 11: Model B
A nonrecursive, two-group model
Felson and Bohrnstedt (1979) girls' data
Unstandardized estimates

And the output for the boys is:

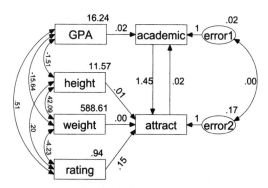

Example 11: Model B
A nonrecursive, two-group model
Felson and Bohrnstedt (1979) boys' data
Unstandardized estimates

Fitting Models A and B in a Single Analysis

It is possible to fit both Model A and Model B in the same analysis. The file
Ex11-ab.amw in the Amos *Examples* directory shows how to do this.

Model C for Girls and Boys

You might consider adding additional constraints to Model B, such as requiring every
parameter to have the same value for boys as for girls. This would imply that the entire
variance/covariance matrix of the observed variables is the same for boys as for girls,
while also requiring that the Felson and Bohrnstedt model be correct for both groups.
Instead of following this course, we will now abandon the Felson and Bohrnstedt
model and concentrate on the hypothesis that the observed variables have the same
variance/covariance matrix for girls and boys. We will construct a model (Model C)
that embodies this hypothesis.

▶ Start with the path diagram for Model A or Model B and delete (Edit → Erase) every
object in the path diagram except the six observed variables. The path diagram will
then look something like this:

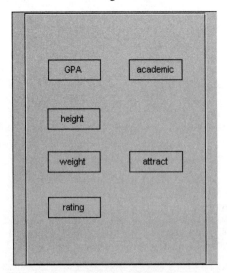

Each pair of rectangles needs to be connected by a double-headed arrow, for a total of
15 double-headed arrows.

▶ To improve the appearance of the results, from the menus, choose Edit → Move and use the mouse to arrange the six rectangles in a single column like this:

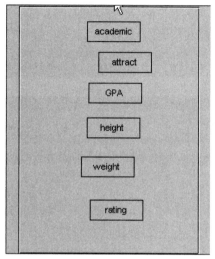

The Drag properties option can be used to put the rectangles in perfect vertical alignment.

▶ From the menus, choose Edit → Drag properties.

▶ In the Drag Properties dialog box, select height, width, and X-coordinate. A check mark will appear next to each one.

▶ Use the mouse to drag these properties from *academic* to *attract*.

This gives *attract* the same x coordinate as *academic*. In other words, it aligns them vertically. It also makes *attract* the same size as *academic* if they are not already the same size.

▶ Then drag from *attract* to *GPA*, *GPA* to *height*, and so on. Keep this up until all six variables are lined up vertically.

194

Example 11

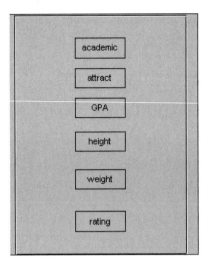

▶ To even out the spacing between the rectangles, from the menus, choose Edit → Select All.

▶ Then choose Edit → Space Vertically.

There is a special button for drawing large numbers of double-headed arrows at once. With all six variables still selected from the previous step:

▶ From the menus, choose Tools → Macro → Draw Covariances.

Amos draws all possible covariance paths among the selected variables.

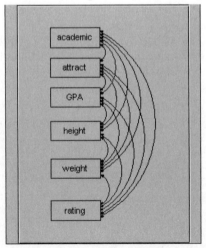

▶ Label all variances and covariances with suitable names; for example, label them with letters *a* through *u*. In the Object Properties dialog box, always put a check mark next to All groups when you name a parameter.

▶ From the menus, choose Analyze → Manage Models and create a second group for the boys.

▶ Choose File → Data Files and specify the boys' dataset (*Fels_mal.sav*) for this group.

The file *Ex11-c.amw* contains the model specification for Model C. Here is the input path diagram, which is the same for both groups:

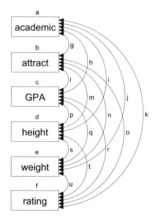

Example 11: Model C
Test of variance/covariance homogeneity
Felson and Bohrnstedt (1979) girls' data
Model Specification

Results for Model C

Model C has to be rejected at any conventional significance level.

Chi-square = 48.977
Degrees of freedom = 21
Probability level = 0.001

This result means that you should not waste time proposing models that allow no differences at all between boys and girls.

Example 11

Modeling in VB.NET

Model A

The following program fits Model A. It is saved as *Ex11-a.vb*.

```
Sub Main()
  Dim Sem As New AmosEngine
  Try
    Sem.TextOutput()

    Sem.BeginGroup(Sem.AmosDir & "Examples\Fels_fem.sav")
    Sem.GroupName("girls")
    Sem.AStructure("academic = GPA + attract + error1 (1)")
    Sem.AStructure _
      ("attract  = height + weight + rating + academic + error2 (1)")
    Sem.AStructure("error2 <--> error1")

    Sem.BeginGroup(Sem.AmosDir & "Examples\Fels_mal.sav")
    Sem.GroupName("boys")
    Sem.AStructure("academic = GPA + attract + error1 (1)")
    Sem.AStructure _
      ("attract  = height + weight + rating + academic + error2 (1)")
    Sem.AStructure("error2 <--> error1")

    Sem.FitModel()
  Finally
    Sem.Dispose()
  End Try
End Sub
```

Model B

The following program fits Model B, in which parameter labels *p1* through *p6* are used to impose equality constraints across groups. The program is saved in *Ex11-b.vb.*

```
Sub Main()
  Dim Sem As New AmosEngine
  Try
    Sem.TextOutput()

    Sem.BeginGroup(Sem.AmosDir & "Examples\Fels_fem.sav")
    Sem.GroupName("girls")
    Sem.AStructure("academic = (p1) GPA + (p2) attract + (1) error1")
    Sem.AStructure("attract  = " & _
      "(p3) height + (p4) weight + (p5) rating + (p6) academic + (1) error2")
    Sem.AStructure("error2 <--> error1")

    Sem.BeginGroup(Sem.AmosDir & "Examples\Fels_mal.sav")
    Sem.GroupName("boys")
    Sem.AStructure("academic = (p1) GPA + (p2) attract + (1) error1")
    Sem.AStructure("attract  = " & _
      "(p3) height + (p4) weight + (p5) rating + (p6) academic + (1) error2")
    Sem.AStructure("error2 <--> error1")

    Sem.FitModel()
  Finally
    Sem.Dispose()
  End Try
End Sub
```

Model C

The VB.NET program for Model C is not displayed here. It is saved in the file *Ex11-c.vb.*

Example 11

Fitting Multiple Models

The following program fits both Models A and B. The program is saved in the file *Ex11-ab.vb.*

```
Sub Main()
  Dim Sem As New AmosEngine
  Try
    Sem.TextOutput()

    Sem.BeginGroup(Sem.AmosDir & "Examples\Fels_fem.sav")
    Sem.GroupName("girls")
    Sem.AStructure("academic = (g1) GPA + (g2) attract + (1) error1")
    Sem.AStructure("attract  = " & _
      "(g3) height + (g4) weight + (g5) rating + (g6) academic + (1) error2")
    Sem.AStructure("error2 <--> error1")

    Sem.BeginGroup(Sem.AmosDir & "Examples\Fels_mal.sav")
    Sem.GroupName("boys")
    Sem.AStructure("academic = (b1) GPA + (b2) attract + (1) error1")
    Sem.AStructure("attract  = " & _
      "(b3) height + (b4) weight + (b5) rating + (b6) academic + (1) error2")
    Sem.AStructure("error2 <--> error1")

    Sem.Model("Model_A")
    Sem.Model("Model_B", _
      "g1=b1", "g2=b2", "g3=b3", "g4=b4", "g5=b5", "g6=b6")

    Sem.FitAllModels()
  Finally
    Sem.Dispose()
  End Try
End Sub
```

Example

12

Simultaneous Factor Analysis for Several Groups

Introduction

This example demonstrates how to test whether the same factor analysis model holds for each of several populations, possibly with different parameter values for different populations (Jöreskog 1971).

About the Data

We will use the Holzinger and Swineford (1939) data described in Example 8. This time, however, data from the 72 boys in the Grant-White sample will be analyzed along with data from the 73 girls studied in Example 8. The girls' data are in the file *Grnt_fem.sav* and were described in Example 8. The following is a sample of the boys' data in the file *Grnt_mal.sav*:

	visperc	cubes	lozenges	paragrap	sentence	wordmean
1	23.00	19.00	4.00	10.00	17.00	10.00
2	34.00	24.00	22.00	11.00	19.00	19.00
3	29.00	23.00	9.00	9.00	19.00	11.00
4	16.00	25.00	10.00	8.00	25.00	24.00
5	27.00	26.00	6.00	10.00	16.00	13.00
6	32.00	21.00	8.00	1.00	7.00	11.00
7	38.00	31.00	12.00	10.00	11.00	14.00

Model A for the Holzinger and Swineford Boys and Girls

Consider the hypothesis that the common factor analysis model of Example 8 holds for boys as well as for girls. The path diagram from Example 8 can be used as a starting point for this two-group model. By default, Amos Graphics assumes that both groups have the same path diagram, so the path diagram does not have to be drawn a second time for the second group.

In Example 8, where there was only one group, the name of the group didn't matter. Accepting the default name *Group number 1* was good enough. Now that there are two groups to keep track of, the groups should be given meaningful names.

Naming the Groups

▶ From the menus, choose Analyze → Manage Groups.

▶ In the Manage Groups dialog box, type Girls for Group Name.

▶ While the Manage Groups dialog box is open, create another group by clicking New.

▶ Then, type Boys in the Group Name text box.

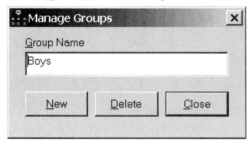

▶ Click Close to close the Manage Groups dialog box.

Specifying the Data

▶ From the menus, choose File → Data Files.

▶ In the Data Files dialog box, double-click Girls and specify the data file *Grnt_fem.sav*.

▶ Then double-click Boys and specify the data file *Grnt_mal.sav*.

▶ Click OK to close the Data Files dialog box.

Your path diagram should look something like this for the girls' sample:

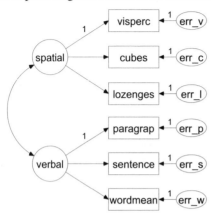

Example 12: Model A
Factor analysis: Girls' sample
Holzinger and Swineford (1939)
Model Specification

The boys' path diagram is identical. Note, however, that the parameter estimates are allowed to be different for the two groups.

Results for Model A

Text Output

In the calculation of degrees of freedom for this model, all of the numbers from Example 8 are exactly doubled.

Computation of degrees of freedom: (Default model)	
Number of distinct sample moments:	42
Number of distinct parameters to be estimated:	26
Degrees of freedom (42 – 26):	16

Model A is acceptable at any conventional significance level. If Model A had been rejected, we would have had to make changes in the path diagram for at least one of the two groups.

Chi-square = 16.480
Degrees of freedom = 16
Probability level = 0.420

Graphics Output

Here are the (unstandardized) parameter estimates for the 73 girls. They are the same estimates that were obtained in Example 8 where the girls alone were studied.

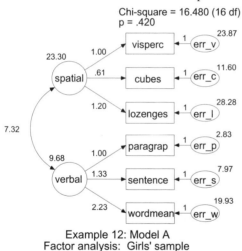

Example 12: Model A
Factor analysis: Girls' sample
Holzinger and Swineford (1939)
Unstandardized estimates

The corresponding output path diagram for the 72 boys is:

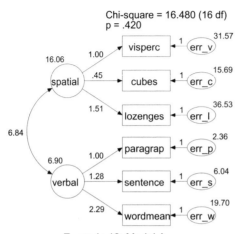

Example 12: Model A
Factor analysis: Boys' sample
Holzinger and Swineford (1939)
Unstandardized estimates

Notice that the estimated regression weights vary little across groups. It seems plausible that the two populations have the same regression weights—a hypothesis that we will test in Model B.

Model B for the Holzinger and Swineford Boys and Girls

We now accept the hypothesis that boys and girls have the same path diagram. The next step is to ask whether boys and girls have the same parameter values. The next model (Model B) does not go as far as requiring that every parameter for the population of boys be equal to the corresponding parameter for girls. It does require that the factor pattern (that is, the regression weights) be the same for both groups. Model B still permits different unique variances for boys and girls. The common factor variances and covariances may also differ across groups.

▶ Take Model A as a starting point for Model B.

▶ First, display the girls' path diagram by clicking Girls in the Groups panel at the left of the path diagram.

▶ Right-click the arrow that points from *spatial* to *cubes* and choose Object Properties from the pop-up menu.

▶ In the Object Properties dialog box, click the Parameters tab.

▶ Type cube_s in the Regression weight text box.

▶ Select All groups. A check mark appears next to it. The effect of the check mark is to assign the same name to this regression weight in both groups.

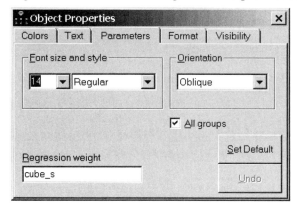

▶ Leaving the Object Properties dialog box open, click each of the remaining single-headed arrows in turn, each time typing a name in the Regression weight text box. Keep this up until you have named every regression weight. Always make sure to select (put a check mark next to) All groups. (Any regression weights that are already fixed at 1 should be left alone.)

The path diagram for either of the two samples should now look something like this:

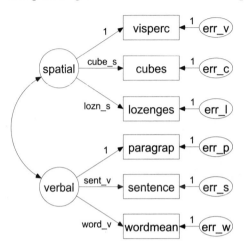

Results for Model B

Text Output

Because of the additional constraints in Model B, four fewer parameters have to be estimated from the data, increasing the number of degrees of freedom by 4.

Computation of degrees of freedom: (Default model)	
Number of distinct sample moments:	42
Number of distinct parameters to be estimated:	22
Degrees of freedom (42 – 20):	20

The chi-square fit statistic is acceptable.

Chi-square = 18.292
Degrees of freedom = 20
Probability level = 0.568

The chi-square difference between Models A and B, $18.292 - 16.480 = 1.812$, is not significant at any conventional level. Thus, Model B, which specifies a group-invariant factor pattern, is supported by the Holzinger and Swineford data.

Graphics Output

Here are the parameter estimates for the 73 girls:

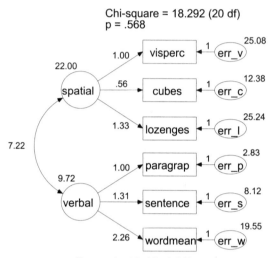

Chi-square = 18.292 (20 df)
p = .568

Example 12: Model B
Factor analysis: Girls' sample
Holzinger and Swineford (1939)
Unstandardized estimates

Here are the parameter estimates for the 72 boys:

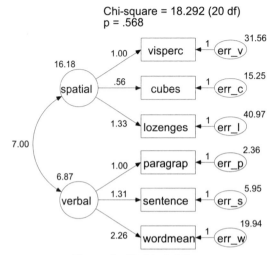

Example 12: Model B
Factor analysis: Boys' sample
Holzinger and Swineford (1939)
Unstandardized estimates

Not surprisingly, the Model B parameter estimates are different from the Model A estimates. The following table shows estimates and standard errors for the two models side by side:

Parameters	Model A		Model B	
Girls' sample	**Estimate**	**Standard Error**	**Estimate**	**Standard Error**
g: cubes <--- spatial	0.610	0.143	0.557	0.114
g: lozenges <--- spatial	1.198	0.272	1.327	0.248
g: sentence <--- verbal	1.334	0.160	1.305	0.117
g: wordmean <--- verbal	2.234	0.263	2.260	0.200
g: spatial <---> verbal	7.315	2.571	7.225	2.458
g: var(spatial)	23.302	8.124	22.001	7.078
g: var(verbal)	9.682	2.159	9.723	2.025
g: var(err_v)	23.873	5.986	25.082	5.832
g: var(err_c)	11.602	2.584	12.382	2.481
g: var(err_l)	28.275	7.892	25.244	8.040
g: var(err_p)	2.834	0.869	2.835	0.834
g: var(err_s)	7.967	1.869	8.115	1.816
g: var(err_w)	19.925	4.951	19.550	4.837

Boys' sample	Estimate	Standard Error	Estimate	Standard Error
b: cubes <--- spatial	0.450	0.176	0.557	0.114
b: lozenges <--- spatial	1.510	0.461	1.327	0.248
b: sentence <--- verbal	1.275	0.171	1.305	0.117
b: wordmean <--- verbal	2.294	0.308	2.260	0.200
b: spatial <---> verbal	6.840	2.370	6.992	2.090
b: var(spatial)	16.058	7.516	16.183	5.886
b: var(verbal)	6.904	1.622	6.869	1.465
b: var(err_v)	31.571	6.982	31.563	6.681
b: var(err_c)	15.693	2.904	15.245	2.934
b: var(err_l)	36.526	11.532	40.974	9.689
b: var(err_p)	2.364	0.726	2.363	0.681
b: var(err_s)	6.035	1.433	5.954	1.398
b: var(err_w)	19.697	4.658	19.937	4.470

All but two of the estimated standard errors are smaller in Model B, including those for the unconstrained parameters. This is a reason to use Model B for parameter estimation rather than Model A, assuming, of course, that Model B is correct.

Modeling in VB.NET

Model A

The following program (*Ex12-a.vb*) fits Model A for boys and girls:

```
Sub Main()
  Dim Sem As New AmosEngine
  Try
    Sem.TextOutput()
    Sem.Standardized()
    Sem.Smc()

    Sem.BeginGroup(Sem.AmosDir & "Examples\Grnt_fem.sav")
      Sem.GroupName("Girls")
      Sem.AStructure("visperc  = (1) spatial + (1) err_v")
      Sem.AStructure("cubes    =     spatial + (1) err_c")
      Sem.AStructure("lozenges =     spatial + (1) err_l")

      Sem.AStructure("paragrap = (1) verbal + (1) err_p")
      Sem.AStructure("sentence =     verbal + (1) err_s")
      Sem.AStructure("wordmean =     verbal + (1) err_w")
    Sem.BeginGroup(Sem.AmosDir & "Examples\Grnt_mal.sav")
      Sem.GroupName("Boys")
      Sem.AStructure("visperc  = (1) spatial + (1) err_v")
      Sem.AStructure("cubes    =     spatial + (1) err_c")
      Sem.AStructure("lozenges =     spatial + (1) err_l")

      Sem.AStructure("paragrap = (1) verbal + (1) err_p")
      Sem.AStructure("sentence =     verbal + (1) err_s")
      Sem.AStructure("wordmean =     verbal + (1) err_w")

    Sem.FitModel()
  Finally
    Sem.Dispose()
  End Try
End Sub
```

The same model is specified for boys as for girls. However, the boys' parameter values can be different from the corresponding girls' parameters.

Model B

Here is a program for fitting Model B, in which some parameters are identically named so that they are constrained to be equal. The program is saved as *Ex12-b.vb*.

```
Sub Main()
  Dim Sem As New AmosEngine
  Try
    Sem.TextOutput()
    Sem.Standardized()
    Sem.Smc()

    Sem.BeginGroup(Sem.AmosDir & "Examples\Grnt_fem.sav")
      Sem.GroupName("Girls")
      Sem.AStructure("visperc  =      (1) spatial + (1) err_v")
      Sem.AStructure("cubes    = (cube_s) spatial + (1) err_c")
      Sem.AStructure("lozenges = (lozn_s) spatial + (1) err_l")

      Sem.AStructure("paragrap =      (1) verbal  + (1) err_p")
      Sem.AStructure("sentence = (sent_v) verbal  + (1) err_s")
      Sem.AStructure("wordmean = (word_v) verbal  + (1) err_w")

    Sem.BeginGroup(Sem.AmosDir & "Examples\Grnt_mal.sav")
      Sem.GroupName("Boys")
      Sem.AStructure("visperc  =      (1) spatial + (1) err_v")
      Sem.AStructure("cubes    = (cube_s) spatial + (1) err_c")
      Sem.AStructure("lozenges = (lozn_s) spatial + (1) err_l")

      Sem.AStructure("paragrap =      (1) verbal  + (1) err_p")
      Sem.AStructure("sentence = (sent_v) verbal  + (1) err_s")
      Sem.AStructure("wordmean = (word_v) verbal  + (1) err_w")

    Sem.FitModel()
  Finally
    Sem.Dispose()
  End Try
End Sub
```

Example
13

Estimating and Testing Hypotheses about Means

Introduction

This example demonstrates how to estimate means and how to test hypotheses about means. In large samples, the method demonstrated is equivalent to multivariate analysis of variance.

Means and Intercept Modeling

Amos and similar programs are usually used to estimate variances, covariances, and regression weights, and to test hypotheses about those parameters. Means and intercepts are not usually estimated, and hypotheses about means and intercepts are not usually tested. At least in part, means and intercepts have been left out of structural equation modeling because of the relative difficulty of specifying models that include those parameters.

Amos, however, was designed to make means and intercept modeling easy. The present example is the first of several showing how to estimate means and intercepts and test hypotheses about them. In this example, the model parameters consist only of variances, covariances, and means. Later examples introduce regression weights and intercepts in regression equations.

About the Data

For this example, we will be using Attig's (1983) memory data, which was described in Example 1. We will use data from both young and old subjects. The raw data for the two groups are contained in the Microsoft Excel workbook *UserGuide.xls*, in the *Attg_yng* and *Attg_old* worksheets. In this example, we will be using only the measures *recall1* and *cued1*.

Model A for Young and Old Subjects

In the analysis of Model B of Example 10, we concluded that *recall1* and *cued1* have the same variances and covariance for both old and young people. At least, the evidence against that hypothesis was found to be insignificant. Model A in the present example replicates the analysis in Example 10 of Model B with an added twist. This time, the *means* of the two variables *recall1* and *cued1* will also be estimated.

Mean Structure Modeling in Amos Graphics

In Amos Graphics, estimating and testing hypotheses involving means is not too different from analyzing variance and covariance structures. Take Model B of Example 10 as a starting point. Young and old subjects had the same path diagram:

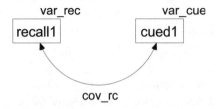

The same parameter names were used in both groups, which had the effect of requiring parameter estimates to be the same in both groups.

Means and intercepts did not appear in Example 10. To introduce means and intercepts into the model:

▶ From the menus, choose View → Analysis Properties.

▶ In the Analysis Properties dialog box, click the Estimation tab.

▶ Select Estimate means and intercepts.

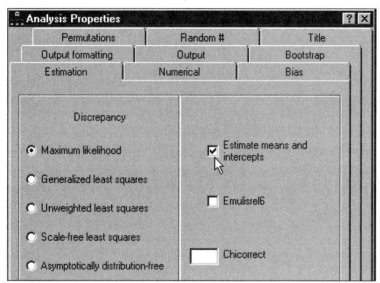

Now the path diagram looks like this (the same path diagram for each group):

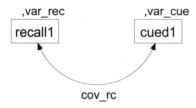

The path diagram now shows a **mean, variance** pair of parameters for each exogenous variable. There are no endogenous variables in this model and hence no intercepts. For each variable in the path diagram, there is a comma followed by the name of a variance. There is only a blank space preceding each comma because the means in the model have not yet been named.

When you choose Calculate Estimates from the Analyze menu, Amos will estimate two means, two variances, and a covariance for each group. The variances and the covariance will be constrained to be equal across groups, while the means will be unconstrained.

The behavior of Amos Graphics changes in several ways when you select (put a check mark next to) Estimate means and intercepts:

- Mean and intercept fields appear on the Parameters tab in the Object Properties dialog box.

- Constraints can be applied to means and intercepts as well as regression weights, variances, and covariances.

- From the menus, choosing Analyze → Calculate Estimates estimates means and intercepts—subject to constraints, if any.

- You have to provide sample means if you provide sample covariances as input.

When you do *not* put a check mark next to Estimate means and intercepts:

- Only fields for variances, covariances, and regression weights are displayed on the Parameters tab in the Object Properties dialog box. Constraints can be placed only on those parameters.

- When Calculate Estimates is chosen, Amos estimates variances, covariances, and regression weights, but *not* means or intercepts.

- You can provide sample covariances as input without providing sample means. If you do provide sample means, they are ignored.

- If you remove the check mark next to Estimate means and intercepts after a means model has already been fitted, the output path diagram will continue to show means and intercepts. To display the correct output path diagram without means or intercepts, *recalculate* the model estimates after removing the check mark next to Estimate means and intercepts.

With these rules, the Estimate mean and intercepts check box makes estimating and testing means models as easy as traditional path modeling.

Results for Model A

Text Output

The number of degrees of freedom for this model is the same as in Example 10, Model B, but we arrive at it in a different way. This time, the number of distinct sample moments includes the sample means as well as the sample variances and covariances. In the young sample, there are two variances, one covariance, and two means, for a total of five sample moments. Similarly, there are five sample moments in the old sample. So, taking both samples together, there are 10 sample moments. As for the parameters to be estimated, there are seven of them, namely *var_rec* (the variance of *recall1*), *var_cue* (the variance of *cued1*), *cov_rc* (the covariance between *recall1* and *cued1*), the means of *recall1* among young and old people (2), and the means of *cued1* among young and old people (2).

The number of degrees of freedom thus works out to be:

Computation of degrees of freedom (Default model)	
Number of distinct sample moments:	10
Number of distinct parameters to be estimated:	7
Degrees of freedom (10 - 7):	3

The chi-square statistic here is also the same as in Model B of Example 10. The hypothesis that old people and young people share the same variances and covariance would be accepted at any conventional significance level.

Chi-square = 4.588
Degrees of freedom = 3
Probability level = 0.205

Here are the parameter estimates for the 40 young subjects:

Means: (young subjects - Default model)

	Estimate	S.E.	C.R.	P	Label
recall1	10.250	.382	26.862	***	
cued1	11.700	.374	31.292	***	

Covariances: (young subjects - Default model)

	Estimate	S.E.	C.R.	P	Label
recall1 <--> cued1	4.056	.780	5.202	***	cov_rc

Variances: (young subjects - Default model)

	Estimate	S.E.	C.R.	P	Label
recall1	5.678	.909	6.245	***	var_rec
cued1	5.452	.873	6.245	***	var_cue

Here are the estimates for the 40 old subjects:

Means: (old subjects - Default model)					
	Estimate	S.E.	C.R.	P	Label
recall1	8.675	.382	22.735	***	
cued1	9.575	.374	25.609	***	
Covariances: (old subjects - Default model)					
	Estimate	S.E.	C.R.	P	Label
recall1 <--> cued1	4.056	.780	5.202	***	cov_rc
Variances: (old subjects - Default model)					
	Estimate	S.E.	C.R.	P	Label
recall1	5.678	.909	6.245	***	var_rec
cued1	5.452	.873	6.245	***	var_cue

Except for the means, these estimates are the same as those obtained in Example 10, Model B. The estimated standard errors and critical ratios are also the same. This demonstrates that merely estimating means, without placing any constraints on them, has no effect on the estimates of the remaining parameters or their standard errors.

Graphics Output

The path diagram output for the two groups follows. Each variable has a *mean, variance* pair displayed next to it. For instance, for young subjects, variable *recall1* has an estimated mean of 10.25 and an estimated variance of 5.68.

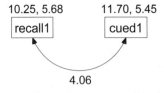

Example 13: Model A
Homogenous covariance structures
Attig (1983) young subjects
Unstandardized estimates

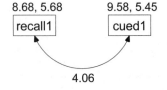

Example 13: Model A
Homogenous covariance structures
Attig (1983) old subjects
Unstandardized estimates

Model B for Young and Old Subjects

From now on, assume that Model A is correct, and consider the more restrictive hypothesis that the means of *recall1* and *cued1* are the same for both groups.

To constrain the means for *recall1* and *cued1*:

▶ Right-click *recall1* and choose Object Properties from the pop-up menu.

▶ In the Object Properties dialog box, click the Parameters tab.

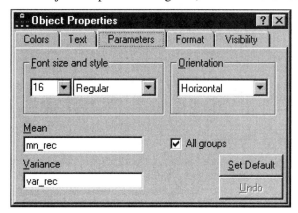

▶ You can enter either a numeric value or a name in the Mean text box. For now, type the name mn_rec.

▶ Select All groups. (A check mark appears next to it. The effect of the check mark is to assign the name *mn_rec* to the mean of *recall1* in every group, requiring the mean of *recall1* to be the same for all groups.)

▶ After giving the name *mn_rec* to the mean of *recall1*, follow the same steps to give the name *mn_cue* to the mean of *cued1*.

The path diagrams for the two groups should now look like this:

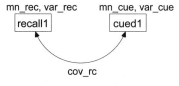

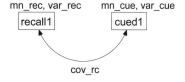

Example 13: Model B
Invariant means and (co-)variances
Attig (1983) young subjects
Model Specification

Example 13: Model B
Invariant means and (co-)variances
Attig (1983) old subjects
Model Specification

These path diagrams are saved in the file *Ex13-b.amw.*

Results for Model B

With the new constraints on the means, Model B has five degrees of freedom.

Computation of degrees of freedom (Default model)	
Number of distinct sample moments:	10
Number of distinct parameters to be estimated:	5
Degrees of freedom (10 - 5):	5

Model B has to be rejected at any conventional significance level.

Chi-square = 19.267
Degrees of freedom = 5
Probability level = 0.002

Comparison of Model B with Model A

If Model A is correct and Model B is wrong (which is plausible, since Model A was accepted and Model B was rejected), then the assumption of equal means must be wrong. A better test of the hypothesis of equal means under the assumption of equal variances and covariances can be obtained in the following way: In comparing Model B with Model A, the chi-square statistics differ by 14.679, with a difference of 2 in degrees of freedom. Since Model B is obtained by placing additional constraints on Model A, we can say that, if Model B is correct, then 14.679 is an observation on a chi-square variable with two degrees of freedom. The probability of obtaining this large a chi-square value is 0.001. Therefore, we reject Model B in favor of Model A, concluding that the two groups have different means.

The comparison of Model B against Model A is as close as Amos can come to conventional multivariate analysis of variance. In fact, the test in Amos is equivalent to a conventional MANOVA, except that the chi-square test provided by Amos is only asymptotically correct. By contrast, MANOVA, for this example, provides an exact test.

Multiple Model Input

It is possible to fit both Model A and Model B in a single analysis. The file *Ex13-all.amw* shows how to do this. One benefit of fitting both models in a single analysis is that Amos will recognize that the two models are nested and will automatically compute the difference in chi-square values as well as the *p* value for testing Model B against Model A.

Mean Structure Modeling in VB.NET

Model A

Here is a program (*Ex13-a.vb*) for fitting Model A. The program keeps the variance and covariance restrictions that were used in Example 10, Model B, and, in addition, places constraints on the means.

```
Sub Main()
   Dim Sem As New AmosEngine
   Try
      Sem.TextOutput()
      Sem.ModelMeansAndIntercepts()

      Sem.BeginGroup(Sem.AmosDir & "Examples\UserGuide.xls", "Attg_yng")
         Sem.GroupName("young_subjects")
         Sem.AStructure("recall1        (var_rec)")
         Sem.AStructure("cued1          (var_cue)")
         Sem.AStructure("recall1 <> cued1  (cov_rc)")
         Sem.Mean("recall1")
         Sem.Mean("cued1")

      Sem.BeginGroup(Sem.AmosDir & "Examples\UserGuide.xls", "Attg_old")
         Sem.GroupName("old_subjects")
         Sem.AStructure("recall1        (var_rec)")
         Sem.AStructure("cued1          (var_cue)")
         Sem.AStructure("recall1 <> cued1  (cov_rc)")
         Sem.Mean("recall1")
         Sem.Mean("cued1")

      Sem.FitModel()
   Finally
      Sem.Dispose()
   End Try
End Sub
```

The ModelMeansAndIntercepts method is used to specify that means (of exogenous variables) and intercepts (in predicting endogenous variables) are to be estimated as explicit model parameters.

The Mean method is used twice in each group in order to estimate the means of *recall1* and *cued1*. If the Mean method had not been used in this program, *recall1* and *cued1* would have had their means fixed at 0. When you use the

ModelMeansAndIntercepts method in an Amos program, Amos assumes that each exogenous variable has a mean of 0 unless you specify otherwise. You need to use the Model method once for each exogenous variable whose mean you want to estimate. It is easy to forget that Amos programs behave this way when you use ModelMeansAndIntercepts.

Note: If you use the Sem.ModelMeansAndIntercepts method in an Amos program, then the Mean method must be called once for each exogenous variable whose mean you want to estimate. Any exogenous variable that is not explicitly estimated through use of the Mean method is assumed to have a mean of 0.

This is different from Amos Graphics, where putting a check mark next to Estimate means and intercepts causes the means of all exogenous variables to be treated as free parameters except for those means that are explicitly constrained.

Model B

The following program (*Ex13-b.vb*) fits Model B. In addition to requiring group-invariant variances and covariances, the program also requires the means to be equal across groups.

```
Sub Main()
    Dim Sem As New AmosEngine
    Try
        Sem.TextOutput()
        Sem.ModelMeansAndIntercepts()

        Sem.BeginGroup(Sem.AmosDir & "Examples\UserGuide.xls", "Attg_yng")
            Sem.GroupName("young_subjects")
            Sem.AStructure("recall1        (var_rec)")
            Sem.AStructure("cued1          (var_cue)")
            Sem.AStructure("recall1 <> cued1  (cov_rc)")
            Sem.Mean("recall1", "mn_rec")
            Sem.Mean("cued1", "mn_cue")

        Sem.BeginGroup(Sem.AmosDir & "Examples\UserGuide.xls", "Attg_old")
            Sem.GroupName("old_subjects")
            Sem.AStructure("recall1        (var_rec)")
            Sem.AStructure("cued1          (var_cue)")
            Sem.AStructure("recall1 <> cued1  (cov_rc)")
            Sem.Mean("recall1", "mn_rec")
            Sem.Mean("cued1", "mn_cue")

        Sem.FitModel()
    Finally
        Sem.Dispose()
    End Try
End Sub
```

Fitting Multiple Models

Both models A and B can be fitted by the following program. It is saved as *Ex13-all.vb.*

```
Sub Main()
   Dim Sem As New AmosEngine
   Try
      Sem.TextOutput()
      Sem.ModelMeansAndIntercepts()

      Sem.BeginGroup(Sem.AmosDir & "Examples\UserGuide.xls", "Attg_yng")
         Sem.GroupName("young subjects")
         Sem.AStructure("recall1        (var_rec)")
         Sem.AStructure("cued1          (var_cue)")
         Sem.AStructure("recall1 <> cued1  (cov_rc)")
         Sem.Mean("recall1", "yng_rec")
         Sem.Mean("cued1", "yng_cue")

      Sem.BeginGroup(Sem.AmosDir & "Examples\UserGuide.xls", "Attg_old")
         Sem.GroupName("old subjects")
         Sem.AStructure("recall1        (var_rec)")
         Sem.AStructure("cued1          (var_cue)")
         Sem.AStructure("recall1 <> cued1  (cov_rc)")
         Sem.Mean("recall1", "old_rec")
         Sem.Mean("cued1", "old_cue")

      Sem.Model("Model_A", "")
      Sem.Model("Model_B", "yng_rec = old_rec", "yng_cue = old_cue")
      Sem.FitAllModels()
   Finally
      Sem.Dispose()
   End Try
End Sub
```

Example

14

Regression with an Explicit Intercept

Introduction

This example shows how to estimate the intercept in an ordinary regression analysis.

Assumptions Made by Amos

Ordinarily, when you specify that some variable depends linearly on some others, Amos assumes that the linear equation expressing the dependency contains an additive constant, or intercept, but does not estimate it. For instance, in Example 4, we specified the variable *performance* to depend linearly on three other variables: *knowledge*, *value*, and *satisfaction*. Amos assumed that the regression equation was of the following form:

$$performance \ = \ a + b_1 \times knowledge + b_2 \times value + b_3 \times satisfaction + error$$

where b_1, b_2, and b_3 are regression weights, and a is the intercept. In Example 4, the regression weights b_1 through b_3 were estimated. Amos did not estimate a in Example 4, and it did not appear in the path diagram. Nevertheless, b_1, b_2, and b_3 were estimated under the assumption that a was present in the regression equation. Similarly, *knowledge*, *value*, and *satisfaction* were assumed to have means, but their means were not estimated and did not appear in the path diagram. You will usually be satisfied with this method of handling means and intercepts in regression equations. Sometimes, however, you will want to see an estimate of an intercept or to test a hypothesis about an intercept. For that, you will need to take the steps demonstrated in this example.

About the Data

We will once again use the data of Warren, White, and Fuller (1974), first used in Example 4. We will use the Excel worksheet *Warren5v* in *UserGuide.xls* found in the *Examples* directory. Here are the sample moments (means, variances, and covariances):

rowtype_	varname_	performance	knowledge	value	satisfaction	past_training
n		98	98	98	98	98
cov	performance	0.0209				
cov	knowledge	0.0177	0.052			
cov	value	0.0245	0.028	0.1212		
cov	satisfaction	0.0046	0.0044	-0.0063	0.0901	
cov	past_training	0.0187	0.0192	0.0353	-0.0066	0.0946
mean		0.0589	1.3796	2.8773	2.4613	2.1174

Specifying the Model

You can specify the regression model exactly as you did in Example 4. In fact, if you have already worked through Example 4, you can use that path diagram as a starting point for this example. Only one change is required to get Amos to estimate the means and the intercept.

▶ From the menus, choose View → Analysis Properties.

▶ In the Analysis Properties dialog box, click the Estimation tab.

▶ Select Estimate means and intercepts.

Your path diagram should then look like this:

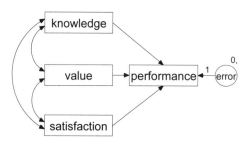

Example 14
Job Performance of Farm Managers
Regression with an explicit intercept
(Model Specification)

Notice the string *0,* displayed above the *error* variable. The *0* to the left of the comma indicates that the mean of the *error* variable is fixed at 0, a standard assumption in linear regression models. The absence of anything to the right of the comma in *0,* means that the variance of *error* is not fixed at a constant and does not have a name.

With a check mark next to Estimate means and intercepts, Amos will estimate a mean for each of the predictors and an intercept for the regression equation that predicts *performance*.

Results of the Analysis

Text Output

The present analysis gives the same results as in Example 4 but with the explicit estimation of three means and an intercept. The number of degrees of freedom is again 0, but the calculation of degrees of freedom goes a little differently. Sample means are required for this analysis; therefore, the number of distinct sample moments includes the sample means as well as the sample variances and covariances. There are four sample means, four sample variances, and six sample covariances, for a total of 14 sample moments. As for the parameters to be estimated, there are three regression weights and an intercept. Also, the three predictors have among them three means, three variances, and three covariances. Finally, there is one error variance, for a total of 14 parameters to be estimated.

Computation of degrees of freedom (Default model)

Number of distinct sample moments:	14
Number of distinct parameters to be estimated:	14
Degrees of freedom (14 - 14):	0

With 0 degrees of freedom, there is no hypothesis to be tested.

> Chi-square = 0.000
> Degrees of freedom = 0
> Probability level cannot be computed

The estimates for regression weights, variances, and covariances are the same as in Example 4, and so are the associated standard error estimates, critical ratios, and *p* values.

Regression Weights: (Group number 1 - Default model)

	Estimate	S.E.	C.R.	P	Label
performance <--- knowledge	.258	.054	4.822	***	
performance <--- value	.145	.035	4.136	***	
performance <--- satisfaction	.049	.038	1.274	.203	

Means: (Group number 1 - Default model)

	Estimate	S.E.	C.R.	P	Label
value	2.877	.035	81.818	***	
knowledge	1.380	.023	59.891	***	
satisfaction	2.461	.030	81.174	***	

Intercepts: (Group number 1 - Default model)

	Estimate	S.E.	C.R.	P	Label
performance	-.834	.140	-5.951	***	

Covariances: (Group number 1 - Default model)

	Estimate	S.E.	C.R.	P	Label
knowledge <--> satisfaction	.004	.007	.632	.528	
value <--> satisfaction	-.006	.011	-.593	.553	
knowledge <--> value	.028	.008	3.276	.001	

Variances: (Group number 1 - Default model)

	Estimate	S.E.	C.R.	P	Label
knowledge	.051	.007	6.964	***	
value	.120	.017	6.964	***	
satisfaction	.089	.013	6.964	***	
error	.012	.002	6.964	***	

Graphics Output

Below is the path diagram that shows the unstandardized estimates for this example. The intercept of –0.83 appears just above the endogenous variable *performance*.

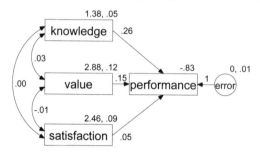

Example 14
Job Performance of Farm Managers
Regression with an explicit intercept
(Unstandardized estimates)

Modeling in VB.NET

As a reminder, here is the Amos program from Example 4 (equation version):

```
Sub Main()
    Dim Sem As New AmosEngine
    Try
        Sem.TextOutput()
        Sem.Standardized()
        Sem.Smc()
        Sem.ImpliedMoments()
        Sem.SampleMoments()

        Sem.BeginGroup(Sem.AmosDir & "Examples\UserGuide.xls", "Warren5v")
        Sem.AStructure _
            ("performance = knowledge + value + satisfaction + error (1)")
        Sem.FitModel()
    Finally
        Sem.Dispose()
    End Try
End Sub
```

The following program for the model of Example 14 gives all the same results, plus mean and intercept estimates. This program is saved as *Ex14.vb.*

```
Sub Main()
    Dim Sem As New AmosEngine
    Try
        Sem.TextOutput()
        Sem.Standardized()
        Sem.Smc()
        Sem.ImpliedMoments()
        Sem.SampleMoments()
        Sem.ModelMeansAndIntercepts()

        Sem.BeginGroup( _
            Sem.AmosDir & "Examples\UserGuide.xls", "Warren5v")
        Sem.AStructure( _
            "performance = () + knowledge + value + satisfaction + error (1)")

        Sem.Mean("knowledge")
        Sem.Mean("value")
        Sem.Mean("satisfaction")

        Sem.FitModel()
    Finally
        Sem.Dispose()
    End Try
End Sub
```

Note the Sem.ModelMeansAndIntercepts statement that causes Amos to treat means and intercepts as explicit model parameters. Another change from Example 4 is that there is now an additional pair of empty parentheses and a *plus* sign in the AStructure line. The extra pair of empty parentheses represents the intercept in the regression equation.

The Sem.Mean statements request estimates for the means of *knowledge*, *value*, and *satisfaction*. Each exogenous variable with a mean other than 0 has to appear as the argument in a call to the Mean method. If the Mean method had not been used in this program, Amos would have fixed the means of the exogenous variables at 0.

Intercept parameters can be specified by an extra pair of parentheses in a Sem.AStructure command (as we just showed) or by using the Intercept method. In the following program, the Intercept method is used to specify that there is an intercept in the regression equation for predicting *performance*:

```
Sub Main()
   Dim Sem As New AmosEngine
   Try
      Sem.TextOutput()
      Sem.Standardized()
      Sem.Smc()
      Sem.ImpliedMoments()
      Sem.SampleMoments()
      Sem.ModelMeansAndIntercepts()

      Sem.BeginGroup( _
         Sem.AmosDir & "Examples\UserGuide.xls", "Warren5v")
      Sem.AStructure("performance <--- knowledge")
      Sem.AStructure("performance <--- value")
      Sem.AStructure("performance <--- satisfaction")
      Sem.AStructure("performance <--- error (1)")

      Sem.Intercept("performance")
      Sem.Mean("knowledge")
      Sem.Mean("value")
      Sem.Mean("satisfaction")

      Sem.FitModel()
   Finally
      Sem.Dispose()
   End Try
End Sub
```

Example
15

Factor Analysis with Structured Means

Introduction

This example demonstrates how to estimate factor means in a common factor analysis of data from several populations.

Factor Means

Conventionally, the common factor analysis model does not make any assumptions about the means of any variables. In particular, the model makes no assumptions about the means of the common factors. In fact, it is not even possible to estimate factor means or to test hypotheses in a conventional, single-sample factor analysis.

However, Sörbom (1974) showed that it *is* possible to make inferences about factor means under reasonable assumptions, as long as you are analyzing data from more than one population. Using Sörbom's approach, you cannot estimate the mean of every factor for every population, but you can estimate *differences* in factor means across populations. For instance, think about Example 12, where a common factor analysis model was fitted simultaneously to a sample of girls and a sample of boys. For each group, there were two common factors, interpreted as *verbal ability* and *spatial ability*. The method used in Example 12 did not permit an examination of mean verbal ability or mean spatial ability. Sörbom's method does. Although his method does not provide mean estimates for either girls or boys, it does give an estimate of the mean difference between girls and boys for each factor. The method also provides a test of significance for differences of factor means.

The identification status of the factor analysis model is a difficult subject when estimating factor means. In fact, Sörbom's accomplishment was to show how to constrain parameters so that the factor analysis model is identified and so that differences in factor means can be estimated. We will follow Sörbom's guidelines for achieving model identification in the present example.

About the Data

We will use the Holzinger and Swineford (1939) data from Example 12. The girls' dataset is in *Grnt_fem.sav*. The boys' dataset is in *Grnt_mal.sav*.

Model A for Boys and Girls

Specifying the Model

We need to construct a model to test the following null hypothesis: Boys and girls have the same average spatial ability and the same average verbal ability, where spatial and verbal ability are common factors. In order for this hypothesis to have meaning, the *spatial* and the *verbal* factors must be related to the observed variables in the same way for girls as for boys. This means that the girls' regression weights and intercepts must be equal to the boys' regression weights and intercepts.

Model B of Example 12 can be used as a starting point for specifying Model A of the present example. Starting with Model B of Example 12:

▶ From the menus, choose View → Analysis Properties.

▶ In the Analysis Properties dialog box, click the Estimation tab.

▶ Select Estimate means and intercepts (a check mark appears next to it).

The regression weights are already constrained to be equal across groups. To begin constraining the intercepts to be equal across groups:

▶ Right-click one of the observed variables, such as *visperc*.

▶ Choose Object Properties from the pop-up menu.

▶ In the Object Properties dialog box, click the Parameters tab.

▶ Enter a parameter name, such as int_vis, in the Intercept text box.

▶ Select All groups, so that the intercept is named *int_vis* in both groups.

▶ Proceed in the same way to give names to the five remaining intercepts.

As Sörbom showed, it is necessary to fix the factor means in one of the groups at a constant. We will fix the means of the boys' *spatial* and *verbal* factors at 0. Example 13 shows how to fix the mean of a variable to a constant value.

Note: When using the Object Properties dialog box to fix the boys' factor means at 0, be sure that you do *not* put a check mark next to All groups.

After fixing the boys' factor means at 0, follow the same procedure to assign names to the girls' factor means. At this point, the girls' path diagram should look something like this:

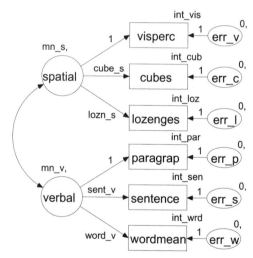

Example 15

The boys' path diagram should look like this:

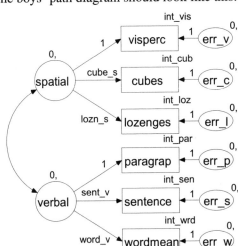

Understanding the Cross-Group Constraints

The cross-group constraints on intercepts and regression weights may or may not be satisfied in the populations. One result of fitting the model will be a test of whether these constraints hold in the populations of girls and boys. The reason for starting out with these constraints is that (as Sörbom points out) it is necessary to impose *some* constraints on the intercepts and regression weights in order to make the model identified when estimating factor means. These are not the only constraints that would make the model identified, but they are plausible ones.

The only difference between the boys' and girls' path diagrams is in the constraints on the two factor means. For boys, the means are fixed at 0. For girls, both factor means are estimated. The girls' factor means are named *mn_s* and *mn_v*, but the factor means are unconstrained because each mean has a unique name.

The boys' factor means were fixed at 0 in order to make the model identified. Sörbom showed that, even with all the other constraints imposed here, it is still not possible to estimate factor means for both boys and girls simultaneously. Take verbal ability, for example. If you fix the boys' mean verbal ability at some constant (like 0), you can then estimate the girls' mean verbal ability. Alternatively, you can fix the girls' mean verbal ability at some constant and then estimate the boys' mean verbal ability. The bad news is that you cannot estimate both means at once. The good news is that the difference between the boys' mean and the girls' mean will be the same, no matter which mean you fix and no matter what value you fix for it.

Results for Model A

Text Output

There is no reason to reject Model A at any conventional significance level.

Chi-square = 22.593
Degrees of freedom = 24
Probability level = 0.544

Graphics Output

We are primarily interested in estimates of mean verbal ability and mean spatial ability, and not so much in estimates of the other parameters. However, as always, all the estimates should be inspected to make sure that they are reasonable. Here are the unstandardized parameter estimates for the 73 girls:

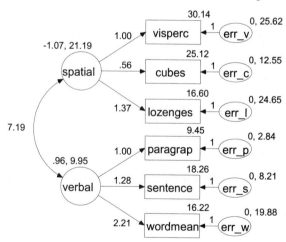

Here are the boys' estimates:

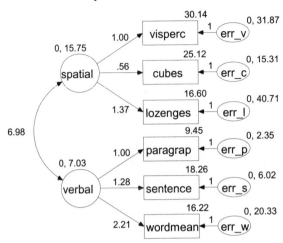

Girls have an estimated mean spatial ability of –1.07. We fixed the mean of boys' spatial ability at 0. Thus, girls' mean spatial ability is estimated to be 1.07 units *below* boys' mean spatial ability. This difference is not affected by the initial decision to fix the boys' mean at 0. If we had fixed the boys' mean at 10.000, the girls' mean would have been estimated to be 8.934. If we had fixed the girls' mean at 0, the boys' mean would have been estimated to be 1.07.

What unit is spatial ability expressed in? A difference of 1.07 verbal ability units may be important or not, depending on the size of the unit. Since the regression weight for regressing *visperc* on spatial ability is equal to 1, we can say that spatial ability is expressed in the same units as scores on the *visperc* test. Of course, this is useful information only if you happen to be familiar with the *visperc* test. There is another approach to evaluating the mean difference of 1.07, which does not involve *visperc*. A portion of the text output not reproduced here shows that *spatial* has an estimated variance of 15.752 for boys, or a standard deviation of about 4.0. For girls, the variance of *spatial* is estimated to be 21.188, so that its standard deviation is about 4.6. With standard deviations this large, a difference of 1.07 would not be considered very large for most purposes.

The statistical significance of the 1.07 unit difference between girls and boys is easy to evaluate. Since the boys' mean was fixed at 0, we need to ask only whether the girls' mean differs significantly from 0.

Here are the girls' factor mean estimates from the text output:

Means: (Girls - Default model)				
	Estimate	S.E.	C.R.	P	Label
spatial	-1.066	.881	-1.209	.226	mn_s
verbal	.956	.521	1.836	.066	mn_v

The girls' mean spatial ability has a critical ratio of -1.209 and is not significantly different from 0 ($p = 0.226$). In other words, it is not significantly different from the boys' mean.

Turning to verbal ability, the girls' mean is estimated 0.96 units *above* the boys' mean. Verbal ability has a standard deviation of about 2.7 among boys and about 3.15 among girls. Thus, 0.96 verbal ability units is about one-third of a standard deviation in either group. The difference between boys and girls approaches significance at the 0.05 level ($p = 0.066$).

Model B for Boys and Girls

In the discussion of Model A, we used critical ratios to carry out two tests of significance: a test for sex differences in spatial ability and a test for sex differences in verbal ability. We will now carry out a single test of the null hypothesis that there are no sex differences, either in spatial ability or in verbal ability. To do this, we will repeat the previous analysis with the additional constraint that boys and girls have the same mean on spatial ability and on verbal ability. Since the boys' means are already fixed at 0, requiring the girls' means to be the same as the boys' means amounts to setting the girls' means to 0 also.

The girls' factor means have already been named *mn_s* and *mn_v*. To fix the means at 0:

▶ From the menus, choose Analyze → Manage Models.

▶ In the Manage Models dialog box, type Model A in the Model Name text box,

▶ Leave the Parameter Constraints box empty.

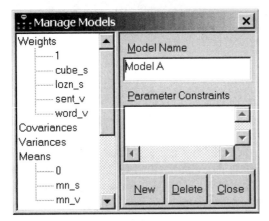

▶ Click **New**.

▶ Type **Model B** in the Model Name text box.

▶ Type the constraints mn_s = 0 and mn_v = 0 in the Parameter Constraints text box.

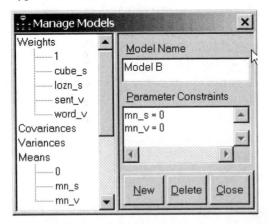

▶ Click Close.

Now when you choose Analyze → Calculate Estimates, Amos will fit both Model A and Model B. The file *Ex15-all.amw* contains this two-model setup.

Results for Model B

If we did not have Model A as a basis for comparison, we would now accept Model B, using any conventional significance level.

Chi-square = 30.624
Degrees of freedom = 26
Probability level = 0.243

Comparing Models A and B

An alternative test of Model B can be obtained by assuming that Model A is correct and testing whether Model B fits significantly worse than Model A. A chi-square test for this comparison is given in the text output.

▶ In the Amos Output window, click Model Comparison in the tree diagram in the upper left pane.

Assuming model Model A to be correct:

Model	DF	CMIN	P	NFI Delta-1	IFI Delta-2	RFI rho-1	TLI rho2
Model B	2	8.030	.018	.024	.026	.021	.023

The table shows that Model B has two more degrees of freedom than Model A, and a chi-square statistic that is larger by 8.030. If Model B is correct, the probability of such a large difference in chi-square values is 0.018, providing some evidence against Model B.

Modeling in VB.NET

Model A

The following program fits Model A. It is saved as *Ex15-a.vb*.

```
Sub Main()
    Dim Sem As New AmosEngine
    Try
        Sem.TextOutput()
        Sem.Standardized()
        Sem.Smc()
        Sem.ModelMeansAndIntercepts()

        Sem.BeginGroup(Sem.AmosDir & "Examples\Grnt_fem.sav")
            Sem.GroupName("Girls")
            Sem.AStructure("visperc  = (int_vis) +     (1) spatial + (1) err_v")
            Sem.AStructure("cubes    = (int_cub) + (cube_s) spatial + (1) err_c")
            Sem.AStructure("lozenges = (int_loz) + (lozn_s) spatial + (1) err_l")
            Sem.AStructure("paragrap = (int_par) +     (1) verbal  + (1) err_p")
            Sem.AStructure("sentence = (int_sen) + (sent_v) verbal  + (1) err_s")
            Sem.AStructure("wordmean = (int_wrd) + (word_v) verbal  + (1) err_w")
            Sem.Mean("spatial", "mn_s")
            Sem.Mean("verbal", "mn_v")

        Sem.BeginGroup(Sem.AmosDir & "Examples\Grnt_mal.sav")
            Sem.GroupName("Boys")
            Sem.AStructure("visperc  = (int_vis) +     (1) spatial + (1) err_v")
            Sem.AStructure("cubes    = (int_cub) + (cube_s) spatial + (1) err_c")
            Sem.AStructure("lozenges = (int_loz) + (lozn_s) spatial + (1) err_l")
            Sem.AStructure("paragrap = (int_par) +     (1) verbal  + (1) err_p")
            Sem.AStructure("sentence = (int_sen) + (sent_v) verbal  + (1) err_s")
            Sem.AStructure("wordmean = (int_wrd) + (word_v) verbal  + (1) err_w")
            Sem.Mean("spatial", "0")
            Sem.Mean("verbal", "0")
        Sem.FitModel()
    Finally
        Sem.Dispose()
    End Try
End Sub
```

The AStructure method is called once for each endogenous variable. The Mean method in the girls' group is used to specify that the means of the verbal ability and spatial ability factors are freely estimated. The program also uses the Mean method to specify that verbal ability and spatial ability have zero means in the boys' group. Actually, Amos assumes zero means by default, so the use of the Mean method for the boys is unnecessary.

Model B

The following program fits Model B. In this model, the factor means are fixed at 0 for both boys and girls. The program is saved as *Ex15-b.vb*.

```
Sub Main()
  Dim Sem As New AmosEngine
  Try
    Dim dataFile As String = Sem.AmosDir & "Examples\userguide.xls"
    Sem.TextOutput()
    Sem.Standardized()
    Sem.Smc()
    Sem.ModelMeansAndIntercepts()

    Sem.BeginGroup(dataFile, "grnt_fem")
      Sem.GroupName("Girls")
      Sem.AStructure("visperc  = (int_vis) +     (1) spatial + (1) err_v")
        Sem.AStructure("cubes    = (int_cub) + (cube_s) spatial + (1) err_c")
      Sem.AStructure("lozenges = (int_loz) + (lozn_s) spatial + (1) err_l")
      Sem.AStructure("paragraph = (int_par) +     (1) verbal + (1) err_p")
      Sem.AStructure("sentence  = (int_sen) + (sent_v) verbal + (1) err_s")
      Sem.AStructure("wordmean  = (int_wrd) + (word_v) verbal  + (1) err_w")
      Sem.Mean("spatial", "0")
      Sem.Mean("verbal", "0")
    Sem.BeginGroup(dataFile, "grnt_mal")
      Sem.GroupName("Boys")
      Sem.AStructure("visperc  = (int_vis) +     (1) spatial + (1) err_v")
      Sem.AStructure("cubes    = (int_cub) + (cube_s) spatial + (1) err_c")
      Sem.AStructure("lozenges = (int_loz) + (lozn_s) spatial + (1) err_l")
      Sem.AStructure("paragraph = (int_par) +     (1) verbal + (1) err_p")
      Sem.AStructure("sentence  = (int_sen) + (sent_v) verbal  + (1) err_s")
      Sem.AStructure("wordmean  = (int_wrd) + (word_v) verbal  + (1) err_w")
      Sem.Mean("spatial", "0")
      Sem.Mean("verbal", "0")
    Sem.FitModel()
  Finally
    Sem.Dispose()
  End Try
End Sub
```

Fitting Multiple Models

The following program (*Ex15-all.vb*) fits both models A and B.

```vb
Sub Main()
    Dim Sem As New AmosEngine
    Try
        Sem.TextOutput()
        Sem.Standardized()
        Sem.Smc()
        Sem.ModelMeansAndIntercepts()

        Sem.BeginGroup(Sem.AmosDir & "Examples\Grnt_fem.sav")
            Sem.GroupName("Girls")
            Sem.AStructure("visperc  = (int_vis) +     (1) spatial + (1) err_v")
            Sem.AStructure("cubes    = (int_cub) + (cube_s) spatial + (1) err_c")
            Sem.AStructure("lozenges = (int_loz) + (lozn_s) spatial + (1) err_l")
            Sem.AStructure("paragrap = (int_par) +     (1) verbal  + (1) err_p")
            Sem.AStructure("sentence = (int_sen) + (sent_v) verbal  + (1) err_s")
            Sem.AStructure("wordmean = (int_wrd) + (word_v) verbal  + (1) err_w")
            Sem.Mean("spatial", "mn_s")
            Sem.Mean("verbal", "mn_v")

        Sem.BeginGroup(Sem.AmosDir & "Examples\Grnt_mal.sav")
            Sem.GroupName("Boys")
            Sem.AStructure("visperc  = (int_vis) +     (1) spatial + (1) err_v")
            Sem.AStructure("cubes    = (int_cub) + (cube_s) spatial + (1) err_c")
            Sem.AStructure("lozenges = (int_loz) + (lozn_s) spatial + (1) err_l")
            Sem.AStructure("paragrap = (int_par) +     (1) verbal  + (1) err_p")
            Sem.AStructure("sentence = (int_sen) + (sent_v) verbal  + (1) err_s")
            Sem.AStructure("wordmean = (int_wrd) + (word_v) verbal  + (1) err_w")
            Sem.Mean("spatial", "0")
            Sem.Mean("verbal", "0")

        Sem.Model("Model A")                  ' Sex difference in factor means.
        Sem.Model("Model B", "mn_s=0", "mn_v=0") ' Equal factor means.
        Sem.FitAllModels()
    Finally
        Sem.Dispose()
    End Try
End Sub
```

Example

16

Sörbom's Alternative to Analysis of Covariance

Introduction

This example demonstrates latent structural equation modeling with longitudinal observations in two or more groups, models that generalize traditional analysis of covariance techniques by incorporating latent variables and autocorrelated residuals (compare to Sörbom 1978), and how assumptions employed in traditional analysis of covariance can be tested.

Assumptions

Example 9 demonstrated an alternative to conventional analysis of covariance that works even with unreliable covariates. Unfortunately, analysis of covariance also depends on other assumptions besides the assumption of perfectly reliable covariates, and the method of Example 9 also depends on those. Sörbom (1978) developed a more general approach that allows testing many of those assumptions and relaxing some of them.

The present example uses the same data that Sörbom used to introduce his method. The exposition closely follows Sörbom's.

About the Data

We will again use the Olsson (1973) data introduced in Example 9. The sample means, variances, and covariances from the 108 experimental subjects are in the Microsoft Excel worksheet *Olss_exp* in the workbook *UserGuide.xls*.

rowtype_	varname_	pre_syn	pre_opp	post_syn	post_opp
n		108	108	108	108
cov	pre_syn	50.084			
cov	pre_opp	42.373	49.872		
cov	post_syn	40.76	36.094	51.237	
cov	post_opp	37.343	40.396	39.89	53.641
mean		20.556	21.241	25.667	25.87

The sample means, variances, and covariances from the 105 control subjects are in the worksheet *Olss_cnt*.

rowtype_	varname_	pre_syn	pre_opp	post_syn	post_opp
n		105	105	105	105
cov	pre_syn	37.626			
cov	pre_opp	24.933	34.68		
cov	post_syn	26.639	24.236	32.013	
cov	post_opp	23.649	27.76	23.565	33.443
mean		18.381	20.229	20.4	21.343

Both datasets contain the customary unbiased estimates of variances and covariances. That is, the elements in the covariance matrix were obtained by dividing by $(N-1)$. This also happens to be the default setting used by Amos for *reading* covariance matrices. However, for model fitting, the default behavior is to use the maximum likelihood estimate of the population covariance matrix (obtained by dividing by N) as the sample covariance matrix. Amos performs the conversion from unbiased estimates to maximum likelihood estimates automatically.

Changing the Default Behavior

▶ From the menus, choose View → Analysis Properties.

▶ In the Analysis Properties dialog box, click the Bias tab.

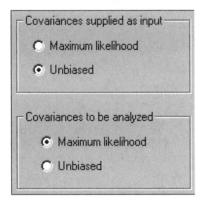

The default setting used by Amos yields results that are consistent with missing data modeling (discussed in Example 17 and Example 18). Other SEM programs like LISREL (Jöreskog and Sörbom 1989) and EQS (Bentler 1985) analyze unbiased moments instead, resulting in slightly different results when sample sizes are small. Selecting both Unbiased options on the Bias tab causes Amos to produce the same estimates as LISREL or EQS. Appendix B discusses further the tradeoffs in choosing whether to fit the maximum likelihood estimate of the covariance matrix or the unbiased estimate.

Model A

Specifying the Model

Consider Sörbom's initial model (Model A) for the Olsson data. The path diagram for the control group is:

Example 16

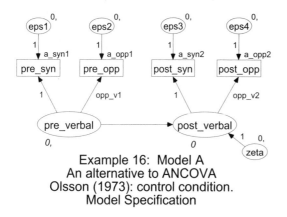

Example 16: Model A
An alternative to ANCOVA
Olsson (1973): control condition.
Model Specification

The following path diagram is Model A for the experimental group:

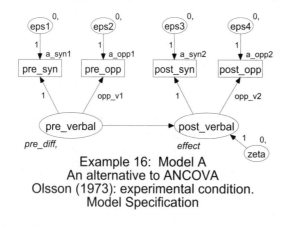

Example 16: Model A
An alternative to ANCOVA
Olsson (1973): experimental condition.
Model Specification

Means and intercepts are an important part of this model, so be sure that you do the following:

▶ From the menus, choose View → Analysis Properties.

▶ Click the Estimation tab.

▶ Select Estimate means and intercepts (a check mark appears next to it).

In each group, Model A specifies that *pre_syn* and *pre_opp* are indicators of a single latent variable called *pre_verbal* and that *post_syn* and *post_opp* are indicators of another latent variable called *post_verbal*. The latent variable *pre_verbal* is interpreted as verbal ability at the beginning of the study, and *post_verbal* is interpreted as verbal ability at the conclusion of the study. This is Sörbom's **measurement** model. The **structural** model specifies that *post_verbal* depends linearly on *pre_verbal*.

The labels *opp_v1* and *opp_v2* require the regression weights in the measurement model to be the same for both groups. Similarly, the labels *a_syn1*, *a_opp1*, *a_syn2*, and *a_opp2* require the intercepts in the measurement model to be the same for both groups. These equality constraints are assumptions that could be wrong. In fact, one result of the upcoming analyses will be a test of these assumptions. As Sörbom points out, some assumptions have to be made about the parameters in the measurement model in order to make it possible to estimate and test hypotheses about parameters in the structural model.

For the control subjects, the mean of *pre_verbal* and the intercept of *post_verbal* are fixed at 0. This establishes the control group as the reference group for the group comparison. You have to pick such a reference group to make the latent variable means and intercepts identified.

For the experimental subjects, the mean and intercept parameters of the latent factors are allowed to be nonzero. The latent variable mean labeled *pre_diff* represents the difference in verbal ability prior to treatment, and the intercept labeled *effect* represents the improvement of the experimental group relative to the control group. The path diagram for this example is saved in *Ex16-a.amw*.

Note that Sörbom's model imposes no cross-group constraints on the variances of the six unobserved exogenous variables. That is, the four observed variables may have different unique variances in the control and experimental conditions, and the variances of *pre_verbal* and *zeta* may also be different in the two groups. We will investigate these assumptions more closely when we get to Models X, Y, and Z.

Results for Model A

Text Output

In the Amos Output window, clicking Notes for Model in the tree diagram in the upper left pane shows that Model A cannot be accepted at any conventional significance level.

Chi-square = 34.775
Degrees of freedom = 6
Probability level = 0.000

We also get the following message that provides further evidence that Model A is wrong:

The following variances are negative. (control - Default model)

zeta
-2.868

Can we modify Model A so that it will fit the data while still permitting a meaningful comparison of the experimental and control groups? It will be helpful here to repeat the analysis and request modification indices. To obtain modification indices:

▶ From the menus, choose View → Analysis Properties.

▶ In the Analysis Properties dialog box, click the Output tab.

▶ Select Modification indices and enter a suitable threshold in the text box to its right. For this example, the threshold will be left at its default value of 4.

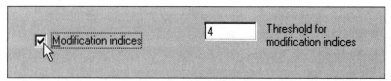

Here is the modification index output from the experimental group:

Modification Indices (experimental - Default model)
Covariances: (experimental - Default model)

	M.I.	Par Change
eps2 <--> eps4	10.508	4.700
eps2 <--> eps3	8.980	-4.021
eps1 <--> eps4	8.339	-3.908
eps1 <--> eps3	7.058	3.310

Variances: (experimental - Default model)

M.I.   Par Change

Regression Weights: (experimental - Default model)

M.I.   Par Change

Means: (experimental - Default model)

M.I.   Par Change

Intercepts: (experimental - Default model)

M.I.   Par Change

In the control group, no parameter had a modification index greater than the threshold of 4.

Model B

The largest modification index obtained with Model A suggests adding a covariance between *eps2* and *eps4* in the experimental group. The modification index indicates that the chi-square statistic will drop by at least 10.508 if *eps2* and *eps4* are allowed to have a nonzero covariance. The parameter change statistic of 4.700 indicates that the covariance estimate will be positive if it is allowed to take on any value. The suggested modification is plausible. *Eps2* represents unique variation in *pre_opp*, and *eps4* represents unique variation in *post_opp*, where measurements on *pre_opp* and *post_opp* are obtained by administering the same test, *opposites*, on two different occasions. It is therefore reasonable to think that *eps2* and *eps4* might be positively correlated.

The next step is to consider a revised model, called Model B, in which *eps2* and *eps4* are allowed to be correlated in the experimental group. To obtain Model B from Model A:

▶ Draw a double-headed arrow connecting *eps2* and *eps4*.

This allows *eps2* and *eps4* to be correlated in both groups. We do not want them to be correlated in the control group, so the covariance must be fixed at 0 in the control group. To accomplish this:

▶ Click control in the Groups panel (at the left of the path diagram) to display the path diagram for the control group.

▶ Right-click the double-headed arrow and choose Object Properties from the pop-up menu.

▶ In the Object Properties dialog box, click the Parameters tab.

▶ Type 0 in the Covariance text box.

▶ Make sure the All groups check box is empty. With the check box empty, the constraint on the covariance applies to only the control group.

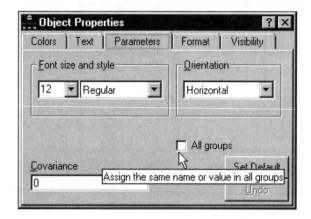

For Model B, the path diagram for the control group is:

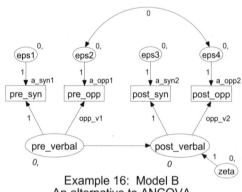

Example 16: Model B
An alternative to ANCOVA
Olsson (1973): control condition.
Model Specification

For the experimental group, the path diagram is:

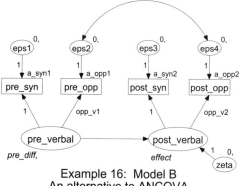

Example 16: Model B
An alternative to ANCOVA
Olsson (1973): experimental condition.
Model Specification

Results for Model B

In moving from Model A to Model B, the chi-square statistic dropped by 17.712 (more than the promised 10.508) while the number of degrees of freedom dropped by just 1.

Chi-square = 17.063
Degrees of freedom = 5
Probability level = 0.004

Model B is an improvement over Model A but not enough of an improvement. Model B still does not fit the data well. Furthermore, the variance of *zeta* in the control group has a negative estimate (not shown here), just as it had for Model A. These two facts argue strongly against Model B. There is room for hope, however, because the modification indices suggest further modifications of Model B. The modification indices for the control group are:

Modification Indices (control - Default model)
Covariances: (control - Default model)

	M.I.	Par Change
eps2 <--> eps4	4.727	2.141
eps1 <--> eps4	4.086	-2.384

Variances: (control - Default model)

	M.I.	Par Change

Regression Weights: (control - Default model)

	M.I.	Par Change

Means: (control - Default model)

	M.I.	Par Change

Intercepts: (control - Default model)

	M.I.	Par Change

The largest modification index (4.727) suggests allowing *eps2* and *eps4* to be correlated in the control group. (*Eps2* and *eps4* are already correlated in the experimental group.) Making this modification leads to Model C.

Model C

Model C is just like Model B except that the terms *eps2* and *eps4* are correlated in both the control group and the experimental group.

To specify Model C, just take Model B and remove the constraint on the covariance between *eps2* and *eps4* in the control group. Here is the new path diagram for the control group, as found in file *Ex16-c.amw*:

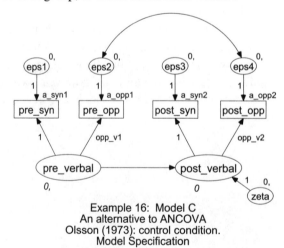

Example 16: Model C
An alternative to ANCOVA
Olsson (1973): control condition.
Model Specification

Results for Model C

Finally, we have a model that fits.

Chi-square = 2.797
Degrees of freedom = 4
Probability level = 0.592

From the point of view of statistical goodness of fit, there is no reason to reject Model C. It is also worth noting that all the variance estimates are positive. The following are the parameter estimates for the 105 control subjects:

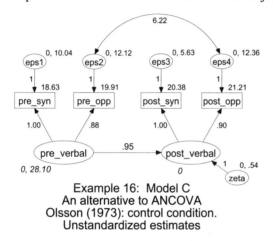

Example 16: Model C
An alternative to ANCOVA
Olsson (1973): control condition.
Unstandardized estimates

Next is a path diagram displaying parameter estimates for the 108 experimental subjects:

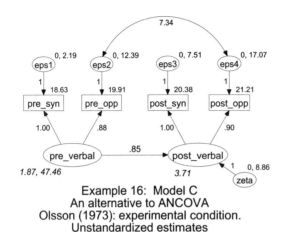

Example 16: Model C
An alternative to ANCOVA
Olsson (1973): experimental condition.
Unstandardized estimates

Most of these parameter estimates are not very interesting, although you may want to check and make sure that the estimates are reasonable. We have already noted that the variance estimates are positive. The path coefficients in the measurement model are positive, which is reassuring. A mixture of positive and negative regression weights in the measurement model would have been difficult to interpret and would have cast doubt on the model. The covariance between *eps2* and *eps4* is positive in both groups, as expected.

We are primarily interested in the regression of *post_verbal* on *pre_verbal*. The intercept, which is fixed at 0 in the control group, is estimated to be 3.71 in the experimental group. The regression weight is estimated at 0.95 in the control group and 0.85 in the experimental group. The regression weights for the two groups are close enough that they might even be identical in the two populations. Identical regression weights would allow a greatly simplified evaluation of the treatment by limiting the comparison of the two groups to a comparison of their intercepts. It is therefore worthwhile to try a model in which the regression weights are the same for both groups. This will be Model D.

Model D

Model D is just like Model C except that it requires the regression weight for predicting *post_verbal* from *pre_verbal* to be the same for both groups. This constraint can be imposed by giving the regression weight the same name, for example *pre2post*, in both groups. The following is the path diagram for Model D for the experimental group:

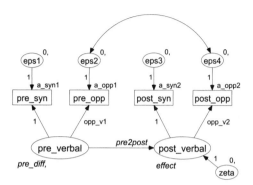

Example 16: Model D
An alternative to ANCOVA
Olsson (1973): experimental condition.
Model Specification

Next is the path diagram for Model D for the control group:

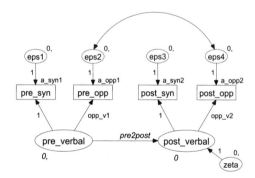

Example 16: Model D
An alternative to ANCOVA
Olsson (1973): control condition.
Model Specification

Results for Model D

Model D would be accepted at conventional significance levels.

Chi-square = 3.976
Degrees of freedom = 5
Probability level = 0.553

Testing Model D against Model C gives a chi-square value of 1.179 (3.976 – 2.797) with 1 degree of freedom (5 – 4). Again, you would accept the hypothesis of equal regression weights (Model D).

With equal regression weights, the comparison of treated and untreated subjects now turns to the difference between their intercepts. Here are the parameter estimates for the 105 control subjects:

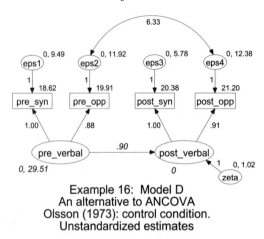

Example 16: Model D
An alternative to ANCOVA
Olsson (1973): control condition.
Unstandardized estimates

The estimates for the 108 experimental subjects are:

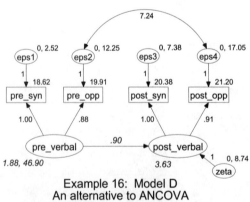

Example 16: Model D
An alternative to ANCOVA
Olsson (1973): experimental condition.
Unstandardized estimates

The intercept for the experimental group is estimated as 3.63. According to the text output (not shown here), the estimate of 3.63 has a critical ratio of 7.59. Thus, the intercept for the experimental group is significantly different from the intercept for the control group (which is fixed at 0).

Model E

Another way of testing the difference in *post_verbal* intercepts for significance is to repeat the Model D analysis with the additional constraint that the intercept be equal across groups. Since the intercept for the control group is already fixed at 0, we need add only the requirement that the intercept be 0 in the experimental group as well. This restriction is used in Model E.

The path diagrams for Model E are just like that for Model D, except that the intercept in the regression of *post_verbal* on *pre_verbal* is fixed at 0 in *both* groups. The path diagrams are not reproduced here. They can be found in *Ex16-e.amw*.

Results for Model E

Model E has to be rejected.

Chi-square = 55.094
Degrees of freedom = 6
Probability level = 0.000

Comparing Model E against Model D yields a chi-square value of 51.018 (55.094 – 3.976) with 1 degree of freedom (6 – 5). Model E has to be rejected in favor of Model D. Because the fit of Model E is significantly worse than that of Model D, the hypothesis of equal intercepts again has to be rejected. In other words, the control and experimental groups differ at the time of the posttest in a way that cannot be accounted for by differences that existed at the time of the pretest.

This concludes Sörbom's (1978) analysis of the Olsson data.

Fitting Models A Through E in a Single Analysis

The example file *Ex16-a2e.amw* fits all five models (A through E) in a single analysis. The procedure for fitting multiple models in a single analysis was shown in detail in Example 6.

Comparison of Sörbom's Method with the Method of Example 9

Sörbom's alternative to analysis of covariance is more difficult to apply than the method of Example 9. On the other hand, Sörbom's method is superior to the method of Example 9 because it is more general. That is, you can duplicate the method of Example 9 by using Sörbom's method with suitable parameter constraints.

We end this example with three additional models called *X*, *Y*, and *Z*. Comparisons among these new models will allow us to duplicate the results of Example 9. However, we will also find evidence that the method used in Example 9 was inappropriate. The purpose of this fairly complicated exercise is to call attention to the limitations of the approach in Example 9 and to show that some of the assumptions of that method can be tested and relaxed in Sörbom's approach.

Model X

First, consider a new model (Model X) that requires that the variances and covariances of the observed variables be the same for the control and experimental conditions. The means of the observed variables may differ between the two populations. Model X does not specify any linear dependencies among the variables. Model X is not, by itself, very interesting; however, Models Y and Z (coming up) *are* interesting, and we will want to know how well they fit the data, compared to Model X.

Modeling in Amos Graphics

Because there are no intercepts or means to estimate, make sure that there is not a check mark next to Estimate means and intercepts on the Estimation tab of the Analysis Properties dialog box.

The following is the path diagram for Model X for the control group:

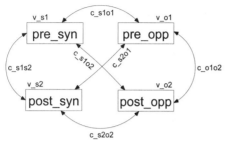

Example 16: Model X
Group-invariant covariance structure
Olsson (1973): control condition
Model Specification

The path diagram for the experimental group is identical. Using the same parameter names for both groups has the effect of requiring the two groups to have the same parameter values.

Results for Model X

Model X would be rejected at any conventional level of significance.

Chi-square = 29.145
Degrees of freedom = 10
Probability level = 0.001

The analyses that follow (Models Y and Z) are actually inappropriate now that we are satisfied that Model X is inappropriate. We will carry out the analyses as an exercise in order to demonstrate that they yield the same results as obtained in Example 9.

Model Y

Consider a model that is just like Model D but with these additional constraints:

- Verbal ability at the pretest (*pre_verbal*) has the same variance in the control and experimental groups.

- The variances of *eps1*, *eps2*, *eps3*, *eps4*, and *zeta* are the same for both groups.

- The covariance between *eps2* and *eps4* is the same for both groups.

Apart from the correlation between *eps2* and *eps4*, Model D required that *eps1*, *eps2*, *eps3*, *eps4*, and *zeta* be uncorrelated among themselves and with every other exogenous variable. These new constraints amount to requiring that the variances and covariances of *all exogenous* variables be the same for both groups.

Altogether, the new model imposes two kinds of constraints:

- All regression weights and intercepts are the same for both groups, except possibly for the intercept used in predicting *post_verbal* from *pre_verbal* (Model D requirements).

- The variances and covariances of the exogenous variables are the same for both groups (additional Model Y requirements).

These are the same assumptions we made in Model B of Example 9. The difference this time is that the assumptions are made explicit and can be tested. Path diagrams for Model Y are shown below. Means and intercepts are estimated in this model, so be sure that you:

▶ From the menus, choose View → Analysis Properties.

▶ Click the Estimation tab.

▶ Select Estimate means and intercepts (a check mark appears next to it).

Here is the path diagram for the experimental group:

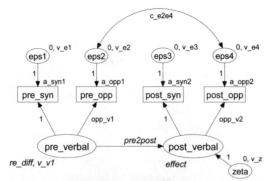

Example 16: Model Y
An alternative to ANCOVA
Olsson (1973): experimental condition.
Model Specification

Here is the path diagram for the control group:

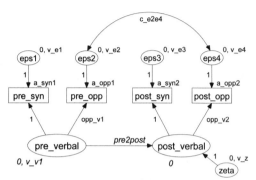

Example 16: Model Y
An alternative to ANCOVA
Olsson (1973): control condition.
Model Specification

Results for Model Y

We must reject Model Y.

> Chi-square = 31.816
> Degrees of freedom = 12
> Probability level = 0.001

This is a good reason for being dissatisfied with the analysis of Example 9, since it depended upon Model Y (which, in Example 9, was called Model B) being correct. If you look back at Example 9, you will see that we accepted Model B there ($\chi^2 = 2.684$, $df = 2$, $p = 0.261$). So how can we say that the same model has to be rejected here ($\chi^2 = 31.816$, $df = 1$, $p = 0.001$)? The answer is that, while the null hypothesis is the same in both cases (Model B in Example 9 and Model Y in the present example), the alternative hypotheses are different. In Example 9, the alternative against which Model B is tested includes the assumption that the variances and covariances of the observed variables are the same for both values of the *treatment* variable (also stated in the assumptions on p. 39). In other words, the test of Model B carried out in Example 9 implicitly assumed homogeneity of variances and covariances for the control and experimental populations. This is the very assumption that is made explicit in Model X of the present example.

Model Y is a restricted version of Model X. It can be shown that the assumptions of Model Y (equal regression weights for the two populations and equal variances and covariances of the exogenous variables) imply the assumptions of Model X (equal covariances for the observed variables). Models X and Y are therefore *nested* models, and it is possible to carry out a *conditional* test of Model Y under the assumption that Model X is true. Of course, it will make sense to do that test only if Model X really is true, and we have already concluded it is not. Nevertheless, let's go through the motions of testing Model Y against Model X. The difference in chi-square values is 2.671 (31.816 – 29.145) with 2 degrees of freedom (12 – 10). These figures are identical (within rounding error) to those of Example 9, Model B. The difference is that in Example 9 we assumed that the test was appropriate. Now we are quite sure (because we rejected Model X) that it is not.

If you have any doubts that the current Model Y is the same as Model B of Example 9, you should compare the parameter estimates from the two analyses. Here are the Model Y parameter estimates for the 108 experimental subjects. See if you can match up these estimates displayed with the unstandardized parameter estimates obtained in Model B of Example 9.

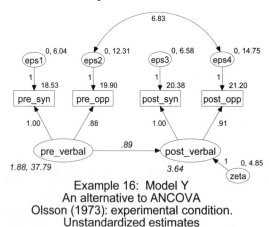

Example 16: Model Y
An alternative to ANCOVA
Olsson (1973): experimental condition.
Unstandardized estimates

Model Z

Finally, construct a new model (Model Z) by starting with Model Y and adding the requirement that the intercept in the equation for predicting *post_verbal* from *pre_verbal* be the same in both populations. This model is equivalent to Model C of Example 9. The path diagrams for Model Z are as follows:

Here is the path diagram for Model Z for the experimental group:

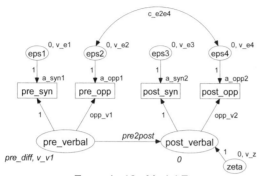

Example 16: Model Z
An alternative to ANCOVA
Olsson (1973): experimental condition.
Model Specification

Here is the path diagram for the control group:

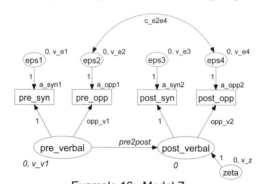

Example 16: Model Z
An alternative to ANCOVA
Olsson (1973): control condition.
Model Specification

Results for Model Z

This model has to be rejected.

Chi-square = 84.280
Degrees of freedom = 13
Probability level = 0.000

Model Z also has to be rejected when compared to Model Y ($\chi^2 = 84.280 - 31.816 = 52.464$, $df = 13 - 12 = 1$). Within rounding error, this is the same difference in chi-square values and degrees of freedom as in Example 9, when Model C was compared to Model B.

Modeling in VB.NET

Model A

The following program fits Model A. It is saved as *Ex16-a.vb*.

```
Sub Main()
    Dim Sem As New AmosEngine
    Try
        Dim dataFile As String = Sem.AmosDir & "Examples\UserGuide.xls"
        Sem.TextOutput()
        Sem.Mods(4)
        Sem.Standardized()
        Sem.Smc()
        Sem.ModelMeansAndIntercepts()

        Sem.BeginGroup(dataFile, "Olss_cnt")
            Sem.GroupName("control")
            Sem.AStructure("pre_syn  = (a_syn1) + (1)     pre_verbal  + (1) eps1")
            Sem.AStructure( _
                "pre_opp  = (a_opp1) + (opp_v1) pre_verbal  + (1) eps2")
            Sem.AStructure("post_syn = (a_syn2) + (1)     post_verbal + (1) eps3")
            Sem.AStructure( _
                "post_opp = (a_opp2) + (opp_v2) post_verbal + (1) eps4")
            Sem.AStructure("post_verbal = (0) + () pre_verbal + (1) zeta")

        Sem.BeginGroup(dataFile, "Olss_exp")
            Sem.GroupName("experimental")
            Sem.AStructure("pre_syn  = (a_syn1) + (1)     pre_verbal  + (1) eps1")
            Sem.AStructure( _
                "pre_opp  = (a_opp1) + (opp_v1) pre_verbal  + (1) eps2")
            Sem.AStructure("post_syn = (a_syn2) + (1)     post_verbal + (1) eps3")
            Sem.AStructure( _
                "post_opp = (a_opp2) + (opp_v2) post_verbal + (1) eps4")
            Sem.AStructure("post_verbal = (effect) + () pre_verbal + (1) zeta")
            Sem.Mean("pre_verbal", "pre_diff")

        Sem.FitModel()
    Finally
        Sem.Dispose()
    End Try
End Sub
```

Model B

To fit Model B, start with the program for Model A and add the line

Sem.AStructure("eps2 <---> eps4")

to the model specification for the experimental group. Here is the resulting program for Model B. It is saved as *Ex16-b.vb*.

```
Sub Main()
    Dim Sem As New AmosEngine
    Try
        Dim dataFile As String = Sem.AmosDir & "Examples\UserGuide.xls"
        Sem.TextOutput()
        Sem.Mods(4)
        Sem.Standardized()
        Sem.Smc()
        Sem.ModelMeansAndIntercepts()

        Sem.BeginGroup(dataFile, "Olss_cnt")
            Sem.GroupName("control")
            Sem.AStructure("pre_syn  = (a_syn1) + (1)     pre_verbal  + (1) eps1")
            Sem.AStructure( _
                "pre_opp  = (a_opp1) + (opp_v1) pre_verbal  + (1) eps2")
            Sem.AStructure("post_syn = (a_syn2) + (1)     post_verbal + (1) eps3")
            Sem.AStructure( _
                "post_opp = (a_opp2) + (opp_v2) post_verbal + (1) eps4")
            Sem.AStructure("post_verbal = (0) + () pre_verbal + (1) zeta")

        Sem.BeginGroup(dataFile, "Olss_exp")
            Sem.GroupName("experimental")
            Sem.AStructure("pre_syn  = (a_syn1) + (1)     pre_verbal  + (1) eps1")
            Sem.AStructure( _
                "pre_opp  = (a_opp1) + (opp_v1) pre_verbal  + (1) eps2")
            Sem.AStructure("post_syn = (a_syn2) + (1)     post_verbal + (1) eps3")
            Sem.AStructure( _
                "post_opp = (a_opp2) + (opp_v2) post_verbal + (1) eps4")
            Sem.AStructure("post_verbal = (effect) + () pre_verbal + (1) zeta")
            Sem.AStructure("eps2 <---> eps4")
            Sem.Mean("pre_verbal", "pre_diff")

        Sem.FitModel()
    Finally
        Sem.Dispose()
    End Try
End Sub
```

Example 16

Model C

The following program fits Model C. The program is saved as *Ex16-c.vb*.

```vb
Sub Main()
    Dim Sem As New AmosEngine
    Try
        Dim dataFile As String = Sem.AmosDir & "Examples\UserGuide.xls"

        Sem.TextOutput()
        Sem.Mods(4)
        Sem.Standardized()
        Sem.Smc()
        Sem.ModelMeansAndIntercepts()

        Sem.BeginGroup(dataFile, "Olss_cnt")
            Sem.GroupName("control")
            Sem.AStructure("pre_syn  = (a_syn1) + (1)     pre_verbal  + (1) eps1")
            Sem.AStructure( _
                "pre_opp  = (a_opp1) + (opp_v1) pre_verbal  + (1) eps2")
            Sem.AStructure("post_syn = (a_syn2) + (1)     post_verbal + (1) eps3")
            Sem.AStructure( _
                "post_opp = (a_opp2) + (opp_v2) post_verbal + (1) eps4")
            Sem.AStructure("post_verbal = (0) + () pre_verbal + (1) zeta")
            Sem.AStructure("eps2 <---> eps4")

        Sem.BeginGroup(dataFile, "Olss_exp")
            Sem.GroupName("experimental")
            Sem.AStructure("pre_syn  = (a_syn1) + (1)     pre_verbal  + (1) eps1")
            Sem.AStructure( _
                "pre_opp  = (a_opp1) + (opp_v1) pre_verbal  + (1) eps2")
            Sem.AStructure("post_syn = (a_syn2) + (1)     post_verbal + (1) eps3")
            Sem.AStructure( _
                "post_opp = (a_opp2) + (opp_v2) post_verbal + (1) eps4")
            Sem.AStructure("post_verbal = (effect) + () pre_verbal + (1) zeta")
            Sem.AStructure("eps2 <---> eps4")
            Sem.Mean("pre_verbal", "pre_diff")

        Sem.FitModel()
    Finally
        Sem.Dispose()
    End Try
End Sub
```

Model D

The following program fits Model D. The program is saved as *Ex16-d.vb.*

```
Sub Main()
  Dim Sem As New AmosEngine
  Try
    Dim dataFile As String = Sem.AmosDir & "Examples\UserGuide.xls"
    Sem.TextOutput()
    Sem.Mods(4)
    Sem.Standardized()
    Sem.Smc()
    Sem.ModelMeansAndIntercepts()

    Sem.BeginGroup(dataFile, "Olss_cnt")
      Sem.GroupName("control")
      Sem.AStructure("pre_syn  = (a_syn1) + (1)     pre_verbal  + (1) eps1")
      Sem.AStructure( _
        "pre_opp  = (a_opp1) + (opp_v1) pre_verbal  + (1) eps2")
      Sem.AStructure("post_syn = (a_syn2) + (1)     post_verbal + (1) eps3")
      Sem.AStructure( _
        "post_opp = (a_opp2) + (opp_v2) post_verbal + (1) eps4")
      Sem.AStructure("post_verbal = (0) + (pre2post) pre_verbal + (1) zeta")
      Sem.AStructure("eps2 <---> eps4")

    Sem.BeginGroup(dataFile, "Olss_exp")
      Sem.GroupName("experimental")
      Sem.AStructure("pre_syn  = (a_syn1) + (1)     pre_verbal  + (1) eps1")
      Sem.AStructure( _
        "pre_opp  = (a_opp1) + (opp_v1) pre_verbal  + (1) eps2")
      Sem.AStructure("post_syn = (a_syn2) + (1)     post_verbal + (1) eps3")
      Sem.AStructure( _
        "post_opp = (a_opp2) + (opp_v2) post_verbal + (1) eps4")
      Sem.AStructure( _
        "post_verbal = (effect) + (pre2post) pre_verbal + (1) zeta")
      Sem.AStructure("eps2 <---> eps4")
      Sem.Mean("pre_verbal", "pre_diff")

    Sem.FitModel()
  Finally
    Sem.Dispose()
  End Try
End Sub
```

Model E

The following program fits Model E. The program is saved as *Ex16-e.vb*.

```
Sub Main()
  Dim Sem As New AmosEngine
  Try
    Dim dataFile As String = Sem.AmosDir & "Examples\UserGuide.xls"
    Sem.TextOutput()
    Sem.Mods(4)
    Sem.Standardized()
    Sem.Smc()
    Sem.ModelMeansAndIntercepts()

    Sem.BeginGroup(dataFile, "Olss_cnt")
      Sem.GroupName("control")
      Sem.AStructure("pre_syn  = (a_syn1) + (1)     pre_verbal  + (1) eps1")
      Sem.AStructure( _
        "pre_opp  = (a_opp1) + (opp_v1) pre_verbal  + (1) eps2")
      Sem.AStructure("post_syn = (a_syn2) + (1)     post_verbal + (1) eps3")
      Sem.AStructure( _
        "post_opp = (a_opp2) + (opp_v2) post_verbal + (1) eps4")
      Sem.AStructure("post_verbal = (0) + (pre2post) pre_verbal + (1) zeta")
      Sem.AStructure("eps2 <---> eps4")

    Sem.BeginGroup(dataFile, "Olss_exp")
      Sem.GroupName("experimental")
      Sem.AStructure("pre_syn  = (a_syn1) + (1)     pre_verbal  + (1) eps1")
      Sem.AStructure( _
        "pre_opp  = (a_opp1) + (opp_v1) pre_verbal  + (1) eps2")
      Sem.AStructure("post_syn = (a_syn2) + (1)     post_verbal + (1) eps3")
      Sem.AStructure( _
        "post_opp = (a_opp2) + (opp_v2) post_verbal + (1) eps4")
      Sem.AStructure("post_verbal = (0) + (pre2post) pre_verbal + (1) zeta")
      Sem.AStructure("eps2 <---> eps4")
      Sem.Mean("pre_verbal", "pre_diff")

    Sem.FitModel()
  Finally
    Sem.Dispose()
  End Try
End Sub
```

Fitting Multiple Models

The following program fits all five models, A through E. The program is saved as *Ex16-a2e.vb.*

```
Sub Main()
   Dim Sem As New AmosEngine
   Try
      Dim dataFile As String = Sem.AmosDir & "Examples\UserGuide.xls"
      Sem.TextOutput()
      Sem.Mods(4)
      Sem.Standardized()
      Sem.Smc()
      Sem.ModelMeansAndIntercepts()

      Sem.BeginGroup(dataFile, "Olss_cnt")
         Sem.GroupName("control")
         Sem.AStructure("pre_syn  = (a_syn1) + (1)     pre_verbal  + (1) eps1")
         Sem.AStructure( _
            "pre_opp  = (a_opp1) + (opp_v1) pre_verbal  + (1) eps2")
         Sem.AStructure("post_syn = (a_syn2) + (1)     post_verbal + (1) eps3")
         Sem.AStructure( _
            "post_opp = (a_opp2) + (opp_v2) post_verbal + (1) eps4")
         Sem.AStructure("post_verbal = (0) + (c_beta) pre_verbal + (1) zeta")
         Sem.AStructure("eps2 <---> eps4  (c_e2e4)")

      Sem.BeginGroup(dataFile, "Olss_exp")
         Sem.GroupName("experimental")
         Sem.AStructure("pre_syn  = (a_syn1) + (1)     pre_verbal  + (1) eps1")
         Sem.AStructure( _
            "pre_opp  = (a_opp1) + (opp_v1) pre_verbal  + (1) eps2")
         Sem.AStructure("post_syn = (a_syn2) + (1)     post_verbal + (1) eps3")
         Sem.AStructure( _
            "post_opp = (a_opp2) + (opp_v2) post_verbal + (1) eps4")
         Sem.AStructure("post_verbal = (effect) + (e_beta) pre_verbal + (1) zeta")
         Sem.AStructure("eps2 <---> eps4  (e_e2e4)")
         Sem.Mean("pre_verbal", "pre_diff")

      Sem.Model("Model A", "c_e2e4 = 0", "e_e2e4 = 0")
      Sem.Model("Model B", "c_e2e4 = 0")
      Sem.Model("Model C")
      Sem.Model("Model D", "c_beta = e_beta")
      Sem.Model("Model E", "c_beta = e_beta", "effect = 0")
      Sem.FitAllModels()
   Finally
      Sem.Dispose()
   End Try
End Sub
```

Example 16

Models X, Y, and Z

VB.NET programs for Models X, Y, and Z will not be discussed here. The programs can be found in the files *Ex16-x.vb*, *Ex16-y.vb*, and *Ex16-z.vb*.

Example

17

Missing Data

Introduction

This example demonstrates the analysis of a dataset in which some values are missing.

Incomplete Data

It often happens that data values that were anticipated in the design of a study fail to materialize. Perhaps a subject failed to participate in part of a study. Or maybe a person filling out a questionnaire skipped a couple of questions. You may find that some people did not tell you their age, some did not report their income, others did not show up on the day you measured reaction times, and so on. For one reason or another, you often end up with a set of data that has gaps in it.

One standard method for dealing with incomplete data is to eliminate from the analysis any observation for which some data value is missing. This is sometimes called **listwise deletion**. For example, if a person fails to report his income, you would eliminate that person from your study and proceed with a conventional analysis based on complete data but with a reduced sample size. This method is unsatisfactory inasmuch as it requires discarding the information contained in the responses that the person did give because of the responses that he did not give. If missing values are common, this method may require discarding the bulk of a sample.

Another standard approach, in analyses that depend on sample moments, is to calculate each sample moment separately, excluding an observation from the calculation only when it is missing a value that is needed for the computation of that particular moment. For example, in calculating the sample mean income, you would exclude only persons whose incomes you do not know. Similarly, in computing the sample covariance between age and income, you would exclude an observation only if age is missing or if income is missing. This approach to missing data is sometimes called **pairwise deletion**.

A third approach is **data imputation**, replacing the missing values with some kind of guess, and then proceeding with a conventional analysis appropriate for complete data. For example, you might compute the mean income of the persons who reported their income and then attribute that income to all persons who did not report their income. Beale and Little (1975) discuss methods for data imputation, which are implemented in many statistical packages.

Amos does not use any of these methods. Even in the presence of missing data, it computes maximum likelihood estimates (Anderson 1957). For this reason, whenever you have missing data, you may prefer to use Amos to do a conventional analysis, such as a simple regression analysis (as in Example 4) or to estimate means (as in Example 13).

It should be mentioned that there is one kind of missing data that Amos cannot deal with. (Neither can any other general approach to missing data, such as the three mentioned above.) Sometimes the very fact that a value is missing conveys information. It could be, for example, that people with very high incomes tend (more than others) not to answer questions about income. Failure to respond may thus convey probabilistic information about a person's income level, beyond the information already given in the observed data. If this is the case, the approach to missing data that Amos uses is inapplicable.

Amos assumes that data values that are missing are *missing at random*. It is not always easy to know whether this assumption is valid or what it means in practice (Rubin 1976). On the other hand, if the *missing at random* condition is satisfied, Amos provides estimates that are efficient and consistent. By contrast, the methods mentioned previously do not provide efficient estimates and provide consistent estimates only under the stronger condition that missing data are missing completely at random (Little and Rubin 1989).

About the Data

For this example, we have modified the Holzinger and Swineford (1939) data used in Example 8. The original dataset (in the SPSS file *Grnt_fem.sav*) contains the scores of 73 girls on six tests, for a total of 438 data values. To obtain a dataset with missing values, each of the 438 data values in *Grnt_fem.sav* was deleted with probability 0.30.

The resulting dataset is in the SPSS file *Grant_x.sav*. Below are the first few cases in that file. A period (.) represents a missing value.

	visperc	cubes	lozenges	paragrap	sentence	wordmean
1	33.00	.	17.00	8.00	17.00	10.00
2	30.00	.	20.00	.	.	18.00
3	.	33.00	36.00	.	25.00	41.00
4	28.00	.	.	10.00	18.00	11.00
5	.	25.00	.	11.00	.	8.00
6	20.00	25.00	6.00	9.00	.	.
7	17.00	21.00	6.00	5.00	10.00	10.00

Amos recognizes the periods in SPSS datasets and treats them as missing data.

Amos recognizes missing data in many other data formats as well. For instance, in an ASCII dataset, two consecutive delimiters indicate a missing value. The seven cases shown above would look like this in ASCII format:

```
visperc,cubes,lozenges,paragraph,sentence,wordmean
33,,17,8,17,10
30,,20,,,18
,33,36,,25,41
28,,,10,18,11
,,25,,11,,8
20,25,6,9,,,,
17,21,6,5,10,10
```

Approximately 27% of the data in *Grant_x.sav* are missing. Complete data are available for only seven cases.

Specifying the Model

We will now fit the common factor analysis model of Example 8 (shown on p. 276) to the Holzinger and Swineford data in the file *Grant_x.sav*. The difference between this analysis and the one in Example 8 is that this time 27% of the data are missing.

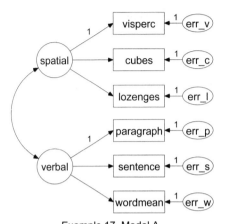

Example 17, Model A
Factor analysis with missing data
Holzinger and Swineford (1939): Girls' sample
Model Specification

After specifying the data file to be *Grant_x.sav* and drawing the above path diagram:

▶ From the menus, choose View → Analysis Properties.

▶ In the Analysis Properties dialog box, click the Estimation tab.

▶ Select Estimate means and intercepts (a check mark appears next to it).

This will give you an estimate of the intercept in each of the six regression equations for predicting the measured variables. Maximum likelihood estimation with missing values works only when you estimate means and intercepts, so you have to estimate them even if you are not interested in the estimates.

Saturated and Independence Models

Computing some fit measures requires fitting the saturated and independence models in addition to your model. This is never a problem with complete data, but fitting these models can require extensive computation when there are missing values. The saturated model is especially problematic. With p observed variables, the saturated model has $p \times (p + 3)/2$ parameters. For example, with 10 observed variables, there are 65 parameters; with 20 variables, there are 230 parameters; with 40 variables, there are 860 parameters; and so on. It may be impractical to fit the saturated model because of the large number of parameters. In addition, some missing data value patterns can make it impossible in principle to fit the saturated model even if it is possible to fit your model.

With incomplete data, Amos Graphics tries to fit the saturated and independence models in addition to your model. If Amos fails to fit the independence model, then fit measures that depend on the fit of the independence model, such as CFI, cannot be computed. If Amos cannot fit the saturated model, the usual chi-square statistic cannot be computed.

Results of the Analysis

Text Output

For this example, Amos succeeds in fitting both the saturated and the independence model. Consequently, all fit measures, including the chi-square statistic, are reported. To see the fit measures:

▶ Click Model Fit in the tree diagram in the upper left corner of the Amos Output window.

The following is the portion of the output that shows the chi-square statistic for the factor analysis model (called *Default model*), the saturated model, and the independence model:

CMIN

Model	NPAR	CMIN	DF	P	CMIN/DF
Default model	19	11.547	8	.173	1.443
Saturated model	27	.000	0		
Independence model	6	117.707	21	.000	5.605

The chi-square value of 11.547 is not very different from the value of 7.853 obtained in Example 8 with the complete dataset. In both analyses, the *p* values are above 0.05.

Parameter estimates, standard errors, and critical ratios have the same interpretation as in an analysis of complete data.

Example 17

Regression Weights: (Group number 1 - Default model)

			Estimate	S.E.	C.R.	P	Label
visperc	<---	spatial	1.000				
cubes	<---	spatial	.511	.153	3.347	***	
lozenges	<---	spatial	1.047	.316	3.317	***	
paragrap	<---	verbal	1.000				
sentence	<---	verbal	1.259	.194	6.505	***	
wordmean	<---	verbal	2.140	.326	6.572	***	

Intercepts: (Group number 1 - Default model)

	Estimate	S.E.	C.R.	P	Label
visperc	28.885	.913	31.632	***	
cubes	24.998	.536	46.603	***	
lozenges	15.153	1.133	13.372	***	
wordmean	18.097	1.055	17.146	***	
paragrap	10.987	.468	23.495	***	
sentence	18.864	.636	29.646	***	

Covariances: (Group number 1 - Default model)

	Estimate	S.E.	C.R.	P	Label
verbal <--> spatial	7.993	3.211	2.490	.013	

Variances: (Group number 1 - Default model)

	Estimate	S.E.	C.R.	P	Label
spatial	29.563	11.600	2.549	.011	
verbal	10.814	2.743	3.943	***	
err_v	18.776	8.518	2.204	.028	
err_c	8.034	2.669	3.011	.003	
err_l	36.625	11.662	3.141	.002	
err_p	2.825	1.277	2.212	.027	
err_s	7.875	2.403	3.277	.001	
err_w	22.677	6.883	3.295	***	

Standardized estimates and squared multiple correlations are as follows:

Standardized Regression Weights: (Group number 1 - Default model)

			Estimate
visperc	<---	spatial	.782
cubes	<---	spatial	.700
lozenges	<---	spatial	.685
paragrap	<---	verbal	.890
sentence	<---	verbal	.828
wordmean	<---	verbal	.828

Correlations: (Group number 1 - Default model)

	Estimate
verbal <--> spatial	.447

Squared Multiple Correlations: (Group number 1 - Default model)

	Estimate
wordmean	.686
sentence	.685
paragrap	.793
lozenges	.469
cubes	.490
visperc	.612

Graphics Output

Here is the path diagram showing the standardized estimates and the squared multiple correlations for the endogenous variables:

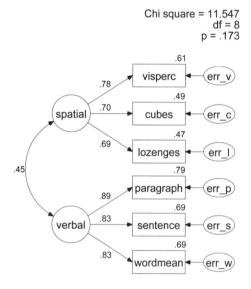

Chi square = 11.547
df = 8
p = .173

Example 17
Factor analysis with missing data
Holzinger and Swineford (1939): Girls' sample
Standardized estimates

The standardized parameter estimates may be compared to those obtained from the complete data in Example 8. The two sets of estimates are identical in the first decimal place.

Modeling in VB.NET

When you write an Amos program to analyze incomplete data, Amos does not automatically fit the independence and saturated models. (Amos Graphics does fit those models automatically.) If you want your Amos program to fit the independence and saturated models, your program has to include code to specify those models. In particular, in order for your program to compute the usual likelihood ratio chi-square statistic, your program must include code to fit the saturated model.

This section outlines three steps necessary for computing the likelihood ratio chi-square statistic:

■ Fitting the factor model

■ Fitting the saturated model

■ Computing the likelihood ratio chi-square statistic and its *p* value

First, the three steps are performed by three separate programs. After that, the three steps will be combined into a single program.

Fitting the Factor Model (Model A)

The following program fits the confirmatory factor model (Model A). It is saved as *Ex17-a.vb.*

```
Sub Main()
    Dim Sem As New AmosEngine
    Try
        Sem.Title("Example 17 a: Factor Model")
        Sem.TextOutput()
        Sem.Standardized()
        Sem.Smc()
        Sem.AllImpliedMoments()
        Sem.ModelMeansAndIntercepts()

        Sem.BeginGroup(Sem.AmosDir & "Examples\Grant_x.sav")
        Sem.AStructure("visperc  = ( ) + (1) spatial + (1) err_v")
        Sem.AStructure("cubes    = ( ) +     spatial + (1) err_c")
        Sem.AStructure("lozenges = ( ) +     spatial + (1) err_l")

        Sem.AStructure("paragrap = ( ) + (1) verbal  + (1) err_p")
        Sem.AStructure("sentence = ( ) +     verbal  + (1) err_s")
        Sem.AStructure("wordmean = ( ) +     verbal  + (1) err_w")

        Sem.FitModel()
    Finally
        Sem.Dispose()
    End Try

End Sub
```

Notice that the ModelMeansAndIntercepts method is used to specify that means and intercepts are parameters of the model and that each of the six regression equations contains a set of empty parentheses representing an intercept. When you analyze data with missing values, means and intercepts must appear in the model as explicit parameters. This is different from the analysis of complete data, where means and intercepts do not have to appear in the model unless you want to estimate them or constrain them.

The fit of Model A is summarized as follows:

> Function of log likelihood = 1375.133
> Number of parameters = 19

The *Function of log likelihood* value is displayed instead of the chi-square fit statistic that you get with complete data. In addition, at the beginning of the *Summary of models section* of the text output, Amos displays the warning:

> The saturated model was not fitted to the data of at least one group. For this reason, only the 'function of log likelihood', AIC and BCC are reported. The likelihood ratio chi-square statistic and other fit measures are not reported.

Whenever Amos prints this note, the values in the *cmin* column of the *Summary of models* section do not contain the familiar fit chi-square statistics. To evaluate the fit of the factor model, its *Function of log likelihood* value has to be compared to that of some less constrained baseline model, such as the saturated model.

Fitting the Saturated Model (Model B)

The saturated model has as many free parameters as there are first and second order moments. When complete data are analyzed, the saturated model always fits the sample data perfectly (with chi-square = 0.00 and $df = 0$). All structural equation models with the same six observed variables are either equivalent to the saturated model or are constrained versions of it. A saturated model will fit the sample data at least as well as any constrained model, and its *Function of log likelihood* value will be no larger and is, typically, smaller.

The following program fits the saturated model (Model B). The program is saved as *Ex17-b.vb*.

```
Sub Main()
    Dim Saturated As New AmosEngine
    Try
        'Set up and estimate Saturated model:
        Saturated.Title("Example 17 b: Saturated Model")
        Saturated.TextOutput()
        Saturated.AllImpliedMoments()
        Saturated.ModelMeansAndIntercepts()

        Saturated.BeginGroup(Saturated.AmosDir & "Examples\Grant_x.sav")
        Saturated.Mean("visperc")
        Saturated.Mean("cubes")
        Saturated.Mean("lozenges")
        Saturated.Mean("paragrap")
        Saturated.Mean("sentence")
        Saturated.Mean("wordmean")

        Saturated.FitModel()
    Finally
        Saturated.Dispose()
    End Try
End Sub
```

Following the BeginGroup line, there are six uses of the Mean method, requesting estimates of means for the six variables. When Amos estimates their means, it will automatically estimate their variances and covariances as well, as long as the program does not explicitly constrain the variances and covariances.

The following are the unstandardized parameter estimates for the saturated Model B:

Means: (Group number 1 - Model 1)

	Estimate	S.E.	C.R.	P	Label
visperc	28.883	.910	31.756	***	
cubes	25.154	.540	46.592	***	
lozenges	14.962	1.101	13.591	***	
paragrap	10.976	.466	23.572	***	
sentence	18.802	.632	29.730	***	
wordmean	18.263	1.061	17.211	***	

Covariances: (Group number 1 - Model 1)

			Estimate	S.E.	C.R.	P	Label
visperc	<-->	cubes	17.484	4.614	3.789	***	
visperc	<-->	lozenges	31.173	9.232	3.377	***	
cubes	<-->	lozenges	17.036	5.459	3.121	.002	
visperc	<-->	paragrap	8.453	3.705	2.281	.023	
cubes	<-->	paragrap	2.739	2.179	1.257	.209	
lozenges	<-->	paragrap	9.287	4.596	2.021	.043	
visperc	<-->	sentence	14.382	5.114	2.813	.005	
cubes	<-->	sentence	1.678	2.929	.573	.567	
lozenges	<-->	sentence	10.544	6.050	1.743	.081	
paragrap	<-->	sentence	13.470	2.945	4.574	***	
visperc	<-->	wordmean	14.665	8.314	1.764	.078	
cubes	<-->	wordmean	3.470	4.870	.713	.476	
lozenges	<-->	wordmean	29.655	10.574	2.804	.005	
paragrap	<-->	wordmean	23.616	5.010	4.714	***	
sentence	<-->	wordmean	29.577	6.650	4.447	***	

Variances: (Group number 1 - Model 1)

	Estimate	S.E.	C.R.	P	Label
visperc	49.584	9.398	5.276	***	
cubes	16.484	3.228	5.106	***	
lozenges	67.901	13.404	5.066	***	
paragrap	13.570	2.515	5.396	***	
sentence	25.007	4.629	5.402	***	
wordmean	73.974	13.221	5.595	***	

Example 17

The AllImpliedMoments method in the program displays the following table of estimates:

Implied (for all variables) Covariances (Group number 1 - Model 1)						
	wordmean	sentence	paragrap	lozenges	cubes	visperc
wordmean	73.974					
sentence	29.577	25.007				
paragrap	23.616	13.470	13.570			
lozenges	29.655	10.544	9.287	67.901		
cubes	3.470	1.678	2.739	17.036	16.484	
visperc	14.665	14.382	8.453	31.173	17.484	49.584

Implied (for all variables) Means (Group number 1 - Model 1)					
wordmean	sentence	paragrap	lozenges	cubes	visperc
18.263	18.802	10.976	14.962	25.154	28.883

These estimates, even the estimated means, are different from the sample values computed using either pairwise or listwise deletion methods. For example, 53 people took the visual perception test (*visperc*). The sample mean of those 53 *visperc* scores is 28.245. One might expect the Amos estimate of the mean visual perception score to be 28.245. In fact it is 28.883.

Amos displays the following fit information for Model B:

Function of log likelihood = 1363.586
Number of parameters = 27

Function of log likelihood values can be used to compare the fit of nested models. In this case, Model A (with a fit statistic of 1375.133 and 19 parameters) is nested within Model B (with a fit statistic of 1363.586 and 27 parameters). When a stronger model (Model A) is being compared to a weaker model (Model B), and where the stronger model is correct, you can say the following: The amount by which the Function of log likelihood increases when you switch from the weaker model to the stronger model is an observation on a chi-square random variable with degrees of freedom equal to the difference in the number of parameters of the two models. In the present example, the Function of log likelihood for Model A exceeds that for Model B by 11.547 (1375.133 − 1363.586). At the same time, Model A requires estimating only 19 parameters while Model B requires estimating 27 parameters, for a difference of 8. In other words, if Model A is correct, 11.547 is an observation on a chi-square variable with 8 degrees of freedom. A chi-square table can be consulted to see whether this chi-square statistic is significant.

Computing the Likelihood Ratio Chi-Square Statistic and P

Instead of consulting a chi-square table, you can use the ChiSquareProbability method to find the probability that a chi-square value as large as 11.547 would have occurred with a correct factor model. The following program shows how the ChiSquareProbability method is used. The program is saved as *Ex17-c.vb.*

```
Sub Main()
    Dim ChiSquare As Double, P As Double
    Dim Df As Integer

    ChiSquare = 1375.133 - 1363.586  'Difference in functions of log-likelihood
    Df = 27 - 19                      'Difference in no. of parameters

    P = AmosEngine.ChiSquareProbability(ChiSquare, CDbl(Df))

    Debug.WriteLine( "Fit of factor model:")
    Debug.WriteLine( "Chi Square = " & ChiSquare.ToString("#,##0.000"))
    Debug.WriteLine("DF = " & Df)
    Debug.WriteLine("P = " & P.ToString("0.000"))
End Sub
```

The program output is displayed in the Debug output panel of the program editor.

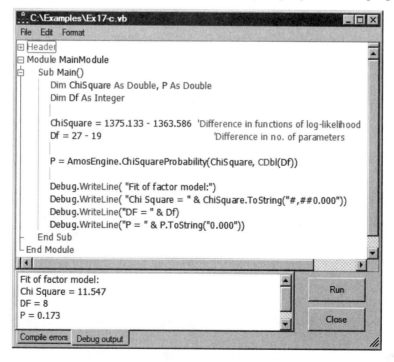

The *p* value is 0.173; therefore, we accept the hypothesis that Model A is correct at the 0.05 level.

As the present example illustrates, in order to test a model with incomplete data, you have to compare its fit to that of another, alternative model. In this example, we wanted to test Model A, and it was necessary also to fit Model B as a standard against which Model A could be compared. The alternative model has to meet two requirements. First, you have to be satisfied that it is correct. Model B certainly meets this criterion, since it places no constraints on the implied moments and cannot be wrong. Second, it must be more general than the model you wish to test. Any model that can be obtained by removing some of the constraints on the parameters of the model under test will meet this second criterion. If you have trouble thinking up an alternative model, you can always use the saturated model, as was done here.

Performing All Steps with One Program

It is possible to write a single program that fits both models (the factor model and the saturated model) and then calculates the chi-square statistic and its *p* value. The program in *Ex17-all.vb* shows how this can be done.

Example
18

More about Missing Data

Introduction

This example demonstrates the analysis of data in which some values are missing by design and then explores the benefits of intentionally collecting incomplete data.

Missing Data

Researchers do not ordinarily like missing data. They typically take great care to avoid these gaps whenever possible. But sometimes it is actually better *not* to observe every variable on every occasion. Matthai (1951) and Lord (1955) described designs where certain data values are intentionally not observed.

The basic principle employed in such designs is that when it is impossible or too costly to obtain sufficient observations on a variable, estimates with improved accuracy can be obtained by taking additional observations on other correlated variables.

Such designs can be highly useful, but because of computational difficulties, they have not previously been employed except in very simple situations. This example describes only one of many possible designs where some data are intentionally not collected. The method of analysis is the same as in Example 17.

About the Data

For this example, the Attig data (introduced in Example 1) was modified by eliminating some of the data values and treating them as missing. A portion of the modified data file for young people, *Atty_mis.sav*, is shown below as it appears in the SPSS Data Editor. The file contains scores of Attig's 40 young subjects on the two vocabulary tests *v_short* and *vocab*. The variable *vocab* is the WAIS vocabulary score. *V_short* is the score on a small subset of items on the WAIS vocabulary test. *Vocab* scores were deleted for 30 randomly picked subjects.

	v_short	vocab
7	6.00	51.00
8	9.00	52.00
9	8.00	60.00
10	5.00	48.00
11	13.00	.
12	12.00	.
13	14.00	.
14	4.00	.
15	5.00	.

A second data file, *Atto_mis.sav*, contains vocabulary test scores for the 40 old subjects, again with 30 randomly picked *vocab* scores deleted.

	v_short	vocab
7	10.00	67.00
8	6.00	47.00
9	4.00	47.00
10	.00	40.00
11	12.00	.
12	14.00	.
13	13.00	.
14	6.00	.
15	7.00	.

Of course, no sensible person deletes data that have already been collected. In order for this example to make sense, imagine this pattern of missing data arising in the following circumstances.

Suppose that *vocab* is the best vocabulary test you know of. It is highly reliable and valid, and it is the vocabulary test that you want to use. Unfortunately, it is an expensive test to administer. Maybe it takes a long time to give the test, maybe it has to be administered on an individual basis, or maybe it has to be scored by a highly trained person. *V_short* is not as good a vocabulary test, but it is short, inexpensive, and easy to administer to a large number of people at once. You administer the cheap test, *v_short*, to 40 young and 40 old subjects. Then you randomly pick 10 people from each group and ask them to take the expensive test, *vocab*.

Suppose the purpose of the research is to:

- Estimate the average *vocab* test score in the population of young people.

- Estimate the average *vocab* score in the population of old people.

- Test the hypothesis that young people and old people have the same average *vocab* score.

In this scenario, you are not interested in the average *v_short* score. However, as will be demonstrated below, the *v_short* scores are still useful because they contain information that can be used to estimate and test hypotheses about *vocab* scores.

The fact that missing values are missing by design does not affect the method of analysis. Two models will be fitted to the data. In both models, means, variances, and the covariance between the two vocabulary tests will be estimated for young people and also for old people. In Model A, there will be no constraints requiring parameter estimates to be equal across groups. In Model B, *vocab* will be required to have the same mean in both groups.

Model A

To estimate means, variances, and the covariance between *vocab* and *v_short*, set up a two-group model for the young and old groups.

▶ Draw a path diagram in which *vocab* and *v_short* appear as two rectangles connected by a double-headed arrow.

▶ From the menus, choose View → Analysis Properties.

▶ In the Analysis Properties dialog box, click the Estimation tab.

▶ Select Estimate means and intercepts (a check mark appears next to it).

▶ While the Analysis Properties dialog box is open, click the Output tab.

▶ Select Standardized estimates and Critical ratios for differences.

Because this example focuses on group differences in the mean of *vocab*, it will be useful to have names for the mean of the young group and the mean of the old group. To give a name to the mean of *vocab* in the young group:

▶ Right-click the *vocab* rectangle in the path diagram for the young group.

▶ Choose Object Properties from the pop-up menu.

▶ In the Object Properties dialog box, click the Parameters tab.

▶ Enter a name, such as *m1_yng*, in the Mean text box.

▶ Follow the same procedure for the old group. Be sure to give the mean of the old group a unique name, such as *m1_old*.

Naming the means does not constrain them as long as each name is unique. After the means are named, the two groups should have path diagrams that look something like this:

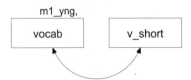

Example 18: Model A
Incompletely observed data.
Attig (1983) young subjects
Model Specification

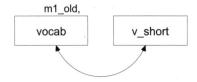

Example 18: Model A
Incompletely observed data.
Attig (1983) old subjects
Model Specification

Results for Model A

Graphics Output

Here are the two path diagrams containing means, variances, and covariances for the young and old subjects, respectively:

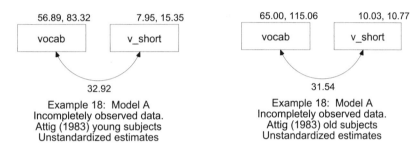

Example 18: Model A
Incompletely observed data.
Attig (1983) young subjects
Unstandardized estimates

Example 18: Model A
Incompletely observed data.
Attig (1983) old subjects
Unstandardized estimates

Text Output

▶ In the Amos Output window, click Notes for Model in the upper left pane.

The text output shows that Model A is saturated, so that the model is not testable.

Number of distinct sample moments:	10
Number of distinct parameters to be estimated:	10
Degrees of freedom (10 − 10):	0

Example 18

The parameter estimates and standard errors for young subjects are:

Means: (young subjects - Default model)

	Estimate	S.E.	C.R.	P	Label
vocab	56.891	1.765	32.232	***	m1_yng
v_short	7.950	.627	12.673	***	par_4

Covariances: (young subjects - Default model)

	Estimate	S.E.	C.R.	P	Label
vocab <--> v_short	32.916	8.694	3.786	***	par_3

Correlations: (young subjects - Default model)

	Estimate
vocab <--> v_short	.920

Variances: (young subjects - Default model)

	Estimate	S.E.	C.R.	P	Label
vocab	83.320	25.639	3.250	.001	par_7
v_short	15.347	3.476	4.416	***	par_8

The parameter estimates and standard errors for old subjects are:

Means: (old subjects - Default model)

	Estimate	S.E.	C.R.	P	Label
vocab	65.001	2.167	29.992	***	m1_old
v_short	10.025	.526	19.073	***	par_6

Covariances: (old subjects - Default model)

	Estimate	S.E.	C.R.	P	Label
vocab <--> v_short	31.545	8.725	3.616	***	par_5

Correlations: (old subjects - Default model)

	Estimate
vocab <--> v_short	.896

Variances: (old subjects - Default model)

	Estimate	S.E.	C.R.	P	Label
vocab	115.063	37.463	3.071	.002	par_9
v_short	10.774	2.440	4.416	***	par_10

The estimates for the mean of *vocab* are 56.891 in the young population and 65.001 in the old population. Notice that these are not the same as the sample means that would have been obtained from the 10 young and 10 old subjects who took the *vocab* test. The sample means of 58.5 and 62 are good estimates of the population means (the best that can be had from the two samples of size 10), but the Amos estimates (56.891 and 65.001) have the advantage of using information in the *v_short* scores.

How much more accurate are the mean estimates that include the information in the *v_short* scores? Some idea can be obtained by looking at estimated standard errors. For the young subjects, the standard error for 56.891 shown above is about 1.765, whereas the standard error of the sample mean, 58.5, is about 2.21. For the old subjects, the standard error for 65.001 is about 2.167 while the standard error of the sample mean,

62, is about 4.21. Although the standard errors just mentioned are only approximations, they still provide a rough basis for comparison. In the case of the young subjects, using the information contained in the *v_short* scores reduces the standard error of the estimated *vocab* mean by about 21%. In the case of the old subjects, the standard error was reduced by about 49%.

Another way to evaluate the additional information that can be attributed to the *v_short* scores is by evaluating the sample size requirements. Suppose you did not use the information in the *v_short* scores. How many more young examinees would have to take the *vocab* test to reduce the standard error of its mean by 21%? Likewise, how many more old examinees would have to take the *vocab* test to reduce the standard error of its mean by 49%? The answer is that, because the standard error of the mean is inversely proportional to the square root of the sample size, it would require about 1.6 times as many young subjects and about 3.8 times as many old subjects. That is, it would require about 16 young subjects and 38 old subjects taking the *vocab* test, instead of 10 young and 10 old subjects taking both tests, and 30 young and 30 old subjects taking the short test alone. Of course, this calculation treats the estimated standard errors as though they were exact standard errors, and so it gives only a rough idea of how much is gained by using scores on the *v_short* test.

Do the young and old populations have different mean *vocab* scores? The estimated mean difference is 8.110 (65.001 – 56.891). A critical ratio for testing this difference for significance can be found in the following table:

Critical Ratios for Differences between Parameters (Default model)

	m1_yng	m1_old	par_3	par_4	par_5	par_6	par_7
m1_yng	.000						
m1_old	2.901	.000					
par_3	-2.702	-3.581	.000				
par_4	-36.269	-25.286	-2.864	.000			
par_5	-2.847	-3.722	-.111	2.697	.000		
par_6	-25.448	-30.012	-2.628	2.535	-2.462	.000	
par_7	1.028	.712	2.806	2.939	1.912	2.858	.000
par_8	-10.658	-12.123	-2.934	2.095	-1.725	1.514	-2.877
par_9	1.551	1.334	2.136	2.859	2.804	2.803	.699
par_10	-15.314	-16.616	-2.452	1.121	-3.023	.300	-2.817

Critical Ratios for Differences between Parameters (Default model)

	par_8	par_9	par_10
par_8	.000		
par_9	2.650	.000	
par_10	-1.077	-2.884	.000

The first two rows and columns, labeled *m1_yng* and *m1_old*, refer to the group means of the *vocab* test. The critical ratio for the mean difference is 2.901, according to which the means differ significantly at the 0.05 level; the older population scores higher on the long test than the younger population.

Another test of the hypothesis of equal *vocab* group means can be obtained by refitting the model with equality constraints imposed on these two means. We will do that next.

Model B

In Model B, *vocab* is required to have the same mean for young people as for old people. There are two ways to impose this constraint. One method is to change the names of the means. In Model A, each mean has a unique name. You can change the names and give each mean the same name. This will have the effect of requiring the two mean estimates to be equal.

A different method of constraining the means will be used here. The name of the means, *m1_yng* and *m1_old*, will be left alone. Amos will use its Model Manager to fit both Model A and Model B in a single analysis. To use this approach:

▶ Start with Model A.

▶ From the menus, choose Analyze → Manage Models.

▶ In the Manage Models dialog box, type Model A in the Model Name text box.

▶ Leave the Parameter Constraints box empty.

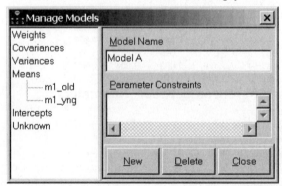

▶ To specify Model B, click New.

▶ In the Model Name text box, change Model Number 2 to Model B.

▶ Type m1_old = m1_yng in the Parameter Constraints text box.

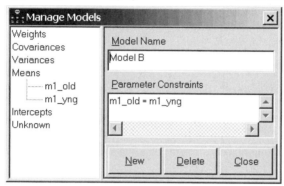

▶ Click Close.

A path diagram that fits both Model A and Model B is saved in the file *Ex18-b.amw.*

Output from Models A and B

▶ To see fit measures for both Model A and Model B, click Model Fit in the tree diagram in the upper left pane of the Amos Output window.

The portion of the output that contains chi-square values is shown here:

CMIN

Model	NPAR	CMIN	DF	P	CMIN/DF
Model A	10	.000	0		
Model B	9	7.849	1	.005	7.849
Saturated model	10	.000	0		
Independence model	4	33.096	6	.000	5.516

If Model B is correct (that is, the young and old populations have the same mean *vocab* score), then 7.849 is an observation on a random variable that has a chi-square distribution with one degree of freedom. The probability of getting a value as large as 7.849 by chance is small ($p = 0.005$), so Model B is rejected. In other words, young and old subjects differ significantly in their mean *vocab* scores.]

Example 18

Modeling in VB.NET

Model A

The following program fits Model A. It estimates means, variances, and covariances of both vocabulary tests in both groups of subjects, without constraints. The program is saved as *Ex18-a.vb.*

```
Sub Main()
   Dim Sem As New AmosEngine
   Try
      Sem.TextOutput()
      Sem.Crdiff()
      Sem.ModelMeansAndIntercepts()

      Sem.BeginGroup(Sem.AmosDir & "Examples\atty_mis.sav")
         Sem.GroupName("young_subjects")
         Sem.Mean("vocab", "m1_yng")
         Sem.Mean("v_short")
      Sem.BeginGroup(Sem.AmosDir & "Examples\atto_mis.sav")
         Sem.GroupName("old_subjects")
         Sem.Mean("vocab", "m1_old")
         Sem.Mean("v_short")
      Sem.FitModel()
   Finally
      Sem.Dispose()
   End Try
End Sub
```

The Crdiff method displays the critical ratios for parameter differences that were discussed earlier.

For later reference, note the value of the *Function of log likelihood* for Model A.

```
Function of log likelihood =   429.963
Number of parameters =   10
```

Model B

Here is a program for fitting Model B. In this program, the same parameter name (*mn_vocab*) is used for the *vocab* mean of the young group as for the *vocab* mean of the old group. In this way, the young group and old group are required to have the same *vocab* mean. The program is saved as *Ex18-b.vb*.

```
Sub Main()
   Dim Sem As New AmosEngine
   Try
      Sem.TextOutput()
      Sem.Crdiff()
      Sem.ModelMeansAndIntercepts()

      Sem.BeginGroup(Sem.AmosDir & "Examples\atty_mis.sav")
         Sem.GroupName("young_subjects")
         Sem.Mean("vocab", "mn_vocab")
         Sem.Mean("v_short")
      Sem.BeginGroup(Sem.AmosDir & "Examples\atto_mis.sav")
         Sem.GroupName("old_subjects")
         Sem.Mean("vocab", "mn_vocab")
         Sem.Mean("v_short")
      Sem.FitModel()
   Finally
      Sem.Dispose()
   End Try
End Sub
```

Amos reports the fit of Model B as:

```
Function of log likelihood =   437.813
Number of parameters =   9
```

The difference in fit measures between Models B and A is 7.85 (= 437.813 – 429.963), and the difference in the number of parameters is 1 (= 10 – 9). These are the same figures we obtained earlier with Amos Graphics.

Example

19

Bootstrapping

Introduction

This example demonstrates how to obtain robust standard error estimates by the bootstrap method.

The Bootstrap Method

The bootstrap (Efron, 1982) is a versatile method for estimating the sampling distribution of parameter estimates. In particular, the bootstrap can be used to find approximate standard errors. As we saw in earlier examples, Amos automatically displays approximate standard errors for the parameters it estimates. In computing these approximations, Amos uses formulas that depend on the assumptions on p. 39.

The bootstrap is a completely different approach to the problem of estimating standard errors. Why would you want another approach? To begin with, Amos does not have formulas for all of the standard errors you might want, such as standard errors for squared multiple correlations. The unavailability of formulas for standard errors is never a problem with the bootstrap, however. The bootstrap can be used to generate an approximate standard error for every estimate that Amos computes, whether or not a formula for the standard error is known. Even when Amos has formulas for standard errors, the formulas are good only under the assumptions on p. 39. Not only that, but the formulas work only when you are using a correct model. Approximate standard errors arrived at by the bootstrap do not suffer from these limitations.

The bootstrap has its own shortcomings, including the fact that it can require fairly large samples. For readers who are new to bootstrapping, we recommend the *Scientific American* article by Diaconis and Efron (1983).

The present example demonstrates the bootstrap with a factor analysis model, but, of course, you can use the bootstrap with any model. Incidentally, don't forget that Amos can solve simple estimation problems like the one in Example 1. You might choose to use Amos for such simple problems just so you can use the bootstrapping capability of Amos.

About the Data

We will use the Holzinger and Swineford (1939) data, introduced in Example 8, for this example. The data are contained in the file *Grnt_fem.sav.*

A Factor Analysis Model

The path diagram for this model (*Ex19.amw*) is the same as in Example 8.

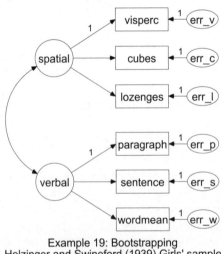

Example 19: Bootstrapping
Holzinger and Swineford (1939) Girls' sample
Model Specification

▶ To request 500 bootstrap replications, from the menus, choose View → Analysis Properties.

▶ Click the Bootstrap tab.

▶ Select Perform bootstrap.

▶ Type 500 in the Number of bootstrap samples text box.

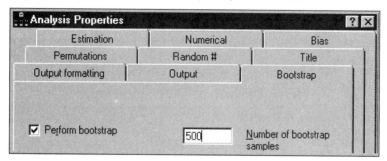

Monitoring the Progress of the Bootstrap

You can monitor the progress of the bootstrap algorithm by watching the Computation summary panel at the left of the path diagram.

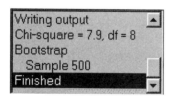

Results of the Analysis

The model fit is, of course, the same as in Example 8.

Chi-square = 7.853
Degrees of freedom = 8
Probability level = 0.448

The parameter estimates are also the same as in Example 8. However, we would now like to look at the standard error estimates based on the maximum likelihood theory, so that we can compare them to standard errors obtained from the bootstrap. Here, then, are the maximum likelihood estimates of parameters and their standard errors:

Example 19

Regression Weights: (Group number 1 - Default model)

			Estimate	S.E.	C.R.	P	Label
visperc	<---	spatial	1.000				
cubes	<---	spatial	.610	.143	4.250	***	
lozenges	<---	spatial	1.198	.272	4.405	***	
paragrap	<---	verbal	1.000				
sentence	<---	verbal	1.334	.160	8.322	***	
wordmean	<---	verbal	2.234	.263	8.482	***	

Standardized Regression Weights: (Group number 1 - Default model)

			Estimate
visperc	<---	spatial	.703
cubes	<---	spatial	.654
lozenges	<---	spatial	.736
paragrap	<---	verbal	.880
sentence	<---	verbal	.827
wordmean	<---	verbal	.841

Covariances: (Group number 1 - Default model)

	Estimate	S.E.	C.R.	P	Label
spatial <--> verbal	7.315	2.571	2.846	.004	

Correlations: (Group number 1 - Default model)

	Estimate
spatial <--> verbal	.487

Variances: (Group number 1 - Default model)

	Estimate	S.E.	C.R.	P	Label
spatial	23.302	8.123	2.868	.004	
verbal	9.682	2.159	4.485	***	
err_v	23.873	5.986	3.988	***	
err_c	11.602	2.584	4.490	***	
err_l	28.275	7.892	3.583	***	
err_p	2.834	.868	3.263	.001	
err_s	7.967	1.869	4.263	***	
err_w	19.925	4.951	4.024	***	

Squared Multiple Correlations: (Group number 1 - Default model)

	Estimate
wordmean	.708
sentence	.684
paragrap	.774
lozenges	.542
cubes	.428
visperc	.494

The bootstrap output begins with a table of diagnostic information that is similar to the following:

```
0 bootstrap samples were unused because of a singular covariance matrix.
0 bootstrap samples were unused because a solution was not found.
500 usable bootstrap samples were obtained.
```

It is possible that one or more bootstrap samples will have a singular covariance matrix, or that Amos will fail to find a solution for some bootstrap samples. If any such samples occur, Amos reports their occurrence and omits them from the bootstrap analysis. In the present example, no bootstrap sample had a singular covariance matrix, and a solution was found for each of the 500 bootstrap samples. The bootstrap estimates of standard errors are:

Example 19

Scalar Estimates (Group number 1 - Default model)

Regression Weights: (Group number 1 - Default model)

Parameter			SE	SE-SE	Mean	Bias	SE-Bias
visperc	<---	spatial	.000	.000	1.000	.000	.000
cubes	<---	spatial	.140	.004	.609	-.001	.006
lozenges	<---	spatial	.373	.012	1.216	.018	.017
paragrap	<---	verbal	.000	.000	1.000	.000	.000
sentence	<---	verbal	.176	.006	1.345	.011	.008
wordmean	<---	verbal	.254	.008	2.246	.011	.011

Standardized Regression Weights: (Group number 1 - Default model)

Parameter			SE	SE-SE	Mean	Bias	SE-Bias
visperc	<---	spatial	.123	.004	.709	.006	.005
cubes	<---	spatial	.101	.003	.646	-.008	.005
lozenges	<---	spatial	.121	.004	.719	-.017	.005
paragrap	<---	verbal	.047	.001	.876	-.004	.002
sentence	<---	verbal	.042	.001	.826	.000	.002
wordmean	<---	verbal	.050	.002	.841	-.001	.002

Covariances: (Group number 1 - Default model)

Parameter			SE	SE-SE	Mean	Bias	SE-Bias
spatial	<-->	verbal	2.393	.076	7.241	-.074	.107

Correlations: (Group number 1 - Default model)

Parameter			SE	SE-SE	Mean	Bias	SE-Bias
spatial	<-->	verbal	.132	.004	.495	.008	.006

Variances: (Group number 1 - Default model)

Parameter	SE	SE-SE	Mean	Bias	SE-Bias
spatial	9.086	.287	23.905	.603	.406
verbal	2.077	.066	9.518	-.164	.093
err_v	9.166	.290	22.393	-1.480	.410
err_c	3.195	.101	11.191	-.411	.143
err_l	9.940	.314	27.797	-.478	.445
err_p	.878	.028	2.772	-.062	.039
err_s	1.446	.046	7.597	-.370	.065
err_w	5.488	.174	19.123	-.803	.245

Squared Multiple Correlations: (Group number 1 - Default model)

Parameter	SE	SE-SE	Mean	Bias	SE-Bias
wordmean	.083	.003	.709	.001	.004
sentence	.069	.002	.685	.001	.003
paragrap	.081	.003	.770	-.004	.004
lozenges	.172	.005	.532	-.010	.008
cubes	.127	.004	.428	.000	.006
visperc	.182	.006	.517	.023	.008

- The first column, labeled *S.E.*, contains bootstrap estimates of standard errors. These estimates may be compared to the approximate standard error estimates obtained by maximum likelihood.

- The second column, labeled *S.E.-S.E.*, gives an approximate standard error for the bootstrap standard error estimate itself.

- The column labeled *Mean* represents the average parameter estimate computed across bootstrap samples. This bootstrap mean is not necessarily identical to the original estimate.

- The column labeled *Bias* gives the difference between the original estimate and the mean of estimates across bootstrap samples. If the mean estimate across bootstrapped samples is higher than the original estimate, then *Bias* will be positive.

- The last column, labeled *S.E.-Bias*, gives an approximate standard error for the bias estimate.

Modeling in VB.NET

The following program (*Ex19.vb*) fits the model of Example 19 and performs a bootstrap with 500 bootstrap samples. The program is the same as in Example 8, but with an additional Bootstrap line.

```
Sub Main()
  Dim Sem As New AmosEngine
  Try
    Sem.TextOutput()
    Sem.Bootstrap(500)
    Sem.Standardized()
    Sem.Smc()

    Sem.BeginGroup(Sem.AmosDir & "Examples\Grnt_fem.sav")

    Sem.AStructure("visperc  = (1) spatial + (1) err_v")
    Sem.AStructure("cubes    =     spatial + (1) err_c")
    Sem.AStructure("lozenges =     spatial + (1) err_l")

    Sem.AStructure("paragrap = (1) verbal  + (1) err_p")
    Sem.AStructure("sentence =     verbal  + (1) err_s")
    Sem.AStructure("wordmean =     verbal  + (1) err_w")

    Sem.FitModel()
  Finally
    Sem.Dispose()
  End Try
End Sub
```

The line Sem.Bootstrap(500) requests bootstrap standard errors based on 500 bootstrap samples.

20

Bootstrapping for Model Comparison

Introduction

This example demonstrates the use of the bootstrap for model comparison.

Bootstrap Approach to Model Comparison

The problem addressed by this method is not that of evaluating an individual model in absolute terms but of choosing among two or more competing models. Bollen and Stine (1992), Bollen (1982), and Stine (1989) suggested the possibility of using the bootstrap for model selection in analysis of moment structures. Linhart and Zucchini (1986) described a general schema for bootstrapping and model selection that is appropriate for a large class of models, including structural modeling. The Linhart and Zucchini approach is employed here.

The bootstrap approach to model comparison can be summarized as follows:

- Generate several bootstrap samples by sampling with replacement from the original sample. In other words, the *original sample* serves as the *population* for purposes of bootstrap sampling.

- Fit every competing model to every bootstrap sample. After each analysis, calculate the discrepancy between the implied moments obtained from the bootstrap sample and the moments of the bootstrap population.

- Calculate the average (across bootstrap samples) of the discrepancies for each model from the previous step.

- Choose the model whose average discrepancy is smallest.

About the Data

The present example uses the combined male and female data from the Grant-White high school sample of the Holzinger and Swineford (1939) study, previously discussed in Examples 8, 12, 15, 17, and 19. The 145 combined observations are given in the file *Grant.sav*.

Five Models

Five measurement models will be fitted to the six psychological tests. Model 1 is a factor analysis model with one factor.

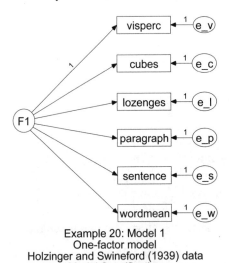

Example 20: Model 1
One-factor model
Holzinger and Swineford (1939) data
Model Specification

Model 2 is an unrestricted factor analysis with two factors. Note that fixing two of the regression weights at 0 does not constrain the model but serves only to make the model identified (Anderson, 1984; Bollen and Jöreskog, 1985; Jöreskog, 1979).

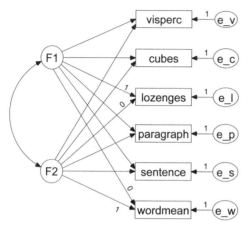

Example 20: Model 2
Two unconstrained factors
Holzinger and Swineford (1939) data
Model Specification

Model 2R is a restricted factor analysis model with two factors, in which the first three tests depend upon only one of the factors while the remaining three tests depend upon only the other factor.

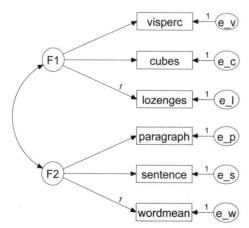

Example 20: Model 2R
Restricted two-factor model
Holzinger and Swineford (1939) data
Model Specification

The remaining two models provide customary points of reference for evaluating the fit of the previous models. In the saturated model, the variances and covariances of the observed variables are unconstrained.

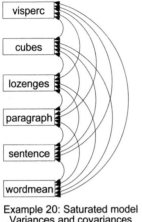

Example 20: Saturated model
Variances and covariances
Holzinger and Swineford (1939) data
Model Specification

In the independence model, the variances of the observed variables are unconstrained and their covariances are required to be 0.

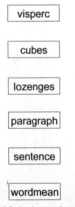

Example 20: Independence model
Only variances are estimated
Holzinger and Swineford (1939) data
Model Specification

You would not ordinarily fit the saturated and independence models separately, since Amos automatically reports fit measures for those two models in the course of every analysis. However, it is necessary to specify explicitly the saturated and independence models in order to get bootstrap results for those models. Five separate bootstrap analyses must be performed, one for each model. For *each* of the five analyses:

▶ From the menus, choose View → Analysis Properties.

▶ In the Analysis Properties dialog box, click the Bootstrap tab.

▶ Select Perform bootstrap (a check mark appears next to it).

▶ Type 1000 in the Number of bootstrap samples text box.

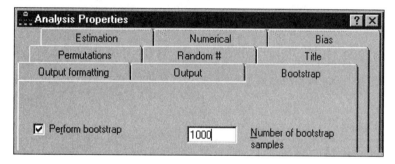

▶ Click the Random # tab and enter a value for Seed for random numbers.

It does not matter what seed you choose, but in order to draw the exact same set of samples in each of several Amos sessions, the same seed number must be given each time. For this example, we used a seed of 3.

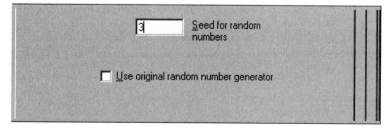

Occasionally, bootstrap samples are encountered for which the minimization algorithm does not converge. To keep overall computation times in check:

▶ Click the Numerical tab and limit the number of iterations to a realistic figure (such as 40) in the Iteration limit field.

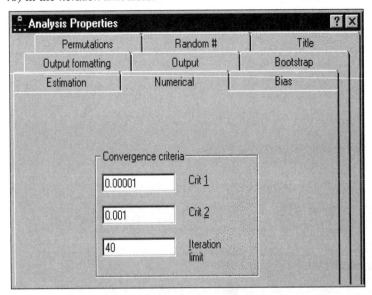

Amos Graphics input files for the five models have been saved with the names *Ex20-1.amw, Ex20-2.amw, Ex20-2r.amw, Ex20-sat.amw,* and *Ex20-ind.amw.*

Text Output

▶ In viewing the text output for Model 1, click Summary of Bootstrap Iterations in the tree diagram in the upper left pane of the Amos Output window.

The following message shows that it was not necessary to discard any bootstrap samples. All 1,000 bootstrap samples were used.

> 0 bootstrap samples were unused because of a singular covariance matrix.
> 0 bootstrap samples were unused because a solution was not found.
> 1000 usable bootstrap samples were obtained.

▶ Click Bootstrap Distributions in the tree diagram to see a histogram of

$$C_{ML}\left(\hat{\alpha}_b, \mathbf{a}\right) = C_{KL}\left(\hat{\alpha}_b, \mathbf{a}\right) - C_{KL}\left(\mathbf{a}, \mathbf{a}\right), \quad b = 1, \ldots, 1000$$

where *a* contains sample moments from the original sample of 145 Grant-White students (that is, the moments in the bootstrap population), and $\hat{\alpha}_b$ contains the implied moments obtained from fitting Model 1 to the *b-th* bootstrap sample. Thus, $C_{\mathrm{ML}}(\hat{\alpha}_b, \mathbf{a})$ is a measure of how much the population moments differ from the moments estimated from the *b-th* bootstrap sample using Model 1.

```
 ML discrepancy (implied vs pop) (Default model)
                              |--------------------
                    48.268    |**
                    52.091    |*********
                    55.913    |*************
                    59.735    |*********************
                    63.557    |******************
                    67.379    |************
                    71.202    |********
  N = 1000          75.024    |******
  Mean = 64.162     78.846    |***
  S. e. = .292      82.668    |*
                    86.490    |**
                    90.313    |**
                    94.135    |*
                    97.957    |*
                   101.779    |*
                              |--------------------
```

The average of $C_{\mathrm{ML}}(\hat{\alpha}_b, \mathbf{a})$ over 1,000 bootstrap samples was 64.162 with a standard error of 0.292. Similar histograms, along with means and standard errors, are displayed for the other four models but are not reproduced here. The average discrepancies for the five competing models are shown in the table below, along with values of BCC, AIC, and CAIC. The table provides fit measures for five competing models (standard errors in parentheses).

Model	Failures	Mean Discrepancy	BCC	AIC	CAIC
1	0	64.16 (0.29)	68.17	66.94	114.66
2	19	29.14 (0.35	36.81	35.07	102.68
2R	0	26.57 (0.30)	30.97	29.64	81.34
Sat.	0	32.05 (0.37)	44.15	42.00	125.51
Indep.	0	334.32 (0.24)	333.93	333.32	357.18

The *Failures* column in the table indicates that the likelihood function of Model 2 could not be maximized for 19 of the 1,000 bootstrap samples, at least not with the iteration limit of 40. Nineteen additional bootstrap samples were generated for Model 2 in order to bring the total number of bootstrap samples to the target of 1,000. The 19 samples where Model 2 could not be fitted successfully caused no problem with the other four models. Consequently, 981 bootstrap samples were common to all five models.

No attempt was made to find out why Model 2 estimates could not be computed for 19 bootstrap samples. As a rule, algorithms for analysis of moment structures tend to fail for models that fit poorly. If some way could be found to successfully fit Model 2 to these 19 samples—for example, with hand-picked start values or a superior algorithm—it seems likely that the discrepancies would be large. According to this line of reasoning, discarding bootstrap samples for which estimation failed would lead to a downward bias in the mean discrepancy. Thus, you should be concerned by estimation failures during bootstrapping, primarily when they occur for the model with the lowest mean discrepancy.

In this example, the lowest mean discrepancy (26.57) occurs for Model 2R, confirming the model choice based on the BCC, AIC, and CAIC criteria. The differences among the mean discrepancies are large compared to their standard errors. Since all models were fitted to the same bootstrap samples (except for samples where Model 2 was not successfully fitted), you would expect to find positive correlations across bootstrap samples between discrepancies for similar models. Unfortunately, Amos does not report those correlations. Calculating the correlations by hand shows that they are close to 1, so that standard errors for the differences between means in the table are, on the whole, even smaller than the standard errors of the means.

Summary

The bootstrap can be a practical aid in model selection for analysis of moment structures. The Linhart and Zucchini (1986) approach uses the expected discrepancy between implied and population moments as the basis for model comparisons. The method is conceptually simple and easy to apply. It does not employ any arbitrary *magic number* such as a significance level. Of course, the theoretical appropriateness of competing models and the reasonableness of their associated parameter estimates are not taken into account by the bootstrap procedure and need to be given appropriate weight at some other stage in the model evaluation process.

Modeling in VB.NET

Visual Basic programs for this example are in the files *Ex20-1.vb, Ex20-2.vb, Ex20-2r.vb, Ex20-ind.vb*, and *Ex20-sat.vb*.

Example

21

Bootstrapping to Compare Estimation Methods

Introduction

This example demonstrates how bootstrapping can be used to choose among competing estimation criteria.

Estimation Methods

The discrepancy between the population moments and the moments implied by a model depends not only on the model but also on the estimation method. The technique used in Example 20 to compare models can be adapted to the comparison of estimation methods. This capability is particularly needed when choosing among estimation methods that are known to be optimal only asymptotically, and whose relative merits in finite samples would be expected to depend on the model, the sample size, and the population distribution. The principal obstacle to carrying out this program for comparing estimation methods is that it requires a prior decision about how to measure the discrepancy between the population moments and the moments implied by the model. There appears to be no way to make this decision without favoring some estimation criteria over others. Of course, if every choice of population discrepancy leads to the same conclusion, questions about which is the appropriate population discrepancy can be considered academic. The present example presents such a clear-cut case.

About the Data

The Holzinger-Swineford (1939) data from Example 20 (in the file *Grant.sav*) are used in the present example.

About the Model

The present example estimates the parameters of Model 2R from Example 20 by four alternative methods: asymptotically distribution-free (ADF), maximum likelihood (ML), generalized least squares (GLS), and unweighted least squares (ULS). To compare the four estimation methods, you need to run Amos four times.

To specify the estimation method and bootstrap parameters:

▶ From the menus, choose View → Analysis Properties.

▶ In the Analysis Properties dialog box, click the Random # tab.

▶ Enter a value for Seed for random numbers.

As we discussed in Example 20, it does not matter what seed value you choose, but in order to draw the exact same set of samples in each of several Amos sessions, the same seed number must be given each time. In this example, we use a seed of 3.

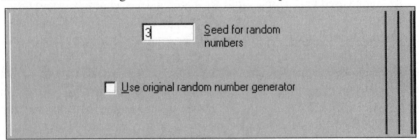

▶ Next, click the Estimation tab.

▶ Select the Asymptotically distribution-free discrepancy.

This discrepancy specifies that ADF estimation should be used to fit the model to each bootstrap sample.

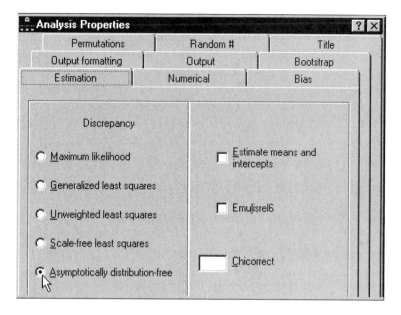

▶ Finally, click the Bootstrap tab.

▶ Select Perform bootstrap and type 1000 for Number of bootstrap samples.

▶ Select Bootstrap ADF, Bootstrap ML, Bootstrap GLS, and Bootstrap ULS.

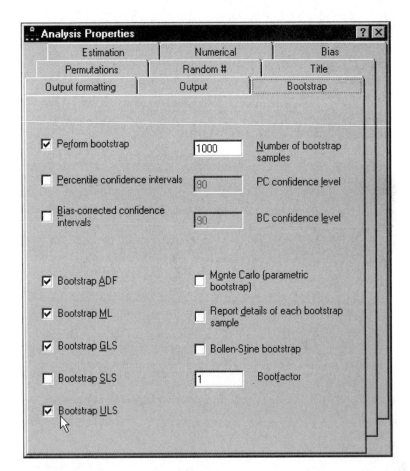

Selecting Bootstrap ADF, Bootstrap ML, Bootstrap GLS, Bootstrap SLS, and Bootstrap ULS specifies that each of C_{ADF}, C_{ML}, C_{GLS}, and C_{ULS} is to be used to measure the discrepancy between the sample moments in the original sample and the implied moments from each bootstrap sample.

To summarize, when you perform the analysis (Analyze → Calculate Estimates), Amos will fit the model to each of 1,000 bootstrap samples using the ADF discrepancy. For each bootstrap sample, the closeness of the implied moments to the population moments will be measured four different ways, using C_{ADF}, C_{ML}, C_{GLS}, and C_{ULS}.

▶ Select the Maximum likelihood discrepancy to repeat the analysis.

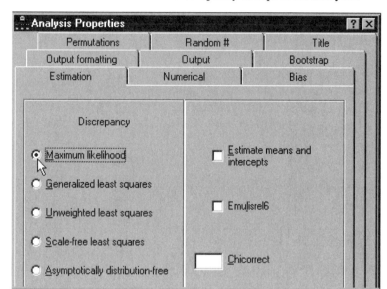

▶ Select the Generalized least squares discrepancy to repeat the analysis again.

▶ Select the Unweighted least squares discrepancy to repeat the analysis one last time.

The four Amos Graphics input files for this example are *Ex21-adf.amw*, *Ex21-ml.amw*, *Ex21-gls.amw*, and *Ex21-uls.amw*.

Text Output

In the first of the four analyses (as found in *Ex21-adf.amw*), estimation using ADF produces the following histogram output. To view this histogram:

▶ Click Bootstrap Distributions → ADF Discrepancy (implied vs pop) in the tree diagram in the upper left pane of the Amos Output window.

```
┌─────────────────────────────────────────────────────────┐
│ ADF discrepancy (implied vs pop) (Default model)         │
│                        |---------------------             │
│              7.359     |*                                 │
│             10.817     |********                          │
│             14.274     |****************                  │
│             17.732     |*********************             │
│             21.189     |********************              │
│             24.647     |*************                     │
│             28.104     |********                          │
│   N = 1000  31.562     |****                              │
│ Mean = 20.601  35.019  |**                                │
│  S. e. = .218  38.477  |**                                │
│             41.934     |*                                 │
│             45.392     |*                                 │
│             48.850     |*                                 │
│             52.307     |*                                 │
│             55.765     |*                                 │
│                        |---------------------             │
└─────────────────────────────────────────────────────────┘
```

This portion of the output shows the distribution of the population discrepancy $C_{\text{ADF}}(\hat{\alpha}_b, \mathbf{a})$ across 1,000 bootstrap samples, where $\hat{\alpha}_b$ contains the implied moments obtained by minimizing $C_{\text{ADF}}(\hat{\alpha}_b, \mathbf{a}_b)$, that is, the sample discrepancy. The average of $C_{\text{ADF}}(\hat{\alpha}_b, \mathbf{a})$ across 1,000 bootstrap samples is 20.601, with a standard error of 0.218.

The following histogram shows the distribution of $C_{\text{ML}}(\hat{\alpha}_b, \mathbf{a})$. To view this histogram:

▶ Click Bootstrap Distributions → ML Discrepancy (implied vs pop) in the tree diagram in the upper left pane of the Amos Output window.

```
┌─────────────────────────────────────────────────────────┐
│ ML discrepancy (implied vs pop) (Default model)          │
│                        |---------------------             │
│             11.272     |****                              │
│             22.691     |*********************             │
│             34.110     |*********************             │
│             45.530     |***********                       │
│             56.949     |*****                             │
│             68.368     |***                               │
│             79.787     |**                                │
│   N = 1000  91.207     |*                                 │
│ Mean = 36.860  102.626 |*                                 │
│  S. e. = .571  114.045 |*                                 │
│            125.464     |*                                 │
│            136.884     |                                  │
│            148.303     |                                  │
│            159.722     |                                  │
│            171.142     |*                                 │
│                        |---------------------             │
└─────────────────────────────────────────────────────────┘
```

The following histogram shows the distribution of $C_{GLS}(\hat{\alpha}_b, \mathbf{a})$. To view this histogram:

▶ Click Bootstrap Distributions → GLS Discrepancy (implied vs pop) in the tree diagram in the upper left pane of the Amos Output window.

```
GLS discrepancy (implied vs pop) (Default model)
                       |--------------------
              7.248    |**
             11.076    |*********
             14.904    |***************
             18.733    |*********************
             22.561    |**************
             26.389    |***********
             30.217    |*******
N = 1000     34.046    |****
Mean = 21.827 37.874   |**
S. e. = .263 41.702    |***
             45.530    |*
             49.359    |*
             53.187    |*
             57.015    |*
             60.844    |*
                       |--------------------
```

The following histogram shows the distribution of $C_{ULS}(\hat{\alpha}_b, \mathbf{a})$. To view this histogram:

▶ Click Bootstrap Distributions → ULS Discrepancy (implied vs pop) in the tree diagram in the upper left pane of the Amos Output window.

```
ULS discrepancy (implied vs pop) (Default model)
                         |--------------------
              5079.897   |******
             30811.807   |********************
             56543.716   |********
             82275.625   |****
            108007.534   |**
            133739.443   |*
            159471.352   |*
N = 1000    185203.261   |*
Mean = 43686.444 210935.170 |
S. e. = 1011.591 236667.079 |*
            262398.988   |
            288130.897   |
            313862.806   |
            339594.715   |
            365326.624   |*
                         |--------------------
```

Below is a table showing the mean of $C(\hat{\alpha}_b, \mathbf{a})$ across 1,000 bootstrap samples with the standard errors in parentheses. The four distributions just displayed are summarized in the first row of the table. The remaining three rows show the results of estimation by minimizing C_{ML}, C_{GLS}, and C_{ULS}, respectively.

		Population discrepancy for evaluation: $C(\hat{\alpha}_b, \mathbf{a}_b)$			
		C_{ADF}	C_{ML}	C_{GLS}	C_{ULS}
Sample discrepancy for estimation $C(\hat{\alpha}_b, \mathbf{a}_b)$	C_{ADF}	20.60 (0.22)	36.86 (0.57)	21.83 (0.26)	43686 (1012)
	C_{ML}	19.19 (0.20)	26.57 (0.30)	18.96 (0.22)	34760 (830)
	C_{GLS}	19.45 (0.20)	31.45 (0.40)	19.03 (0.21)	37021 (830)
	C_{ULS}	24.89 (0.35)	31.78 (0.43)	24.16 (0.33)	35343 (793)

The first column, labeled C_{ADF}, shows the relative performance of the four estimation methods according to the population discrepancy, C_{ADF}. Since 19.19 is the smallest mean discrepancy in the C_{ADF} column, C_{ML} is the best estimation method according to the C_{ADF} criterion. Similarly, examining the C_{ML} column of the table shows that C_{ML} is the best estimation method according to the C_{ML} criterion.

Although the four columns of the table disagree on the exact ordering of the four estimation methods, ML is, in all cases, the method with the lowest mean discrepancy. The difference between ML estimation and GLS estimation is slight in some cases. Unsurprisingly, ULS estimation performed badly, according to all of the population discrepancies employed. More interesting is the poor performance of ADF estimation, indicating that ADF estimation is unsuited to this combination of model, population, and sample size.

Modeling in VB.NET

Visual Basic programs for this example are in the files *Ex21-adf.vb*, *Ex21-gls.vb*, *Ex21-ml.vb*, and *Ex21-uls.vb*.

Example

22

Specification Search

Introduction

This example takes you through two specification searches: one is largely confirmatory (with few optional arrows), and the other is largely exploratory (with many optional arrows).

About the Data

This example uses the Felson and Bohrnstedt (1979) girls' data, also used in Example 7.

About the Model

The initial model for the specification search comes from Felson and Bohrnstedt (1979), as seen in Figure 22-1:

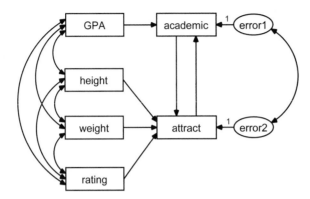

Figure 22-1: Felson and Bohrnstedt's model for girls

Specification Search with Few Optional Arrows

Felson and Bohrnstedt were primarily interested in the two single-headed arrows, *academic←attract* and *attract←academic*. The question was whether one or both, or possibly neither, of the arrows was needed. For this reason, you will make both arrows optional during this specification search. The double-headed arrow connecting *error1* and *error2* is an undesirable feature of the model because it complicates the interpretation of the effects represented by the single-headed arrows, and so you will also make it optional. The specification search will help to decide which of these three optional arrows, if any, are essential to the model.

This specification search is largely confirmatory because most arrows are required by the model, and only three are optional.

Specifying the Model

▶ Open *Ex22a.amw*. If you performed a typical installation, the path is *C:\Program Files\Amos 7\Examples\Ex22a.amw*.

The path diagram opens in the drawing area. Initially, there are no optional arrows, as seen in Figure 22-1.

▶ From the menus, choose Analyze → Specification Search.

The Specification Search window appears. Initially, only the toolbar is visible.

▶ Click  on the Specification Search toolbar, and then click the double-headed arrow that connects *error1* and *error2*. The arrow changes color to indicate that the arrow is optional.

Tip: If you want the optional arrow to be dashed as well as colored, as seen below, choose View → Interface Properties from the menus, click the Accessibility tab, and select the Alternative to color check box.

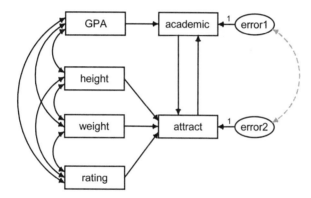

▶ To make the arrow required again, click 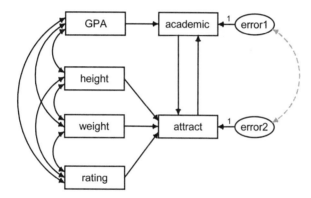 on the Specification Search toolbar, and then click the arrow. When you move the pointer away, the arrow will again display as a required arrow.

▶ Click again, and then click the arrows in the path diagram until it looks like this:

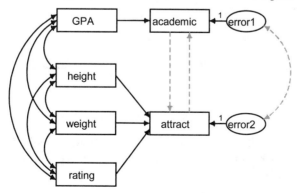

Example 22

When you perform the exploratory analysis later on, the program will treat the three colored arrows as optional and will try to fit the model using every possible subset of them.

Selecting Program Options

▶ Click the Options button 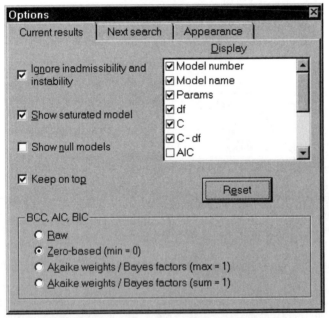 on the Specification Search toolbar.

▶ In the Options dialog box, click the Current results tab.

▶ Click Reset to ensure that your options are the same as those used in this example.

▶ Now click the Next search tab. The text at the top indicates that the exploratory analysis will fit eight (that is, 2^3) models.

▶ In the Retain only the best ___ models box, change the value from 10 to 0.

With a default value of 10, the specification search reports at most 10 one-parameter models, at most 10 two-parameter models, and so on. If the value is set to 0, there is no limitation on the number of models reported.

Limiting the number of models reported can speed up a specification search significantly. However, only eight models in total will be encountered during the specification search for this example, and specifying a nonzero value for Retain only the best ___ models would have the undesirable effect of inhibiting the program from normalizing Akaike weights and Bayes factors so that they sum to 1 across all models, as seen later.

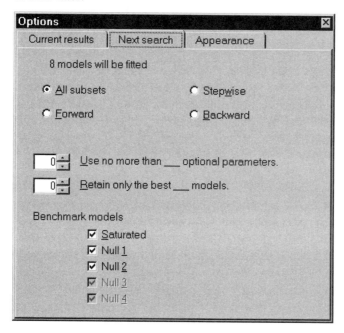

▶ Close the Options dialog box.

Performing the Specification Search

▶ Click ▶ on the Specification Search toolbar.

The program fits the model eight times, using every subset of the optional arrows. When it finishes, the Specification Search window expands to show the results.

Example 22

The following table summarizes fit measures for the eight models and the saturated model:

Model	Params	df	C	C-df	BCC_0	BIC_0	C / df	p	Notes
1	19	2	2.761	0.761	3.830	10.375	1.381	0.251	
2	18	3	19.155	16.155	18.154	21.427	6.385	0.000	
3	17	4	19.215	15.215	16.144	16.144	4.804	0.001	
4	16	5	67.342	62.342	62.201	58.929	13.468	0.000	
5	17	4	27.911	23.911	24.840	24.840	6.978	0.000	
6	18	3	2.763	-0.237	1.761	5.034	0.921	0.430	
7	17	4	3.071	-0.929	0.000	0.000	0.768	0.546	
8	18	3	2.895	-0.105	1.894	5.167	0.965	0.408	
Sat	21	0	0.000	0.000	5.208	18.299			

The *Model* column contains an arbitrary index number from 1 through 8 for each of the models fitted during the specification search. *Sat* identifies the saturated model. Looking at the first row, Model 1 has 19 parameters and 2 degrees of freedom. The discrepancy function (which in this case is the likelihood ratio chi-square statistic) is 2.761. Elsewhere in Amos output, the minimum value of the discrepancy function is referred to as *CMIN*. Here it is labeled *C* for brevity. To get an explanation of any column of the table, right-click anywhere in the column and choose What's This? from the pop-up menu.

Notice that the best value in each column is underlined, except for the *Model* and *Notes* columns.

Many familiar fit measures (*CFI* and *RMSEA*, for example) are omitted from this table. Appendix E gives a rationale for the choice of fit measures displayed.

Viewing Generated Models

▶ You can double-click any row in the table (other than the *Sat* row) to see the corresponding path diagram in the drawing area. For example, double-click the row for Model 7 to see its path diagram.

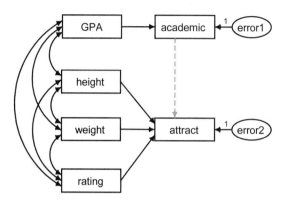

Figure 22-2: Path diagram for Model 7

Viewing Parameter Estimates for a Model

▶ Click 🟦 on the Specification Search toolbar.

▶ In the Specification Search window, double-click the row for Model 7.

The drawing area displays the parameter estimates for Model 7.

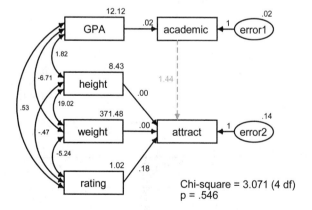

Figure 22-3: Parameter estimates for Model 7

Using BCC to Compare Models

▶ In the Specification Search window, click the column heading BCC_0.

The table sorts according to *BCC* so that the best model according to *BCC* (that is, the model with the smallest *BCC*) is at the top of the list.

Model	Params	df	C	C-df	BCC_0	BIC_0	C / df	p	Notes
7	17	4	3.071	-0.929	0.000	0.000	0.768	0.546	
6	18	3	2.763	-0.237	1.761	5.034	0.921	0.430	
8	18	3	2.895	-0.105	1.894	5.167	0.965	0.408	
1	19	2	2.761	0.761	3.830	10.375	1.381	0.251	
Sat	21	0	0.000	0.000	5.208	18.299			
3	17	4	19.215	15.215	16.144	16.144	4.804	0.001	
2	18	3	19.155	16.155	18.154	21.427	6.385	0.000	
5	17	4	27.911	23.911	24.840	24.840	6.978	0.000	
4	16	5	67.342	62.342	62.201	58.929	13.468	0.000	

Based on a suggestion by Burnham and Anderson (1998), a constant has been added to all the *BCC* values so that the smallest *BCC* value is 0. The *0* subscript on BCC_0 serves as a reminder of this rescaling. *AIC* (not shown in the above figure) and *BIC* have been similarly rescaled. As a rough guideline, Burnham and Anderson (1998, p. 128) suggest the following interpretation of AIC_0. BCC_0 can be interpreted similarly.

AIC_0 or BCC_0	Burnham and Anderson interpretation
0 – 2	There is no credible evidence that the model should be ruled out as being the actual *K-L* best model for the population of possible samples. (See Burnham and Anderson for the definition of *K-L best*.)
2 – 4	There is weak evidence that the model is not the *K-L* best model.
4 – 7	There is definite evidence that the model is not the *K-L* best model.
7 – 10	There is strong evidence that the model is not the *K-L* best model.
>10	There is very strong evidence that the model is not the *K-L* best model.

Although Model 7 is estimated to be the best model according to Burnham and Anderson's guidelines, Models 6 and 8 should not be ruled out.

Viewing the Akaike Weights

▶ Click the Options button 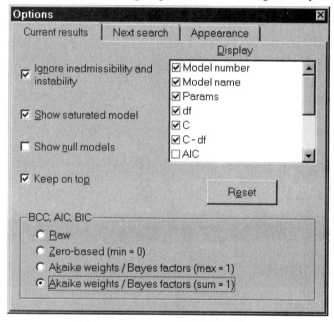 on the Specification Search toolbar.

▶ In the Options dialog box, click the Current results tab.

▶ In the BCC, AIC, BIC group, select Akaike weights / Bayes factors (sum = 1).

In the table of fit measures, the column that was labeled BCC_0 is now labeled BCC_p and contains Akaike weights. (See Appendix G.)

Model	Params	df	C	C-df	**BCCp**	BICp	C / df	p	Notes
7	17	4	3.071	-0.929	0.494	0.860	0.768	0.546	
6	18	3	2.763	-0.237	0.205	0.069	0.921	0.430	
8	18	3	2.895	-0.105	0.192	0.065	0.965	0.408	
1	19	2	2.761	0.761	0.073	0.005	1.381	0.251	
Sat	21	0	0.000	0.000	0.037	0.000			
3	17	4	19.215	15.215	0.000	0.000	4.804	0.001	
2	18	3	19.155	16.155	0.000	0.000	6.385	0.000	
5	17	4	27.911	23.911	0.000	0.000	6.978	0.000	
4	16	5	67.342	62.342	0.000	0.000	13.468	0.000	

The Akaike weight has been interpreted (Akaike, 1978; Bozdogan, 1987; Burnham and Anderson, 1998) as the likelihood of the model given the data. With this interpretation, the estimated *K-L* best model (Model 7) is only about 2.4 times more likely (0.494 / 0.205 = 2.41) than Model 6. Bozdogan (1987) points out that if it is possible to assign prior probabilities to the candidate models, the prior probabilities can be used together with the Akaike weights (interpreted as model likelihoods) to obtain posterior probabilities. With equal prior probabilities, the Akaike weights are themselves posterior probabilities, so that one can say that Model 7 is the *K-L* best model with probability 0.494, Model 6 is the *K-L* best model with probability 0.205, and so on. The four most probable models are Models 7, 6, 8, and 1. After adding their probabilities (0.494 + 0.205 + 0.192 + 0.073 = 0.96), one can say that there is a 96% chance that the *K-L* best model is among those four. (Burnham and Anderson, 1998, pp. 127-129). The p subscript on BCC_p serves as a reminder that BCC_p can be interpreted as a probability under some circumstances.

Using BIC to Compare Models

▶ On the Current results tab of the Options dialog box, select Zero-based (min = 0) in the BCC, AIC, BIC group.

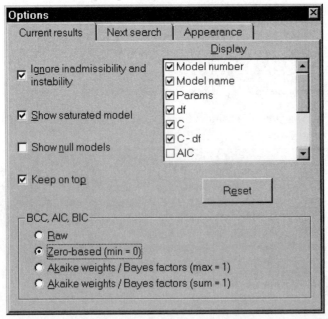

▶ In the Specification Search window, click the column heading BIC_0.

The table is now sorted according to *BIC* so that the best model according to *BIC* (that is, the model with the smallest *BIC*) is at the top of the list.

Model	Params	df	C	C-df	BCC_0	BIC_0	C / df	p	Notes
7	17	4	3.071	-0.929	0.000	0.000	0.768	0.546	
6	18	3	2.763	-0.237	1.761	5.034	0.921	0.430	
8	18	3	2.895	-0.105	1.894	5.167	0.965	0.408	
1	19	2	2.761	0.761	3.830	10.375	1.381	0.251	
3	17	4	19.215	15.215	16.144	16.144	4.804	0.001	
Sat	21	0	0.000	0.000	5.208	18.299			
2	18	3	19.155	16.155	18.154	21.427	6.385	0.000	
5	17	4	27.911	23.911	24.840	24.840	6.978	0.000	
4	16	5	67.342	62.342	62.201	58.929	13.468	0.000	

Model 7, with the smallest *BIC*, is the model with the highest approximate posterior probability (using equal prior probabilities for the models and using a particular prior distribution for the parameters of each separate model). Raftery (1995) suggests the following interpretation of BIC_0 values in judging the evidence for Model 7 against a competing model:

BIC_0	Raftery (1995) interpretation
0 – 2	Weak
2 – 6	Positive
6 – 10	Strong
>10	Very strong

Using these guidelines, you have *positive* evidence against Models 6 and 8, and *very strong* evidence against all of the other models as compared to Model 7.

Using Bayes Factors to Compare Models

▶ On the Current results tab of the Options dialog box, select Akaike weights / Bayes factors (sum = 1) in the BCC, AIC, BIC group.

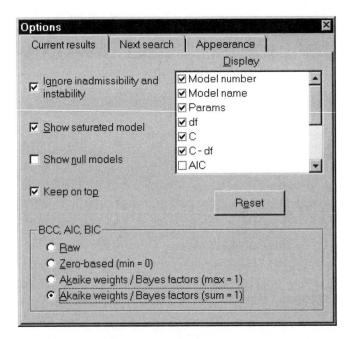

In the table of fit measures, the column that was labeled BIC_0 is now labeled BIC_p and contains Bayes factors scaled so that they sum to 1.

Model	Params	df	C	C-df	BCCp	**BICp**	C / df	p	Notes
7	17	4	3.071	-0.929	0.494	0.860	0.768	0.546	
6	18	3	2.763	-0.237	0.205	0.069	0.921	0.430	
8	18	3	2.895	-0.105	0.192	0.065	0.965	0.408	
1	19	2	2.761	0.761	0.073	0.005	1.381	0.251	
3	17	4	19.215	15.215	0.000	0.000	4.804	0.001	
Sat	21	0	0.000	0.000	0.037	0.000			
2	18	3	19.155	16.155	0.000	0.000	6.385	0.000	
5	17	4	27.911	23.911	0.000	0.000	6.978	0.000	
4	16	5	67.342	62.342	0.000	0.000	13.468	0.000	

With equal prior probabilities for the models and using a particular prior distribution of the parameters of each separate model (Raftery, 1995; Schwarz, 1978), BIC_p values are approximate posterior probabilities. Model 7 is the correct model with probability 0.860. One can be 99% sure that the correct model is among Models 7, 6, and 8 (0.860 + 0.069 + 0.065 = 0.99). The *p* subscript is a reminder that BIC_p values can be interpreted as probabilities.

Madigan and Raftery (1994) suggest that only models in *Occam's window* be used for purposes of model averaging (a topic not discussed here). The **symmetric** Occam's window is the subset of models obtained by excluding models that are much less probable (Madigan and Raftery suggest something like 20 times less probable) than the most probable model. In this example, the symmetric Occam's window contains models 7, 6, and 8 because these are the models whose probabilities (BIC_p values) are greater than $0.860 / 20 = 0.043$.

Rescaling the Bayes Factors

▶ On the Current results tab of the Options dialog box, select Akaike weights / Bayes factors (max = 1) in the BCC, AIC, BIC group.

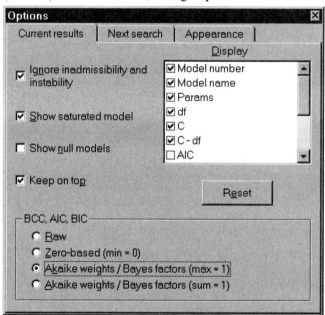

In the table of fit measures, the column that was labeled BIC_p is now labeled BIC_L and contains Bayes factors scaled so that the largest value is 1. This makes it easier to pick out Occam's window. It consists of models whose BIC_L values are greater than $1/20 = 0.05$; in other words, Models 7, 6, and 8. The L subscript on BIC_L is a reminder that the analogous statistic BCC_L can be interpreted as a likelihood.

Example 22

Model	Params	df	C	C - df	BCC~L~	BIC~L~	C / df	p	Notes
7	17	4	3.071	-0.929	1.000	1.000	0.768	0.546	
6	18	3	2.763	-0.237	0.414	0.081	0.921	0.430	
8	18	3	2.895	-0.105	0.388	0.076	0.965	0.408	
1	19	2	2.761	0.761	0.147	0.006	1.381	0.251	
3	17	4	19.215	15.215	0.000	0.000	4.804	0.001	
Sat	21	0	0.000	0.000	0.074	0.000			
2	18	3	19.155	16.155	0.000	0.000	6.385	0.000	
5	17	4	27.911	23.911	0.000	0.000	6.978	0.000	
4	16	5	67.342	62.342	0.000	0.000	13.468	0.000	

Examining the Short List of Models

▶ Click ⊞ on the Specification Search toolbar. This displays a short list of models.

In the figure below, the short list shows the best model for each number of parameters. It shows the best 16-parameter model, the best 17-parameter model, and so on. Notice that all criteria agree on the best model when the comparison is restricted to models with a fixed number of parameters. The overall best model must be on this list, no matter which criterion is employed.

Model	**Params**	df	C	C - df	BCC~L~	BIC~L~	C / df	p	Notes
4	16	5	67.342	62.342	0.000	0.000	13.468	0.000	
7	17	4	3.071	-0.929	1.000	1.000	0.768	0.546	
6	18	3	2.763	-0.237	0.414	0.081	0.921	0.430	
1	19	2	2.761	0.761	0.147	0.006	1.381	0.251	
Sat	21	0	0.000	0.000	0.074	0.000			

Figure 22-4: The best model for each number of parameters

This table shows that the best 17-parameter model fits substantially better than the best 16-parameter model. Beyond 17 parameters, adding additional parameters yields relatively small improvements in fit. In a cost-benefit analysis, stepping from 16 parameters to 17 parameters has a relatively large payoff, while going beyond 17 parameters has a relatively small payoff. This suggests adopting the best 17-parameter model, using a heuristic *point of diminishing returns* argument. This approach to determining the number of parameters is pursued further later in this example (see "Viewing the Best-Fit Graph for C" on p. 342 and "Viewing the Scree Plot for C" on p. 344).

Viewing a Scatterplot of Fit and Complexity

▶ Click 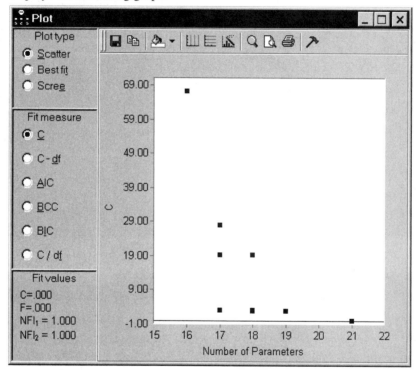 on the Specification Search toolbar. This opens the Plot window, which displays the following graph:

The graph shows a scatterplot of fit (measured by C) versus complexity (measured by the number of parameters) where each point represents a model. The graph portrays the trade-off between fit and complexity that Steiger characterized as follows:

> In the final analysis, it may be, in a sense, impossible to define one *best* way to combine measures of complexity and measures of badness-of-fit in a single numerical index, because the precise nature of the *best* numerical trade-off between complexity and fit is, to some extent, a matter of personal taste. The choice of a model is a classic problem in the two-dimensional analysis of preference. (Steiger, 1990, p. 179.)

▶ Click any of the points in the scatterplot to display a menu that indicates which models are represented by that point and any overlapping points.

▶ Choose one of the models from the pop-up menu to see that model highlighted in the table of model fit statistics and, at the same time, to see the path diagram of that model in the drawing area.

In the following figure, the cursor points to two overlapping points that represent Model 6 (with a discrepancy of 2.76) and Model 8 (with a discrepancy of 2.90).

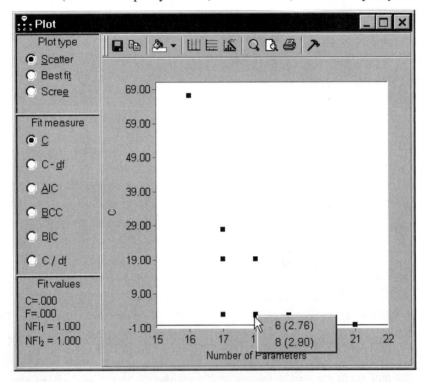

The graph contains a horizontal line representing points for which C is constant. Initially, the line is centered at 0 on the vertical axis. The Fit values panel at the lower left shows that, for points on the horizontal line, $C = 0$ and also $F = 0$. (F is referred to as *FMIN* in Amos output.) NFI_1 and NFI_2 are two versions of NFI that use two different baseline models (see Appendix F).

Initially, both NFI_1 and NFI_2 are equal to 1 for points on the horizontal line. The location of the horizontal line is adjustable. You can move the line by dragging it with the mouse. As you move the line, you can see the changes in the location of the line reflected in the fit measures in the lower left panel.

Adjusting the Line Representing Constant Fit

▶ Move your mouse over the adjustable line. When the pointer changes to a hand, drag the line so that NFI_1 is equal to 0.900. (Keep an eye on NFI_1 in the lower left panel while you reposition the adjustable line.)

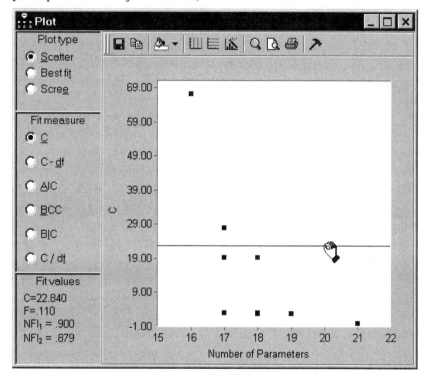

NFI_1 is the familiar form of the NFI statistic for which the baseline model requires the observed variables to be uncorrelated without constraining their means and variances. Points that are below the line have $NFI_1 > 0.900$ and those above the line have $NFI_1 < 0.900$. That is, the adjustable line separates the acceptable models from the unacceptable ones according to a widely used convention based on a remark by Bentler and Bonett (1980).

Example 22

Viewing the Line Representing Constant C – df

▶ In the Plot window, select C – df in the Fit measure group. This displays the following:

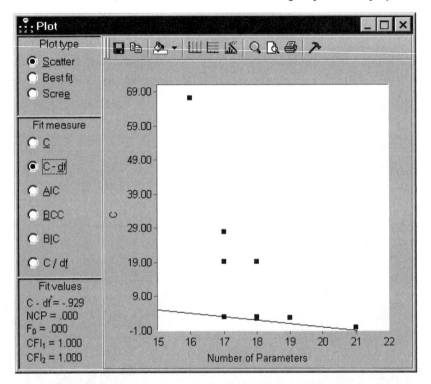

The scatterplot remains unchanged except for the position of the adjustable line. The adjustable line now contains points for which $C - df$ is constant. Whereas the line was previously horizontal, it is now tilted downward, indicating that $C - df$ gives some weight to complexity in assessing model adequacy. Initially, the adjustable line passes through the point for which $C - df$ is smallest.

▶ Click that point, and then choose Model 7 from the pop-up menu.

This highlights Model 7 in the table of fit measures and also displays the path diagram for Model 7 in the drawing area.

The panel in the lower left corner shows the value of some fit measures that depend only on $C - df$ and that are therefore, like $C - df$ itself, constant along the adjustable line. CFI_1 and CFI_2 are two versions of CFI that use two different baseline models (see

Appendix G). Initially, both CFI_1 and CFI_2 are equal to 1 for points on the adjustable line. When you move the adjustable line, the fit measures in the lower left panel change to reflect the changing position of the line.

Adjusting the Line Representing Constant C – df

▶ Drag the adjustable line so that CFI_1 is equal to 0.950.

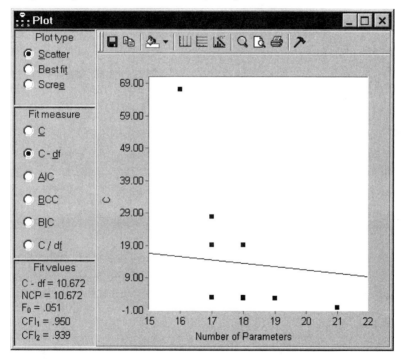

CFI_1 is the usual CFI statistic for which the baseline model requires the observed variables to be uncorrelated without constraining their means and variances. Points that are below the line have $CFI_1 > 0.950$ and those above the line have $CFI_1 < 0.950$. That is, the adjustable line separates the acceptable models from the unacceptable ones according to the recommendation of Hu and Bentler (1999).

Example 22

Viewing Other Lines Representing Constant Fit

▶ Click AIC, BCC, and BIC in turn.

Notice that the slope of the adjustable line becomes increasingly negative. This reflects the fact that the five measures (C, $C - df$, AIC, BCC, and BIC) give increasing weight to model complexity. For each of these five measures, the adjustable line has constant slope, which you can confirm by dragging the line with the mouse. By contrast, the slope of the adjustable line for C / df is not constant (the slope of the line changes when you drag it with the mouse) and so the slope for C / df cannot be compared to the slopes for C, $C - df$, AIC, BCC, and BIC.

Viewing the Best-Fit Graph for C

▶ In the Plot window, select Best fit in the Plot type group.

▶ In the Fit measure group, select C.

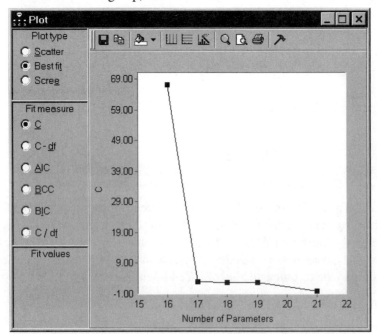

Figure 22-5: Smallest value of C for each number of parameters

Each point in this graph represents a model for which C is less than or equal to that of any other model that has the same number of parameters. The graph shows that the best 16-parameter model has $C = 67.342$, the best 17-parameter model has $C = 3.071$, and so on. While Best fit is selected, the table of fit measures shows the best model for each number of parameters. This table appeared earlier on p. 336.

Model	Params	df	C	C-df	BCC$_L$	BIC$_L$	C / df	p	Notes
4	16	5	67.342	62.342	0.000	0.000	13.468	0.000	
7	17	4	3.071	-0.929	1.000	1.000	0.768	0.546	
6	18	3	2.763	-0.237	0.414	0.081	0.921	0.430	
1	19	2	2.761	0.761	0.147	0.006	1.381	0.251	
Sat	21	0	0.000	0.000	0.074	0.000			

Notice that the best model for a fixed number of parameters does not depend on the choice of fit measure. For example, Model 7 is the best 17-parameter model according to $C - df$, and also according to C / df and every other fit measure. This short list of best models is guaranteed to contain the overall best model, no matter which fit measure is used as the criterion for model selection.

You can view the short list at any time by clicking 🔳. The best-fit graph suggests the choice of 17 as the correct number of parameters on the heuristic grounds that it is the *point of diminishing returns*. That is, increasing the number of parameters from 16 to 17 buys a comparatively large improvement in C ($67.342 - 3.071 = 64.271$), while increasing the number of parameters beyond 17 yields relatively small improvements.

Viewing the Best-Fit Graph for Other Fit Measures

▶ While Best fit is selected, try selecting the other choices in the Fit measure group: C – df, AIC, BCC, BIC, and C / df. For example, if you click BIC, you will see this:

Example 22

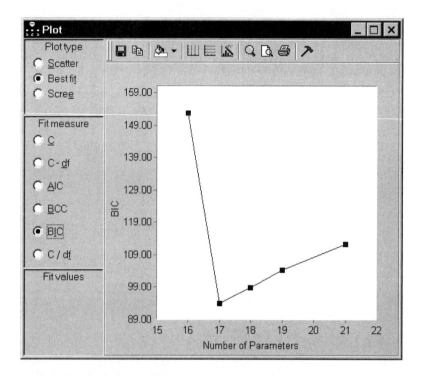

BIC is the measure among *C*, *C – df*, *AIC*, *BCC,* and *BIC* that imposes the greatest penalty for complexity. The high penalty for complexity is reflected in the steep positive slope of the graph as the number of parameters increases beyond 17. The graph makes it clear that, according to *BIC*, the best 17-parameter model is superior to any other candidate model.

Notice that clicking different fit measures changes the vertical axis of the best-fit graph and changes the shape of the configuration of points.[1] However, the identity of each point is preserved. The best 16-parameter model is always Model 4, the best 17-parameter model is always Model 7, and so on. This is because, for a fixed number of parameters, the rank order of models is the same for every fit measure.

Viewing the Scree Plot for C

▶ In the Plot window, select Scree in the Plot type group.

---

1 The saturated model is missing from the *C / df* graph because *C / df* is not defined for the saturated model.

▶ In the Fit measure group, select C.

The Plot window displays the following graph:

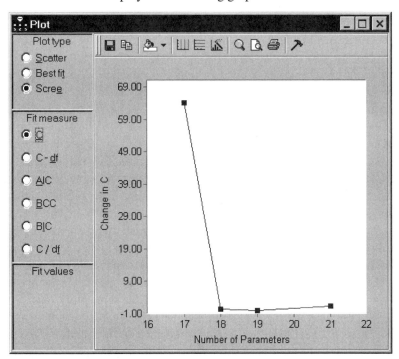

Figure 22-6: Scree plot for C

In this scree plot, the point with coordinate 17 on the horizontal axis has coordinate 64.271 on the vertical axis. This represents the fact that the best 17-parameter model ($C = 3.071$) fits better than the best 16-parameter model ($C = 67.342$), with the difference being $67.342 - 3.071 = 64.271$. Similarly, the height of the graph at 18 parameters shows the improvement in C obtained by moving from the best 17-parameter model to the best 18-parameter model, and so on. The point located above 21 on the horizontal axis requires a separate explanation. There is no 20-parameter model with which the best 21-parameter model can be compared. (Actually, there is only one 21-parameter model—the saturated model.) The best 21-parameter model ($C = 0$) is therefore compared to the best 19-parameter model ($C = 2.761$). The height of the 21-parameter point is calculated as $(2.761 - 0)/2$. That is, the improvement in C obtained by moving from the 19-parameter model to the 21-parameter model is expressed as the amount of reduction in C *per parameter*.

The figure on either p. 342 or p. 345 can be used to support a heuristic *point of diminishing returns* argument in favor of 17 parameters. There is this difference: In the best-fit graph (p. 342), one looks for an *elbow* in the graph, or a place where the slope changes from relatively steep to relatively flat. For the present problem, this occurs at 17 parameters, which can be taken as support for the best 17-parameter model. In the scree plot (p. 345), one also looks for an elbow, but the elbow occurs at 18 parameters in this example. This is also taken as support for the best 17-parameter model. In a scree plot, an elbow at k parameters provides support for the best $(k-1)$ parameter model.

The scree plot is so named because of its similarity to the graph known as a scree plot in principal components analysis (Cattell, 1966). In principal components analysis, a scree plot shows the improvement in model fit that is obtained by adding components to the model, one component at a time. The scree plot presented here for *SEM* shows the improvement in model fit that is obtained by incrementing the number of model parameters. The scree plot for *SEM* is not identical in all respects to the scree plot for principal components analysis. For example, in principal components, one obtains a sequence of nested models when introducing components one at a time. This is not necessarily the case in the scree plot for *SEM*. The best 17-parameter model, say, and the best 18-parameter model may or may not be nested. (In the present example, they are.) Furthermore, in principal components, the scree plot is always monotone non-increasing, which is not guaranteed in the case of the scree plot for *SEM*, even with nested models. Indeed, the scree plot for the present example is not monotone.

In spite of the differences between the traditional scree plot and the scree plot presented here, it is proposed that the new scree plot be used in the same heuristic fashion as the traditional one. A two-stage approach to model selection is suggested. In the first stage, the number of parameters is selected by examining either the scree plot or the short list of models. In the second stage, the best model is chosen from among those models that have the number of parameters determined in the first stage.

Viewing the Scree Plot for Other Fit Measures

▶ With Scree selected in the Plot type group, select the other choices in the Fit measure group: C – df, AIC, BCC, and BIC (but not C / df).

For example, if you select BIC, you will see this:

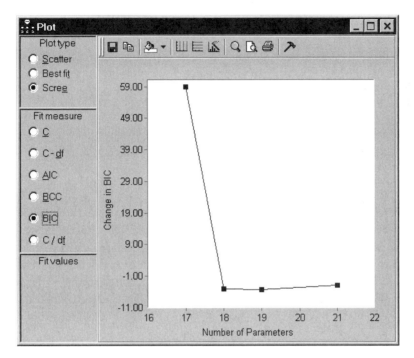

For *C – df*, *AIC*, *BCC*, and *BIC*, the units and the origin of the vertical axis are different than for *C*, but the graphs are otherwise identical. This means that the final model selected by the scree test is independent of which measure of fit is used (unless *C / df* is used). This is the advantage of the scree plot over the *best-fit* plot demonstrated earlier in this example (see "Viewing the Best-Fit Graph for C" on p. 342, and "Viewing the Best-Fit Graph for Other Fit Measures" on p. 343). The best-fit plot and the scree plot contain nearly the same information, but the shape of the best-fit plot depends on the choice of fit measure while the shape of the scree plot does not (with the exception of *C / df*).

Both the best-fit plot and the scree plot are independent of sample size in the sense that altering the sample size without altering the sample moments has no effect other than to rescale the vertical axis.

Specification Search with Many Optional Arrows

The previous specification search was largely confirmatory in that there were only three optional arrows. You can take a much more exploratory approach to constructing a model for the Felson and Bohrnstedt data. Suppose that your only hypothesis about the six measured variables is that

■ *academic* depends on the other five variables, and

■ *attract* depends on the other five variables.

The path diagram shown in Figure 22-7 with 11 optional arrows implements this hypothesis. It specifies which variables are endogenous, and nothing more. Every observed-variable model that is consistent with the hypothesis is included in the specification search. The covariances among the observed, exogenous variables could have been made optional, but doing so would have increased the number of optional arrows from 11 to 17, increasing the number of candidate models from 2,048 (that is, 2^{11}) to 131,072 (that is, 2^{17}). Allowing the covariances among the observed, exogenous variables to be optional would have been costly, and there would seem to be little interest in searching for models in which some pairs of those variables are uncorrelated.

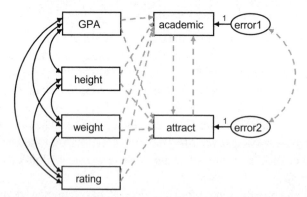

Figure 22-7: Highly exploratory model for Felson and Bohrnstedt's girls' data

Specifying the Model

▶ Open *Ex22b.amw*. If you performed a typical installation, the path will be *C:\Program Files\Amos 7\Examples\Ex22b.amw*.

Tip: If the last file you opened was in the *Examples* folder, you can open the file by double-clicking it in the Files list to the left of the drawing area.

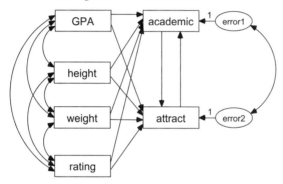

Making Some Arrows Optional

▶ From the menus, choose Analyze → Specification Search.

▶ Click ⊡ on the Specification Search toolbar, and then click the arrows in the path diagram until it looks like the diagram on p. 348.

Tip: You can change multiple arrows at once by clicking and dragging the mouse pointer through them.

Setting Options to Their Defaults

▶ Click the Options button ⊡ on the Specification Search toolbar.

▶ In the Options dialog box, click the Next search tab.

▶ In the Retain only the best ___ models box, change the value from 0 to 10.

Example 22

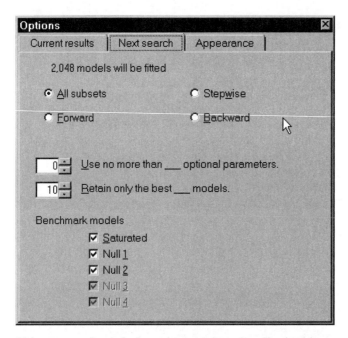

This restores the default setting we altered earlier in this example. With the default setting, the program displays only the 10 best models according to whichever criterion you use for sorting the columns of the model list. This limitation is desirable now because of the large number of models that will be generated for this specification search.

▶ Click the Current results tab.

▶ In the BCC, AIC, BIC group, select Zero-based (min = 0).

Performing the Specification Search

▶ Click on the Specification Search toolbar.

The search takes about 10 seconds on a 1.8 GHz Pentium 4. When it finishes, the Specification Search window expands to show the results.

Using BIC to Compare Models

▶ In the Specification Search window, click the BIC_0 column heading. This sorts the table according to BIC_0.

Model	Params	df	C	C- df	BCC_0	BIC_0	C / df	p	Notes
22	15	6	5.156	-0.844	0.132	0.000	0.859	0.524	
32	16	5	2.954	-2.046	0.000	3.141	0.591	0.707	
33	16	5	3.101	-1.899	0.147	3.288	0.620	0.684	
34	16	5	4.623	-0.377	1.669	4.810	0.925	0.464	
35	16	5	4.623	-0.377	1.669	4.810	0.925	0.464	
36	16	5	4.623	-0.377	1.669	4.810	0.925	0.464	
37	16	5	5.055	0.055	2.101	5.242	1.011	0.409	Unstable
38	16	5	5.055	0.055	2.101	5.242	1.011	0.409	
39	16	5	5.079	0.079	2.125	5.266	1.016	0.406	
40	16	5	5.081	0.081	2.127	5.268	1.016	0.406	

Figure 22-8: The 10 best models according to BIC_0

The sorted table shows that Model 22 is the best model according to BIC_0. (Model numbers depend in part on the order in which the objects in the path diagram were drawn; therefore, if you draw your own path diagram, your model numbers may differ from the model numbers here.) The second-best model according to BIC_0, namely Model 32, is the best according to BCC_0. These models are shown below:

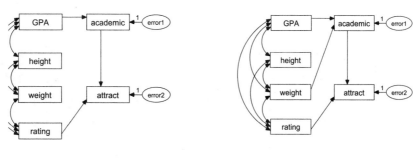

Model 22   Model 32

Viewing the Scree Plot

▶ Click 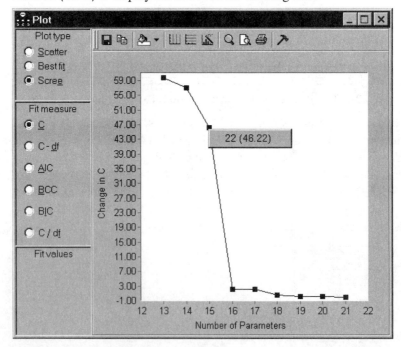 on the Specification Search toolbar.

▶ In the Plot window, select Scree in the Plot type group.

The scree plot strongly suggests that models with 15 parameters provide an optimum trade-off of model fit and parsimony.

▶ Click the point with the horizontal coordinate 15. A pop-up appears that indicates the point represents Model 22, for which the change in chi-square is 46.22.

▶ Click 22 (46.22) to display Model 22 in the drawing area.

Limitations

The specification search procedure is limited to the analysis of data from a single group.

Example

23

Exploratory Factor Analysis by Specification Search

Introduction

This example demonstrates exploratory factor analysis by means of a specification search. In this approach to exploratory factor analysis, any measured variable can (optionally) depend on any factor. A specification search is performed to find the subset of single-headed arrows that provides the optimum combination of simplicity and fit. It also demonstrates a heuristic specification search that is practical for models that are too big for an exhaustive specification search.

About the Data

This example uses the Holzinger and Swineford (1939) girls' data from Example 8.

About the Model

The initial model is shown in Figure 23-1 on p. 354. During the specification search, all single-headed arrows that point from factors to measured variables will be made optional. The purpose of the specification search is to obtain guidance as to which single-headed arrows are essential to the model; in other words, which variables depend on which factors.

The two factor variances are both fixed at 1, as are all the regression weights associated with residual variables. Without these constraints, all the models encountered during the specification search would be unidentified.

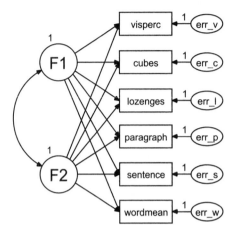

Figure 23-1: Exploratory factor analysis model with two factors

Specifying the Model

▶ Open the file *Ex23.amw*. If you performed a typical installation, the path will be
C:\Program Files\Amos 7\Examples\Ex23.amw.

Initially, the path diagram appears as in Figure 23-1. There is no point in trying to fit this model as it stands because it is not identified, even with the factor variances fixed at 1.

Opening the Specification Search Window

▶ To open the Specification Search window, choose Analyze → Specification Search.

Initially, only the toolbar is visible, as seen here:

Making All Regression Weights Optional

▶ Click 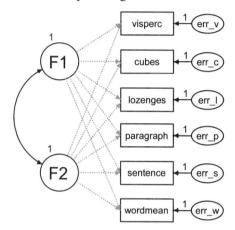 on the Specification Search toolbar, and then click all the single-headed arrows in the path diagram.

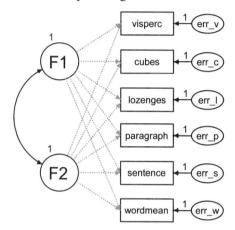

Figure 23-2: Two-factor model with all regression weights optional

During the specification search, the program will attempt to fit the model using every possible subset of the optional arrows.

Setting Options to Their Defaults

▶ Click the Options button ☑ on the Specification Search toolbar.

▶ In the Options dialog box, click the Current results tab.

▶ Click Reset to ensure that your options are the same as those used in this example.

Example 23

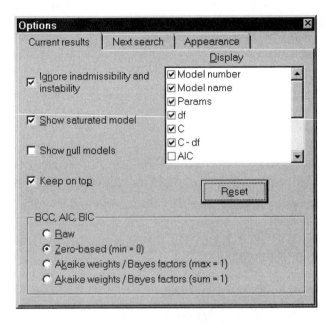

▶ Now click the Next search tab. Notice that the default value for Retain only the best ___ models is 10.

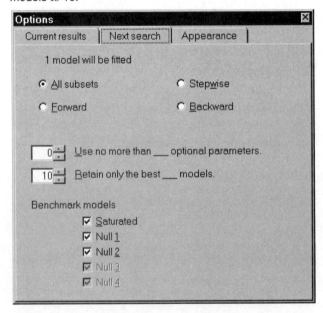

With this setting, the program will display only the 10 best models according to whichever criterion you use for sorting the columns of the model list. For example, if you click the column heading C/df, the table will show the 10 models with the smallest values of C/df, sorted according to C/df. Scatterplots will display only the 10 best 1-parameter models, the 10 best 2-parameter models, and so on. It is useful to place a limit on the number of parameters to be displayed when there are a lot of optional parameters.

In this example, there are 12 optional parameters so that there are $2^{12} = 4096$ candidate models. Storing results for a large number of models can affect performance. Limiting the display to the best 10 models for each number of parameters means that the program has to maintain a list of only about $10 \times 13 = 130$ models. The program will have to fit many more than 130 models in order to find the best 10 models for each number of parameters, but not quite as many as 4,096. The program uses a branch-and-bound algorithm similar to the one used in all-possible-subsets regression (Furnival and Wilson, 1974) to avoid fitting some models unnecessarily.

Performing the Specification Search

▶ Click ▣ on the Specification Search toolbar.

The search takes about 12 seconds on a 1.8 GHz Pentium 4. When it finishes, the Specification Search window expands to show the results.

Initially, the list of models is not very informative. The models are listed in the order in which they were encountered, and the models encountered early in the search were found to be unidentified. The method used for classifying models as unidentified is described in Appendix D.

Model	Params	df	C	C - df	BCC$_0$	BIC$_0$	C / df	p	Notes
1	7	14							Unidentified
2	8	13							Unidentified
3	8	13							Unidentified
4	8	13							Unidentified
5	8	13							Unidentified
6	8	13							Unidentified
7	8	13							Unidentified
8	8	13							Unidentified
9	8	13							Unidentified
10	8	13							Unidentified

Using BCC to Compare Models

▶ In the Specification Search window, click the column heading BCC_0.

The table sorts according to BCC so that the best model according to BCC (that is, the model with the smallest BCC) is at the top of the list.

Model	Params	df	C	C-df	BCC_0	BIC_0	C / df	p	Notes
52	13	8	7.853	-0.147	0.000	0.000	0.982	0.448	
53	13	8	7.853	-0.147	0.000	0.000	0.982	0.448	
62	14	7	5.770	-1.230	0.132	2.207	0.824	0.567	
63	14	7	5.770	-1.230	0.132	2.207	0.824	0.567	
65	14	7	7.155	0.155	1.517	3.593	1.022	0.413	
64	14	7	7.155	0.155	1.517	3.593	1.022	0.413	
67	14	7	7.608	0.608	1.971	4.046	1.087	0.368	
66	14	7	7.608	0.608	1.971	4.046	1.087	0.368	
68	14	7	7.632	0.632	1.995	4.070	1.090	0.366	
69	14	7	7.632	0.632	1.995	4.070	1.090	0.366	

Figure 23-3: The 10 best models according to BCC_0

The two best models according to BCC_0 (Models 52 and 53) have identical fit measures (out to three decimal places anyway). The explanation for this can be seen from the path diagrams for the two models.

▶ In the Specification Search window, double-click the row for Model 52. This displays its path diagram in the drawing area.

▶ To see the path diagram for Model 53, double-click its row.

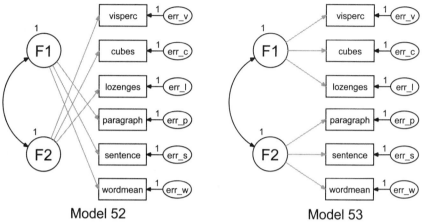

Figure 23-4: Reversing F1 and F2 yields another candidate model

This is just one pair of models where reversing the roles of *F1* and *F2* changes one member of the pair into the other. There are other such pairs. Models 52 and 53 are equivalent, although they are counted separately in the list of 4,096 candidate models. The 10 models in Figure 23-3 on p. 358 come in five pairs, but candidate models do not always come in equivalent pairs, as Figure 23-5 illustrates. The model in that figure does not occur among the 10 best models for six optional parameters and is not identified for that matter, but it does illustrate how reversing *F1* and *F2* can fail to yield a different member of the set of 4,096 candidate models.

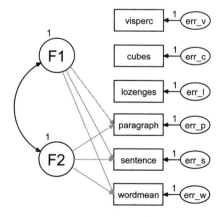

Figure 23-5: Reversing F1 and F2 yields the same candidate model

The occurrence of equivalent candidate models makes it unclear how to apply Bayesian calculations to select a model in this example. Similarly, it is unclear how to use Akaike weights. Furthermore, Burnham and Anderson's guidelines (see p. 330) for the interpretation of BCC_0 are based on reasoning about Akaike weights, so it is not clear whether those guidelines apply in the present example. On the other hand, the use of BCC_0 without reference to the Burnham and Anderson guidelines seems unexceptionable. Model 52 (or the equivalent Model 53) is the best model according to BCC_0.

Although BCC_0 chooses the model employed in Example 8, which was based on a model of Jöreskog and Sörbom (1996), it might be noted that Model 62 (or its equivalent, Model 63) is a very close second in terms of BCC_0 and is the best model according to some other fit measures. Model 63 has the following path diagram:

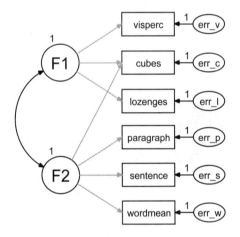

Figure 23-6: Model 63

The factors, *F1* and *F2*, seem roughly interpretable as *spatial ability* and *verbal ability* in both Models 53 and 63. The two models differ in their explanation of scores on the *cubes* test. In Model 53, cubes scores depend entirely on spatial ability. In Model 63, cubes scores depend on both spatial ability and verbal ability. Since it is a close call in terms of every criterion based on fit and parsimony, it may be especially appropriate here to pay attention to interpretability as a model selection criterion. The scree test in the following step, however, does not equivocate as to which is the best model.

Viewing the Scree Plot

▶ Click 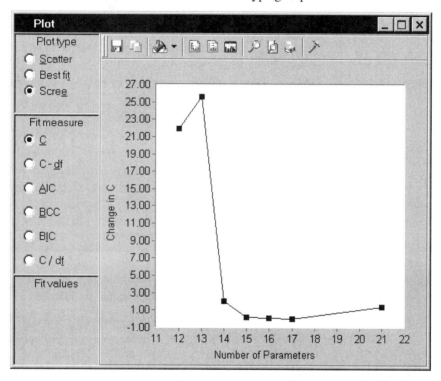 on the Specification Search toolbar.

▶ In the Plot window, select Scree in the Plot type group.

The scree plot strongly suggests the use of 13 parameters because of the way the graph drops abruptly and then levels off immediately after the 13th parameter. Click the point with coordinate 13 on the horizontal axis. A pop-up shows that the point represents Models 52 and 53, as shown in Figure 23-4 on p. 359.

Viewing the Short List of Models

▶ Click 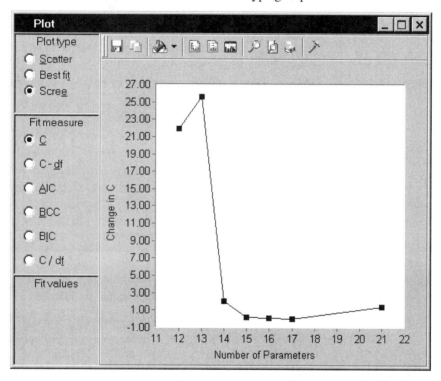 on the Specification Search toolbar. Take note of the short list of models for future reference.

Example 23

Heuristic Specification Search

The number of models that must be fitted in an exhaustive specification search grows rapidly with the number of optional arrows. There are 12 optional arrows in Figure 23-2 on p. 355 so that an exhaustive specification search requires fitting $2^{12} = 4096$ models. (The number of models will be somewhat smaller if you specify a small positive number for Retain only the best___models on the Next search tab of the Options dialog box.) A number of heuristic search procedures have been proposed for reducing the number of models that have to be fitted (Salhi, 1998). None of these is guaranteed to find the best model, but they have the advantage of being computationally feasible in problems with more than, say, 20 optional arrows where an exhaustive specification search is impossible.

Amos provides three heuristic search strategies in addition to the option of an exhaustive search. The heuristic strategies do not attempt to find the overall best model because this would require choosing a definition of *best* in terms of the minimum or maximum of a specific fit measure. Instead, the heuristic strategies attempt to find the 1-parameter model with the smallest discrepancy, the 2-parameter model with the smallest discrepancy, and so on. By adopting this approach, a search procedure can be designed that is independent of the choice of fit measure. You can select among the available search strategies on the Next search tab of the Options dialog box. The choices are as follows:

- **All subsets.** An exhaustive search is performed. This is the default.

- **Forward.** The program first fits the model with no optional arrows. Then it adds one optional arrow at a time, always adding whichever arrow gives the largest reduction in discrepancy.

- **Backward.** The program first fits the model with all optional arrows in the model. Then it removes one optional arrow at a time, always removing whichever arrow gives the smallest increase in discrepancy.

- **Stepwise.** The program alternates between Forward and Backward searches, beginning with a Forward search. The program keeps track of the best 1-optional-arrow model encountered, the best 2-optional-arrow model, and so on. After the first Forward search, the Forward and Backward search algorithms are modified by the following rule: The program will add an arrow or remove an arrow only if the resulting model has a smaller discrepancy than any previously encountered model with the same number of arrows. For example, the program will add an arrow to a 5-optional-arrow model only if the resulting 6-optional-arrow model has a smaller discrepancy than any previously encountered 6-optional-arrow model. Forward and Backward searches are alternated until one Forward or Backward search is completed with no improvement.

Performing a Stepwise Search

▶ Click the Options button ☑ on the Specification Search toolbar.

▶ In the Options dialog box, click the Next search tab.

▶ Select Stepwise.

▶ On the Specification Search toolbar, click ▶.

The results in Figure 23-7 suggest examining the 13-parameter model, Model 7. Its discrepancy *C* is much smaller than the discrepancy for the best 12-parameter model and not much larger than the best 14-parameter model. Model 7 is also best according to both *BCC* and *BIC*. (Your results may differ from those in the figure because of an element of randomness in the heuristic specification search algorithms. When adding an arrow during a forward step or removing an arrow during a backward step, there may not be a unique best choice. In that case, one arrow is picked at random from among the arrows that are tied for best.)

Model	Params	df	C	C - df	BCC_0	BIC_0	C / df	p	Notes
1	7	14							Unidentified
2	8	13							Unidentified
3	9	12							Unidentified
4	10	11							Unidentified
5	11	10	97.475	87.475	85.191	81.041	9.747	0.000	
6	12	9	33.469	24.469	23.401	21.326	3.719	0.000	
7	13	8	7.853	-0.147	0.000	0.000	0.982	0.448	
8	14	7	5.770	-1.230	0.132	2.207	0.824	0.567	
9	15	6	5.594	-0.406	2.172	6.322	0.932	0.470	
10	16	5	5.528	0.528	4.322	10.547	1.106	0.355	
11	17	4	5.476	1.476	6.485	14.785	1.369	0.242	
12	18	3							Unidentified
13	19	2							Unidentified
Sat	21	0	0.000	0.000	9.870	26.471			

Figure 23-7: Results of stepwise specification search

Viewing the Scree Plot

▶ Click 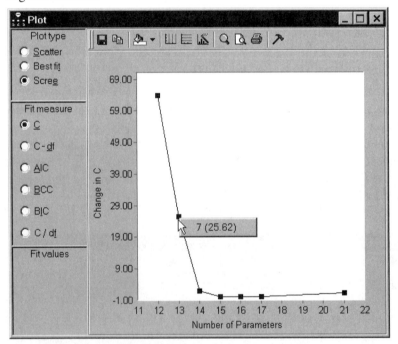 on the Specification Search toolbar.

▶ In the Plot window, select Scree in the Plot type group.

The scree plot confirms that adding a 13th parameter provides a substantial reduction in discrepancy and that adding additional parameters beyond the 13th provides only slight reductions.

Figure 23-8: Scree plot after stepwise specification search

▶ Click the point in the scree plot with horizontal coordinate 13, as in Figure 23-8. The pop-up that appears shows that Model 7 is the best 13-parameter model.

▶ Click 7 (25.62) on the pop-up. This displays the path diagram for Model 7 in the drawing area.

Tip: You can also do this by double-clicking the row for Model 7 in the Specification Search window.

Limitations of Heuristic Specification Searches

A heuristic specification search can fail to find any of the best models for a given number of parameters. In fact, the stepwise search in the present example did fail to find any of the best 11-parameter models. As Figure 23-7 on p. 363 shows, the best 11-parameter model found by the stepwise search had a discrepancy (*C*) of 97.475. An exhaustive search, however, turns up two models that have a discrepancy of 55.382. For every other number of parameters, the stepwise search did find one of the best models.

Of course, it is only when you can perform an exhaustive search to double-check the result of a heuristic search that you can know whether the heuristic search was successful. In those problems where a heuristic search is the only available technique, not only is there no guarantee that it will find one of the best models for each number of parameters, but there is no way to know whether it has succeeded in doing so.

Even in those cases where a heuristic search finds one of the best models for a given number of parameters, it does not (as implemented in Amos) give information about other models that fit equally as well or nearly as well.

Example

24

Multiple-Group Factor Analysis

Introduction

This example demonstrates a two-group factor analysis with automatic specification of cross-group constraints.

About the Data

This example uses the Holzinger and Swineford (1939) girls' and boys' data from Examples 12 and 15.

Model 24a: Modeling without Means and Intercepts

The presence of means and intercepts as explicit model parameters adds to the complexity of a multiple-group analysis. The treatment of means and intercepts will be postponed until Model 24b. For now, consider fitting the following factor analysis model, with no explicit means and intercepts, to the data of girls and of boys:

Example 24

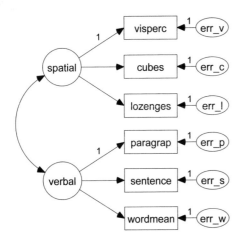

Figure 24-1: Two-factor model for girls and boys

This is the same two-group factor analysis problem that was considered in Example 12. The results obtained in Example 12 will be obtained here automatically.

Specifying the Model

▶ From the menus, choose File → Open.

▶ In the Open dialog box, double-click the file *Ex24a.amw*. If you performed a typical installation, the path will be *C:\Program Files\Amos 7\Examples\Ex24a.amw*.

The path diagram is the same for boys as for girls and is shown in Figure 24-1. Some regression weights are fixed at 1. These regression weights will remain fixed at 1 throughout the analysis to follow. The assisted multiple-group analysis adds constraints to the model you specify but does not remove any constraints.

Opening the Multiple-Group Analysis Dialog Box

▶ From the menus, choose Analyze → Multiple-Group Analysis.

▶ Click OK in the message box that appears. This opens the Multiple-Group Analysis dialog box.

Figure 24-2: The Multiple-Group Analysis dialog box

Most of the time, you will simply click OK. This time, however, let's take a look at some parts of the Multiple-Group Analysis dialog box.

There are eight columns of check boxes. Check marks appear only in the columns labeled 1, 2, and 3. This means that the program will generate three models, each with a different set of cross-group constraints.

Column 1 contains a single check mark in the row labeled Measurement weights, which is short for *regression weights in the measurement part of the model*. In the case of a factor analysis model, these are the *factor loadings*. The following section shows you how to view the measurement weights in the path diagram. Column 1 generates a model in which measurement weights are constant across groups (that is, the same for boys as for girls).

Column 2 contains check marks for Measurement weights and also Structural covariances, which is short for *variances and covariances in the structural part of the model*. In a factor analysis model, these are the factor variances and covariances. The following section shows you how to view the structural covariances in the path diagram. Column 2 generates a model in which measurement weights and structural covariances are constant across groups.

Column 3 contains all the check marks in column 2 and also a check mark next to Measurement residuals, which is short for *variances and covariances of residual (error) variables in the measurement part of the model*. The following section shows you how to view the measurement residuals in the path diagram. The three parameter subsets that appear in a black (that is, not gray) font are mutually exclusive and exhaustive, so that column 3 generates a model in which all parameters are constant across groups.

In summary, columns 1 through 3 generate a hierarchy of models in which each model contains all the constraints of its predecessor. First, the factor loadings are held constant across groups. Then, the factor variances and covariances are held constant. Finally, the residual (unique) variances are held constant.

Viewing the Parameter Subsets

▶ In the Multiple-Group Analysis dialog box, click Measurement weights.

The measurement weights are now displayed in color in the drawing area. If there is a check mark next to Alternative to color on the Accessibility tab of the Interface Properties dialog box, the measurement weights will also display as thick lines, as shown here:

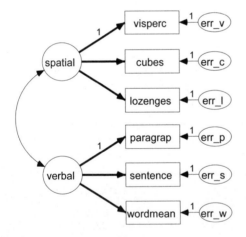

▶ Click Structural covariances to see the factor variances and covariances emphasized.

▶ Click Measurement residuals to see the error variables emphasized.

This is an easy way to visualize which parameters are affected by each cross-group constraint.

Viewing the Generated Models

▶ In the Multiple-Group Analysis dialog box, click OK.

The path diagram now shows names for all parameters. In the panel at the left of the path diagram, you can see that the program has generated three new models in addition to an Unconstrained model in which there are no cross-group constraints at all.

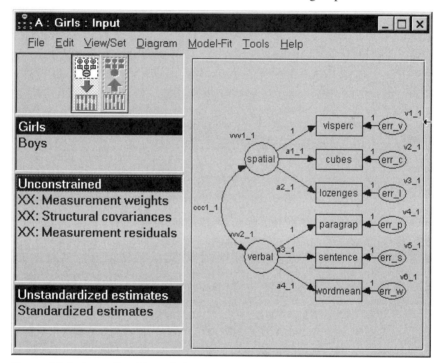

Figure 24-3: Amos Graphics window after automatic constraints

▶ Double-click XX: Measurement weights. This opens the Manage Models dialog box, which shows you the constraints that require the factor loadings to be constant across groups.

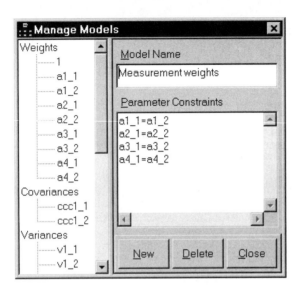

Fitting All the Models and Viewing the Output

▶ From the menus, choose Analyze → Calculate Estimates to fit all models.

▶ From the menus, choose View → Text Output.

▶ In the navigation tree of the output viewer, click the Model Fit node to expand it, and then click CMIN.

The CMIN table shows the likelihood-ratio chi-square statistic for each fitted model. The data do not depart significantly from any of the models. Furthermore, at each step up the hierarchy from the Unconstrained model to the Measurement residuals model, the increase in chi-square is never much larger than the increase in degrees of freedom. There appears to be no significant evidence that girls' parameter values differ from boys' parameter values.

Here is the CMIN table:

Model	NPAR	CMIN	DF	P	CMIN/DF
Unconstrained	26	16.48	16	0.42	1.03
Measurement weights	22	18.29	20	0.57	0.91
Structural covariances	19	22.04	23	0.52	0.96
Measurement residuals	13	26.02	29	0.62	0.90
Saturated model	42	0.00	0		
Independence model	12	337.55	30	0.00	11.25

▶ In the navigation tree, click AIC under the Model Fit node.

AIC and *BCC* values indicate that the best trade-off of model fit and parsimony is obtained by constraining all parameters to be equal across groups (the Measurement residuals model).

Here is the AIC table:

Model	AIC	BCC	BIC	CAIC
Unconstrained	68.48	74.12		
Measurement weights	62.29	67.07		
Structural covariances	60.04	64.16		
Measurement residuals	52.02	54.84		
Saturated model	84.00	93.12		
Independence model	361.55	364.16		

Customizing the Analysis

There were two opportunities to override the automatically generated cross-group constraints. In Figure 24-2 on p. 369, you could have changed the check marks in columns 1, 2, and 3, and you could have generated additional models by placing check marks in columns 4 through 8. Then, in Figure 24-3 on p. 371, you could have renamed or modified any of the automatically generated models listed in the panel at the left of the path diagram.

Model 24b: Comparing Factor Means

Introducing explicit means and intercepts into a model raises additional questions about which cross-group parameter constraints should be tested, and in what order. This example shows how Amos constrains means and intercepts while fitting the factor analysis model in Figure 24-1 on p. 368 to data from separate groups of girls and boys.

This is the same two-group factor analysis problem that was considered in Example 15. The results in Example 15 will be obtained here automatically.

Specifying the Model

▶ From the menus, choose File → Open.

▶ In the Open dialog box, double-click the file *Ex24b.amw*. If you performed a typical installation, the path will be *C:\Program Files\Amos 7\Examples\Ex24b.amw*.

The path diagram is the same for boys as for girls and is shown below. Some regression weights are fixed at 1. The means of all the unobserved variables are fixed at 0. In the following section, you will remove the constraints on the girls' factor means. The other constraints (the ones that you do not remove) will remain in effect throughout the analysis.

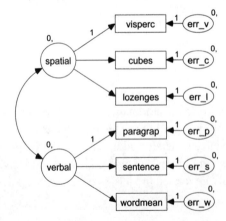

Figure 24-4: Two-factor model with explicit means and intercepts

Removing Constraints

Initially, the factor means are fixed at 0 for both boys and girls. It is not possible to estimate factor means for both groups. However, Sörbom (1974) showed that, by fixing the factor means of a single group to constant values and placing suitable constraints on the regression weights and intercepts in a factor model, it is possible to obtain meaningful estimates of the factor means for all of the other groups. In the present example, this means picking one group, say boys, and fixing their factor means to a constant, say 0, and then removing the constraints on the factor means of the remaining group, the girls. The constraints on regression weights and intercepts required by Sörbom's approach will be generated automatically by Amos.

The boys' factor means are already fixed at 0. To remove the constraints on the girls' factor means, do the following:

▶ In the drawing area of the Amos Graphics window, right-click Spatial and choose Object Properties from the pop-up menu.

▶ In the Object Properties dialog box, click the Parameters tab.

▶ Select the 0 in the Mean box, and press the Delete key.

▶ With the Object Properties dialog box still open, click Verbal in the drawing area. This displays the properties for the *verbal* factor in the Object Properties dialog box.

▶ In the Mean box on the Parameters tab, select 0 and press the Delete key.

▶ Close the Object Properties dialog box.

Now that the constraints on the girls' factor means have been removed, the girls' and boys' path diagrams look like this:

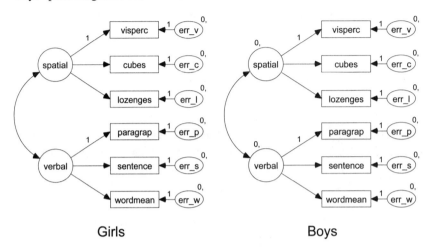

Girls   Boys

Tip: To switch between path diagrams in the drawing area, click either Boys or Girls in the List of Groups pane to the left.

Generating the Cross-Group Constraints

▶ From the menus, choose Analyze → Multiple-Group Analysis.

▶ Click OK in the message box that appears. This opens the Multiple-Group Analysis dialog box.

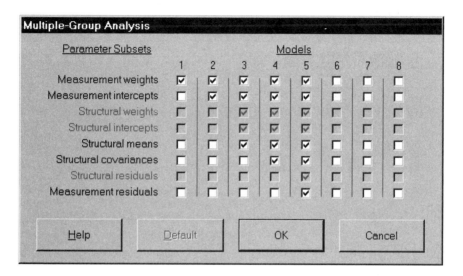

The default settings, as shown above, will generate the following nested hierarchy of five models:

Model	Constraints
Model 1 (column 1)	Measurement weights (factor loadings) are equal across groups.
Model 2 (column 2)	All of the above, and measurement intercepts (intercepts in the equations for predicting measured variables) are equal across groups.
Model 3 (column 3)	All of the above, and structural means (factor means) are equal across groups.
Model 4 (column 4)	All of the above, and structural covariances (factor variances and covariances) are equal across groups.
Model 5 (column 5)	All parameters are equal across groups.

▶ Click OK.

Fitting the Models

▶ From the menus, choose Analyze → Calculate Estimates.

The panel at the left of the path diagram shows that two models could not be fitted to the data. The two models that could not be fitted, the Unconstrained model with no cross-group constraints, and the Measurement weights model with factor loadings held equal across groups, are unidentified.

```
XX: Unconstrained
XX: Measurement weights
OK: Measurement intercepts
OK: Structural means
OK: Structural covariances
OK: Measurement residuals
```

Viewing the Output

▶ From the menus, choose View → Text Output.

▶ In the navigation tree of the output viewer, expand the Model Fit node.

Some fit measures for the four automatically generated and identified models are shown here, along with fit measures for the saturated and independence models.

▶ Click CMIN under the Model Fit node.

The CMIN table shows that none of the generated models can be rejected when tested against the saturated model.

Model	NPAR	CMIN	DF	P	CMIN/DF
Measurement intercepts	30	22.593	24	0.544	0.941
Structural means	28	30.624	26	0.243	1.178
Structural covariances	25	34.381	29	0.226	1.186
Measurement residuals	19	38.459	35	0.316	1.099
Saturated model	54	0.00	0		
Independence model	24	337.553	30	0.00	11.252

On the other hand, the change in chi-square ($30.62 - 22.59 = 8.03$) when introducing the equal-factor-means constraint looks large compared to the change in degrees of freedom ($26 - 24 = 2$).

▶ In the navigation tree, click the Model Comparison node.

Assuming model *Measurement intercepts* to be correct, the following table shows that this chi-square difference is significant:

Model	DF	CMIN	P	NFI Delta-1	IFI Delta-2	RFI rho-1	TLI rho2
Structural means	2	8.030	0.018	0.024	0.026	0.021	0.023
Structural covariances	5	11.787	0.038	0.035	0.038	0.022	0.024
Measurement residuals	11	15.865	0.146	0.047	0.051	0.014	0.015

In the preceding two tables, two chi-square statistics and their associated degrees of freedom are especially important. The first, $\chi^2 = 22.59$ with $df = 24$, allowed accepting the hypothesis of equal intercepts and equal regression weights in the measurement model. It was important to establish the credibility of this hypothesis because, without equal intercepts and equal regression weights, it would be unclear that the factors have the same meaning for boys as for girls and so there would be no interest in comparing their means. The other important chi-square statistic, $\chi^2 = 8.03$ with $df = 2$, leads to rejection of the hypothesis that boys and girls have the same factor means.

Group differences between the boys' and girls' factor means can be determined from the girls' estimates in the Measurement intercepts model.

▶ Select the Measurement intercepts model in the pane at the lower left of the output viewer.

▶ In the navigation tree, click Estimates, then Scalars, and then Means.

The boys' means were fixed at 0, so only the girls' means were estimated, as shown in the following table:

			Estimate	S.E.	C.R.	P	Label
spatial			−1.066	0.881	−1.209	0.226	m1_1
verbal			0.956	0.521	1.836	0.066	m2_1

These estimates were discussed in Model A of Example 15, which is identical to the present Measurement intercepts model. (Model B of Example 15 is identical to the present Structural means model.)

Example

25

Multiple-Group Analysis

Introduction

This example shows you how to automatically implement Sörbom's alternative to analysis of covariance.

Example 16 demonstrates the benefits of Sörbom's approach to analysis of covariance with latent variables. Unfortunately, as Example 16 also showed, the Sörbom approach is difficult to apply, involving many steps. This example automatically obtains the same results as Example 16.

About the Data

The Olsson (1973) data from Example 16 will be used here. The sample moments can be found in the workbook *UserGuide.xls*. Sample moments from the experimental group are in the worksheet *Olss_exp*. Sample moments from the control group are in the worksheet *Olss_cnt*.

About the Model

The model was described in Example 16. The Sörbom method requires that the experimental and the control group have the same path diagram.

Example 25

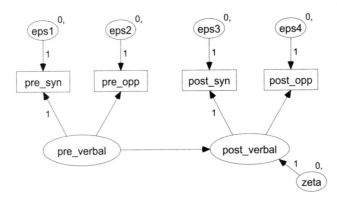

Figure 25-1: Sörbom model for Olsson data

Specifying the Model

▶ Open *Ex25.amw*. If you performed a typical installation, the path will be *C:\Program Files\Amos 7\Examples\Ex25.amw*.

The path diagram is the same for the control and experimental groups and is shown in Figure 25-1. Some regression weights are fixed at 1. The means of all the residual (error) variable means are fixed at 0. These constraints will remain in effect throughout the analysis.

Constraining the Latent Variable Means and Intercepts

The model in Figure 25-1, Sörbom's model for Olsson data, is unidentified and will remain unidentified for every set of cross-group constraints that Amos automatically generates. For every set of cross-group constraints, the mean of *pre_verbal* and the intercept in the equation for predicting *post_verbal* will be unidentified. In order to allow the model to be identified for at least some cross-group constraints, it is necessary to pick one group, such as the control group, and fix the *pre_verbal* mean and the *post_verbal* intercept to a constant, such as 0.

▶ In the List of Groups pane to the left of the path diagram, ensure that Control is selected. This indicates that the path diagram for the control group is displayed in the drawing area.

▶ In the drawing area, right-click pre_verbal and choose Object Properties from the pop-up menu.

▶ In the Object Properties dialog box, click the Parameters tab.

▶ In the Mean text box, type 0.

▶ With the Object Properties dialog box still open, click post_verbal in the drawing area.

▶ In the Intercept text box of the Object Properties dialog box, type 0.

▶ Close the Object Properties dialog box.

Now, the path diagram for the control group appears as follows:

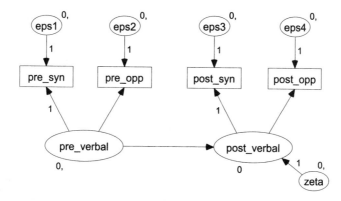

The path diagram for the experimental group continues to look like Figure 25-1.

Generating Cross-Group Constraints

▶ From the menus, choose Analyze → Multiple-Group Analysis.

▶ Click OK in the message box that appears.

The Multiple-Group Analysis dialog box appears.

Example 25

► Click OK to generate the following nested hierarchy of eight models:

Model	Constraints
Model 1 (column 1)	Measurement weights (factor loadings) are constant across groups.
Model 2 (column 2)	All of the above, and measurement intercepts (intercepts in the equations for predicting measured variables) are constant across groups.
Model 3 (column 3)	All of the above, and the structural weight (the regression weight for predicting *post_verbal*) is constant across groups.
Model 4 (column 4)	All of the above, and the structural intercept (the intercept in the equation for predicting *post_verbal*) is constant across groups.
Model 5 (column 5)	All of the above, and the structural mean (the mean of *pre_verbal*) is constant across groups.
Model 6 (column 6)	All of the above, and the structural covariance (the variance of *pre_verbal*) is constant across groups.
Model 7 (column 7)	All of the above, and the structural residual (the variance of *zeta*) is constant across groups.
Model 8 (column 8)	All parameters are constant across groups.

Fitting the Models

▶ From the menus, choose Analyze → Calculate Estimates.

The panel to the left of the path diagram shows that two models could not be fitted to the data. The two models that could not be fitted, the Unconstrained model and the Measurement weights model, are unidentified.

```
XX: Unconstrained
XX: Measurement weights
OK: Measurement intercepts
OK: Structural weights
OK: Structural intercepts
OK: Structural means
OK: Structural covariances
OK: Structural residuals
OK: Measurement residuals
```

Viewing the Text Output

▶ From the menus, choose View → Text Output.

▶ In the navigation tree of the output viewer, expand the Model Fit node, and click CMIN. This displays some fit measures for the seven automatically generated and identified models, along with fit measures for the saturated and independence models, as shown in the following CMIN table:

Model	NPAR	CMIN	DF	P	CMIN/DF
Measurement intercepts	22	34.775	6	0.000	5.796
Structural weights	21	36.340	7	0.000	5.191
Structural intercepts	20	84.060	8	0.000	10.507
Structural means	19	94.970	9	0.000	10.552
Structural covariances	18	99.976	10	0.000	9.998
Structural residuals	17	112.143	11	0.000	10.195
Measurement residuals	13	122.366	15	0.000	8.158
Saturated model	28	0.000	0		
Independence model	16	682.638	12	0.000	56.887

There are many chi-square statistics in this table, but only two of them matter. The Sörbom procedure comes down to two basic questions. First, does the Structural weights model fit? This model specifies that the regression weight for predicting *post_verbal* from *pre_verbal* be constant across groups.

If the Structural weights model is accepted, one follows up by asking whether the next model up the hierarchy, the Structural intercepts model, fits significantly worse. On the other hand, if the Structural weights model has to be rejected, one never gets to the question about the Structural intercepts model. Unfortunately, that is the case here. The Structural weights model, with $\chi^2 = 36.34$ and $df = 7$, is rejected at any conventional significance level.

Examining the Modification Indices

To see if it is possible to improve the fit of the Structural weights model:

▶ Close the output viewer.

▶ From the Amos Graphics menus, choose View → Analysis Properties.

▶ Click the Output tab and select the Modification Indices check box.

▶ Close the Analysis Properties dialog box.

▶ From the menus, choose Analyze → Calculate Estimates to fit all models.

Only the modification indices for the Structural weights model need to be examined because this is the only model whose fit is essential to the analysis.

▶ From the menus, choose View → Text Output, select Modification Indices in the navigation tree of the output viewer, then select Structural weights in the lower left panel.

▶ Expand the Modification Indices node and select Covariances.

As you can see in the following covariance table for the control group, only one modification index exceeds the default threshold of 4:

	M.I.	Par Change
eps2 <--> eps4	4.553	2.073

▶ Now click experimental in the panel on the left. As you can see in the following covariance table for the experimental group, there are four modification indices greater than 4:

	M.I.	Par Change
eps2 <--> eps4	9.314	4.417
eps2 <--> eps3	9.393	−4.117
eps1 <--> eps4	8.513	−3.947
eps1 <--> eps3	6.192	3.110

Of these, only two modifications have an obvious theoretical justification: allowing *eps2* to correlate with *eps4*, and allowing *eps1* to correlate with *eps3*. Between these two, allowing *eps2* to correlate with *eps4* has the larger modification index. Thus the modification indices from the control group and the experimental group both suggest allowing *eps2* to correlate with *eps4*.

Modifying the Model and Repeating the Analysis

▶ Close the output viewer.

▶ From the menus, choose Diagram → Draw Covariances.

▶ Click and drag to draw a double-headed arrow between eps2 and eps4.

▶ From the menus, choose Analyze → Multiple-Group Analysis, and click OK in the message box that appears.

▶ In the Multiple-Group Analysis dialog box, click OK.

▶ From the menus, choose Analyze → Calculate Estimates to fit all models.

▶ From the menus, choose View → Text Output.

▶ Use the navigation tree to view the fit measures for the Structural weights model.

With the additional double-headed arrow connecting *eps2* and *eps4*, the Structural weights model has an adequate fit ($\chi^2 = 3.98$ with $df = 5$), as shown in the following CMIN table:

Example 25

Model	NPAR	CMIN	DF	P	CMIN/DF
Measurement intercepts	24	2.797	4	0.59	0.699
Structural weights	23	3.976	5	0.55	0.795
Structural intercepts	22	55.094	6	0.00	9.182
Structural means	21	63.792	7	0.00	9.113
Structural covariances	20	69.494	8	0.00	8.687
Structural residuals	19	83.194	9	0.00	9.244
Measurement residuals	14	93.197	14	0.00	6.657
Saturated model	28	0.000	0		
Independence model	16	682.638	12	0.00	56.887

Now that the Structural weights model fits the data, it can be asked whether the Structural intercepts model fits significantly worse. Assuming the Structural weights model to be correct:

Model	DF	CMIN	P	NFI Delta-1	IFI Delta-2	RFI rho-1	TLI rho2
Structural intercepts	1	51.118	0.000	0.075	0.075	0.147	0.150
Structural means	2	59.816	0.000	0.088	0.088	0.146	0.149
Structural covariances	3	65.518	0.000	0.096	0.097	0.139	0.141
Structural residuals	4	79.218	0.000	0.116	0.117	0.149	0.151
Measurement residuals	9	89.221	0.000	0.131	0.132	0.103	0.105

The Structural intercepts model does fit significantly worse than the Structural weights model. When the intercept in the equation for predicting *post_verbal* is required to be constant across groups, the chi-square statistic increases by 51.12 while degrees of freedom increases by only 1. That is, the intercept for the experimental group differs significantly from the intercept for the control group. The intercept for the experimental group is estimated to be 3.627.

	Estimate	S.E.	C.R.	P	Label
post_verbal	3.627	0.478	7.591	<0.001	j1_2
pre_syn	18.619	0.594	31.355	<0.001	i1_1
pre_opp	19.910	0.541	36.781	<0.001	i2_1
post_syn	20.383	0.535	38.066	<0.001	i3_1
post_opp	21.204	0.531	39.908	<0.001	i4_1

Recalling that the intercept for the control group was fixed at 0, it is estimated that the treatment increases *post_verbal* scores by 3.63 with *pre_verbal* held constant.

The results obtained in the present example are identical to the results of Example 16. The Structural weights model is the same as Model D in Example 16. The Structural intercepts model is the same as Model E in Example 16.

Example

26

Bayesian Estimation

Introduction

This example demonstrates Bayesian estimation using Amos.

Bayesian Estimation

In maximum likelihood estimation and hypothesis testing, the true values of the model parameters are viewed as *fixed but unknown*, and the estimates of those parameters from a given sample are viewed as *random but known*. An alternative kind of statistical inference, called the **Bayesian** approach, views any quantity that is unknown as a random variable and assigns it a probability distribution. From a Bayesian standpoint, true model parameters are unknown and therefore considered to be random, and they are assigned a joint probability distribution. This distribution is not meant to suggest that the parameters are varying or changing in some fashion. Rather, the distribution is intended to summarize our *state of knowledge,* or what is currently known about the parameters. The distribution of the parameters before the data are seen is called a **prior distribution**. Once the data are observed, the evidence provided by the data is combined with the prior distribution by a well-known formula called **Bayes' Theorem.** The result is an updated distribution for the parameters, called a **posterior distribution**, which reflects a combination of prior belief and empirical evidence (Bolstad, 2004).

Human beings tend to have difficulty visualizing and interpreting the joint posterior distribution for the parameters of a model. Therefore, when performing a Bayesian analysis, one needs summaries of the posterior distribution that are easy to interpret. A good way to start is to plot the marginal posterior density for each parameter, one at a time. Often, especially with large data samples, the marginal posterior distributions for parameters tend to resemble normal distributions. The mean of a marginal posterior distribution, called a **posterior mean**, can be reported as a parameter estimate. The **posterior standard deviation**, the standard deviation of the distribution, is a useful measure of uncertainty similar to a conventional standard error.

The analogue of a confidence interval may be computed from the percentiles of the marginal posterior distribution; the interval that runs from the 2.5 percentile to the 97.5 percentile forms a Bayesian 95% **credible interval**. If the marginal posterior distribution is approximately normal, the 95% credible interval will be approximately equal to the posterior mean ± 1.96 posterior standard deviations. In that case, the credible interval becomes essentially identical to an ordinary confidence interval that assumes a normal sampling distribution for the parameter estimate. If the posterior distribution is not normal, the interval will not be symmetric about the posterior mean. In that case, the Bayesian version often has better properties than the conventional one.

Unlike a conventional confidence interval, the Bayesian credible interval is interpreted as a probability statement about the parameter itself; $\text{Prob}(a \leq \theta \leq b) = 0.95$) literally means that you are 95% sure that the true value of θ lies between a and b. Tail areas from a marginal posterior distribution can even be used as a kind of Bayesian p value for hypothesis testing. If 96.5% of the area under the marginal posterior density for θ lies to the right of some value a, then the Bayesian p value for testing the null hypothesis $\theta \leq a$ against the alternative hypothesis $\theta > a$ is 0.045. In that case, one would actually say, *I'm 96.5% sure that the alternative hypothesis is true.*

Although the idea of Bayesian inference dates back to the late 18th century, its use by statisticians has been rare until recently. For some, reluctance to apply Bayesian methods stems from a philosophical distaste for viewing probability as a state of belief and from the inherent subjectivity in choosing prior distributions. But for the most part, Bayesian analyses have been rare because computational methods for summarizing joint posterior distributions have been difficult or unavailable. Using a new class of simulation techniques called Markov chain Monte Carlo (MCMC), however, it is now possible to draw random values of parameters from high-dimensional joint posterior distributions, even in complex problems. With MCMC, obtaining posterior summaries becomes as simple as plotting histograms and computing sample means and percentiles.

Selecting Priors

A prior distribution quantifies the researcher's belief concerning where the unknown parameter may lie. Knowledge of how a variable is distributed in the population can sometimes be used to help researchers select reasonable priors for parameters of interest. Hox (2002) cites the example of a normed intelligence test with a mean of 100 units and a standard deviation of 15 units in the general population. If the test is given to participants in a study who are fairly representative of the general population, then it would be reasonable to center the prior distributions for the mean and standard deviation of the test score at 100 and 15, respectively. Knowing that an observed variable is bounded may help us to place bounds on the parameters. For instance, the mean of a Likert-type survey item taking values 0, 1, ..., 10 must lie between 0 and 10, and its maximum variance is 25. Prior distributions for the mean and variance of this item can be specified to enforce these bounds.

In many cases, one would like to specify prior distribution that introduces as little information as possible, so that the data may be allowed to speak for themselves. A prior distribution is said to be **diffuse** if it spreads its probability over a very wide range of parameter values. By default, Amos applies a uniform distribution from -3.4×10^{-38} to 3.4×10^{38} to each parameter.

Diffuse prior distributions are often said to be **non-informative**, and we will use that term as well. In a strict sense, however, no prior distribution is ever completely non-informative, not even a uniform distribution over the entire range of allowable values, because it would cease to be uniform if the parameter were transformed. (Suppose, for example, that the variance of a variable is uniformly distributed from 0 to ∞; then the standard deviation will not be uniformly distributed.) Every prior distribution carries with it at least some information. As the size of a dataset grows, the evidence from the data eventually swamps this information, and the influence of the prior distribution diminishes. Unless your sample is unusually small or if your model and/or prior distribution are strongly contradicted by the data, you will find that the answers from a Bayesian analysis tend to change very little if the prior is changed. Amos makes it easy for you to change the prior distribution for any parameter, so you can easily perform this kind of sensitivity check.

Performing Bayesian Estimation Using Amos Graphics

To illustrate Bayesian estimation using Amos Graphics, we revisit Example 3, which shows how to test the null hypothesis that the covariance between two variables is 0 by fixing the value of the covariance between *age* and *vocabulary* to 0.

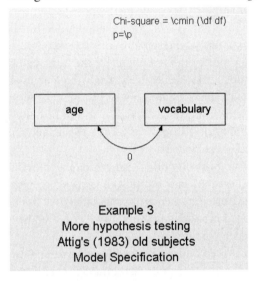

Estimating the Covariance

The first thing we need to do for the present example is to remove the zero constraint on the covariance so that the covariance can be estimated.

▶ Open *Ex03.amw*. If you performed a typical installation, the path is *C:\Program Files\Amos 7\Examples*.

▶ Right-click the double-headed arrow in the path diagram and choose Object Properties from the pop-up menu.

▶ In the Object Properties dialog box, click the Parameters tab.

▶ Delete the 0 in the Covariance text box.

▶ Close the Object Properties dialog box.

This is the resulting path diagram (you can also find it in *Ex26.amw*):

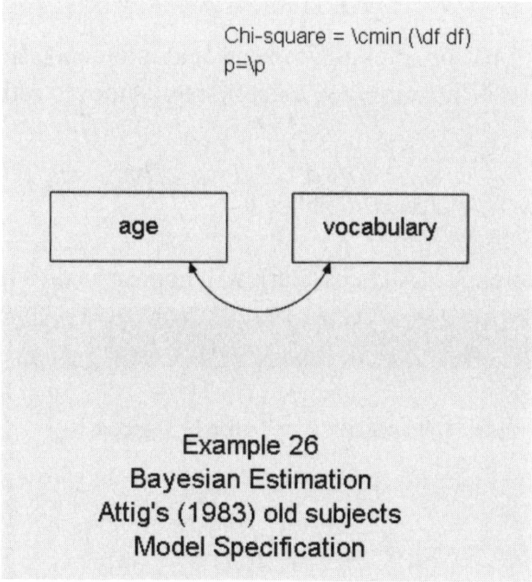

Chi-square = \cmin (\df df)
p=\p

age   vocabulary

Example 26
Bayesian Estimation
Attig's (1983) old subjects
Model Specification

Results of Maximum Likelihood Analysis

Before performing a Bayesian analysis of this model, we perform a maximum likelihood analysis for comparison purposes.

▶ From the menus, choose Analyze → Calculate Estimates to display the following parameter estimates and standard errors:

Covariances: (Group number 1 - Default model)

	Estimate	S.E.	C.R.	P	Label
age <--> vocabulary	−5.014	8.560	−0.586	0.558	

Variances: (Group number 1 - Default model)

	Estimate	S.E.	C.R.	P	Label
age	21.574	4.886	4.416	***	
vocabulary	131.294	29.732	4.416	***	

Example 26

Bayesian Analysis

Bayesian analysis requires estimation of explicit means and intercepts. Before performing any Bayesian analysis in Amos, you must first tell Amos to estimate means and intercepts.

▶ From the menus, choose View → Analysis Properties.

▶ Select Estimate means and intercepts. (A check mark will appear next to it.)

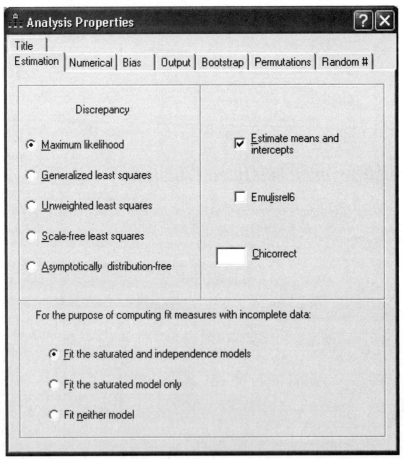

▶ To perform a Bayesian analysis, from the menus, choose Analyze → Bayesian Estimation, or press the keyboard combination Ctrl+B.

The Bayesian SEM window appears, and the MCMC algorithm immediately begins generating samples.

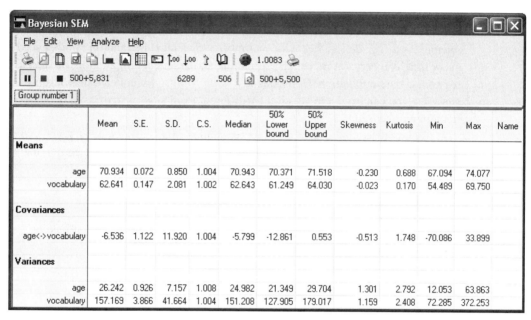

The Bayesian SEM window has a toolbar near the top of the window and has a results summary table below. Each row of the summary table describes the marginal posterior distribution of a single model parameter. The first column, labeled *Mean*, contains the posterior mean, which is the center or average of the posterior distribution. This can be used as a Bayesian point estimate of the parameter, based on the data and the prior distribution. With a large dataset, the posterior mean will tend to be close to the maximum likelihood estimate. (In this case, the two are somewhat close; compare the posterior mean of –6.536 for the *age-vocabulary* covariance to the maximum likelihood estimate of –5.014 reported earlier.)

Example 26

Replicating Bayesian Analysis and Data Imputation Results

The multiple imputation and Bayesian estimation algorithms implemented in Amos make extensive use of a stream of random numbers that depends on an initial *random number seed*. The default behavior of Amos is to change the random number seed every time you perform Bayesian estimation, Bayesian data imputation, or stochastic regression data imputation. Consequently, when you try to replicate one of those analyses, you can expect to get slightly different results because of using a different random number seed.

If, for any reason, you need an exact replication of an earlier analysis, you can do so by starting with the same random number seed that was used in the earlier analysis.

Examining the Current Seed

To find out what the current random number seed is or to change its value:

▶ From the menus, choose Tools → Seed Manager.

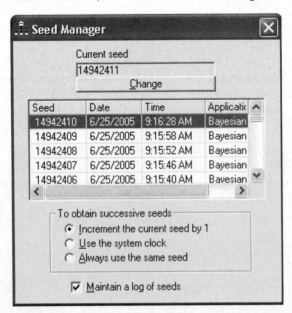

By default, Amos increments the current random number seed by one for each invocation of a simulation method that makes use of random numbers (either Bayesian SEM, stochastic regression data imputation, or Bayesian data imputation). Amos maintains a log of previous seeds used, so it is possible to match the file creation dates of previously generated analysis results or imputed datasets with the dates reported in the Seed Manager.

Changing the Current Seed

▶ Click Change and enter a previously used seed before performing an analysis.

Amos will use the same stream of random numbers that it used the last time it started out with that seed. For example, we used the Seed Manager to discover that Amos used a seed of 14942405 when the analysis for this example was performed. To generate the same Bayesian analysis results as we did:

▶ Click Change and change the current seed to 14942405.

The following figure shows the Seed Manager dialog box after making the change:

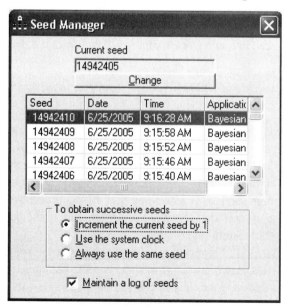

A more proactive approach is to select a fixed seed value prior to running a Bayesian or data imputation analysis. You can have Amos use the same seed value for all analyses if you select the Always use the same seed option.

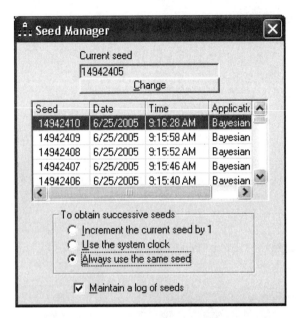

Record the value of this seed in a safe place so that you can replicate the results of your analysis at a later date.

Tip: We use the same seed value of 14942405 for all examples in this guide so that you can reproduce our results.

We mentioned earlier that the MCMC algorithm used by Amos draws random values of parameters from high-dimensional joint posterior distributions via Monte Carlo simulation of the posterior distribution of parameters. For instance, the value reported in the *Mean* column is not the exact posterior mean but is an estimate obtained by averaging across the random samples produced by the MCMC procedure. It is important to have at least a rough idea of how much uncertainty in the posterior mean is attributable to Monte Carlo sampling.

The second column, labeled *S.E.*, reports an estimated standard error that suggests how far the Monte-Carlo estimated posterior mean may lie from the true posterior mean. As the MCMC procedure continues to generate more samples, the estimate of the posterior mean becomes more precise, and the *S.E.* gradually drops. Note that *this S.E. is not an estimate of how far the posterior mean may lie from the unknown true value of the parameter*. That is, one would not use ± 2 S.E. values as the width of a 95% interval for the parameter.

The likely distance between the posterior mean and the unknown true parameter is reported in the third column, labeled *S.D.*, and that number is analogous to the standard error in maximum likelihood estimation. Additional columns contain the *convergence statistic* (*C.S.*), the median value of each parameter, the lower and upper 50% boundaries of the distribution of each parameter, and the skewness, kurtosis, minimum value, and maximum value of each parameter. The lower and upper 50% boundaries are the endpoints of a 50% Bayesian credible set, which is the Bayesian analogue of a 50% confidence interval. Most of us are accustomed to using a confidence level of 95%, so we will soon show you how to change to 95%.

When you choose Analyze → Bayesian Estimation, the MCMC algorithm begins sampling immediately, and it continues until you click the Pause Sampling button to halt the process. In the figure on p. 395, sampling was halted after 500 + 5831 = 6331 completed samples. Amos generated and discarded 500 *burn-in* samples prior to drawing the first sample that was retained for the analysis. Amos draws burn-in samples to allow the MCMC procedure to converge to the true joint posterior distribution. After Amos draws and discards the burn-in samples, it draws additional samples to give us a clear picture of what this joint posterior distribution looks like. In the example shown on p. 395, Amos has drawn 5,831 of these *analysis samples*, and it is upon these analysis samples that the results in the summary table are based. Actually, the displayed results are for 500 burn-in and 5,500 analysis samples. Because the sampling algorithm Amos uses is very fast, updating the summary table after each sample would lead to a rapid, incomprehensible blur of changing results in the Bayesian SEM window. It would also slow the analysis down. To avoid both problems, Amos refreshes the results after every 1,000 samples.

Changing the Refresh Options

To change the refresh interval:

▶ From the menus, choose View → Options.

▶ Click the Refresh tab in the Options dialog box to show the refresh options.

Example 26

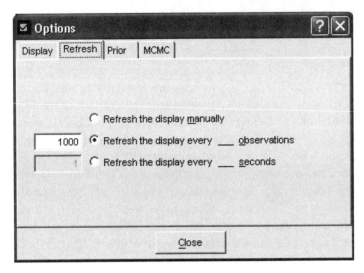

You can change the refresh interval to something other than the default of 1,000 observations. Alternatively, you can refresh the display at a regular time interval that you specify.

If you select Refresh the display manually, the display will never be updated automatically. Regardless of what you select on the Refresh tab, you can refresh the display manually at any time by clicking the Refresh button on the Bayesian SEM toolbar.

Assessing Convergence

Are there enough samples to yield stable estimates of the parameters? Before addressing this question, let us briefly discuss what it means for the procedure to have converged. Convergence of an MCMC algorithm is quite different from convergence of a nonrandom method such as maximum likelihood. To properly understand MCMC convergence, we need to distinguish two different types.

The first type, which we may call **convergence in distribution**, means that the analysis samples are, in fact, being drawn from the actual joint posterior distribution of the parameters. Convergence in distribution takes place in the burn-in period, during which the algorithm gradually forgets its initial starting values. Because these samples may not be representative of the actual posterior distribution, they are discarded. The default burn-in period of 500 is quite conservative, much longer than needed for most problems. Once the burn-in period is over and Amos begins to collect the analysis samples, one may ask whether there are enough of these samples to accurately estimate the summary statistics, such as the posterior mean.

That question pertains to the second type of convergence, which we may call **convergence of posterior summaries**. Convergence of posterior summaries is complicated by the fact that the analysis samples are not independent but are actually an autocorrelated time series. The 1001th sample is correlated with the 1000th, which, in turn, is correlated with the 999th, and so on. These correlations are an inherent feature of MCMC, and because of these correlations, the summary statistics from 5,500 (or whatever number of) analysis samples have more variability than they would if the 5,500 samples had been independent. Nevertheless, as we continue to accumulate more and more analysis samples, the posterior summaries gradually stabilize.

Amos provides several diagnostics that help you check convergence. Notice the value 1.0083 on the toolbar of the Bayesian SEM window on p. 395. This is an overall convergence statistic based on a measure suggested by Gelman, Carlin, Stern, and Rubin (2004). Each time the screen refreshes, Amos updates the *C.S.* for each parameter in the summary table; the *C.S.* value on the toolbar is the largest of the individual *C.S.* values. By default, Amos judges the procedure to have converged if the largest of the *C.S.* values is less than 1.002. By this standard, the maximum *C.S.* of 1.0083 is not small enough. Amos displays an unhappy face 😟 when the overall *C.S.* is not small enough. The *C.S.* compares the variability within parts of the analysis sample to the variability across these parts. A value of 1.000 represents perfect convergence, and larger values indicate that the posterior summaries can be made more precise by creating more analysis samples.

Clicking the Pause Sampling button a second time instructs Amos to resume the sampling process. You can also pause and resume sampling by choosing Pause Sampling from the Analyze menu, or by using the keyboard combination Ctrl+E. The next figure shows the results after resuming the sampling for a while and pausing again.

	Mean	S.E.	S.D.	C.S.	Median	50% Lower bound	50% Upper bound	Skewness	Kurtosis	Min	Max	Name
Means												
age	70.969	0.024	0.811	1.000	70.972	70.431	71.500	-0.090	0.355	67.094	74.077	
vocabulary	62.570	0.055	2.002	1.000	62.566	61.228	63.874	-0.032	0.252	53.845	69.860	
Covariances												
age<->vocabulary	-6.462	0.334	10.902	1.000	-6.214	-13.214	0.421	-0.160	0.860	-70.086	43.096	
Variances												
age	26.170	0.328	6.824	1.001	24.979	21.458	29.697	1.213	2.577	12.053	70.861	
vocabulary	158.773	1.965	39.617	1.001	152.990	130.336	180.134	0.959	1.417	72.285	372.253	

At this point, we have 22,501 analysis samples, although the display was most recently updated at the 22,500th sample. The largest *C.S.* is 1.0012, which is below the 1.002 criterion that indicates acceptable convergence. Reflecting the satisfactory convergence, Amos now displays a happy face ☺. Gelman et al. (2004) suggest that for many analyses, values of 1.10 or smaller are sufficient. The default criterion of 1.002 is conservative. Judging that the MCMC chain has converged by this criterion does not mean that the summary table will stop changing. The summary table will continue to change as long as the MCMC algorithm keeps running. As the overall *C.S.* value on the toolbar approaches 1.000, however, there is not much more precision to be gained by taking additional samples, so we might as well stop.

Diagnostic Plots

In addition to the *C.S.* value, Amos offers several plots that can help you check convergence of the Bayesian MCMC method. To view these plots:

▶ From the menus, choose View → Posterior.

Amos displays the Posterior dialog box.

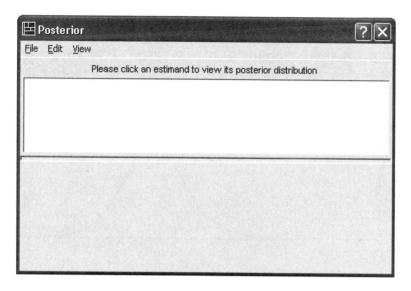

▶ Select the age< - >vocabulary parameter from the Bayesian SEM window.

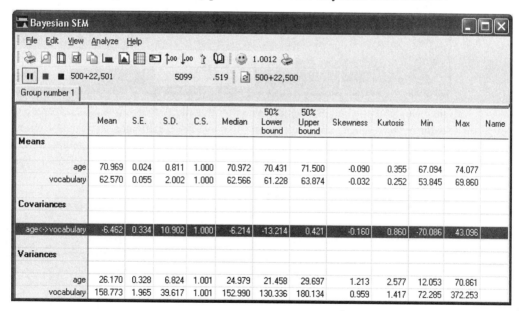

	Mean	S.E.	S.D.	C.S.	Median	50% Lower bound	50% Upper bound	Skewness	Kurtosis	Min	Max	Name
Means												
age	70.969	0.024	0.811	1.000	70.972	70.431	71.500	-0.090	0.355	67.094	74.077	
vocabulary	62.570	0.055	2.002	1.000	62.566	61.228	63.874	-0.032	0.252	53.845	69.860	
Covariances												
age<->vocabulary	-6.462	0.334	10.902	1.000	-6.214	-13.214	0.421	-0.160	0.860	-70.086	43.096	
Variances												
age	26.170	0.328	6.824	1.001	24.979	21.458	29.697	1.213	2.577	12.053	70.861	
vocabulary	158.773	1.965	39.617	1.001	152.990	130.336	180.134	0.959	1.417	72.285	372.253	

The Posterior dialog box now displays a frequency polygon of the distribution of the *age-vocabulary* covariance across the 22,500 samples.

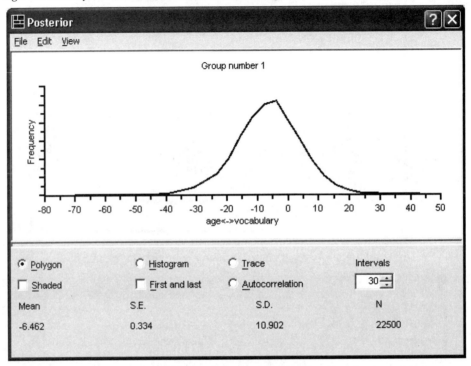

One visual aid you can use to judge whether it is likely that Amos has converged to the posterior distribution is a simultaneous display of two estimates of the distribution, one obtained from the first third of the accumulated samples and another obtained from the last third. To display the two estimates of the marginal posterior on the same graph:

▶ Select First and last. (A check mark will appear next to the option.)

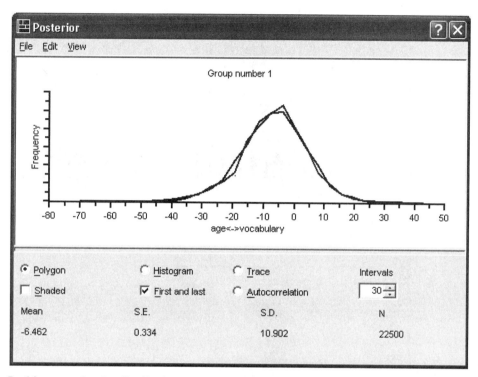

In this example, the distributions of the first and last thirds of the analysis samples are almost identical, which suggests that Amos has successfully identified the important features of the posterior distribution of the *age-vocabulary* covariance. Note that this posterior distribution appears to be centered at some value near –6, which agrees with the *Mean* value for this parameter. Visual inspection suggests that the standard deviation is roughly 10, which agrees with the value of *S.D.*

Notice that more than half of the sampled values are to the left of 0. This provides mild evidence that the true value of the covariance parameter is negative, but this result is not *statistically significant* because the proportion to the right of 0 is still quite large. If the proportion of sampled values to the right of 0 were very small—for example, less than 5%—then we would be able to reject the null hypothesis that the covariance parameter is greater than or equal to 0. In this case, however, we cannot.

Another plot that helps in assessing convergence is the **trace plot**. The trace plot, sometimes called a **time-series plot**, shows the sampled values of a parameter over time. This plot helps you to judge how quickly the MCMC procedure converges in distribution—that is, how quickly it forgets its starting values.

▶ To view the trace plot, select Trace.

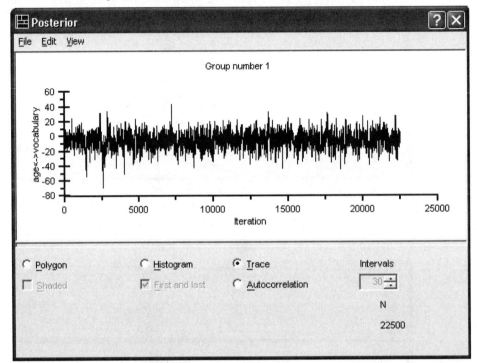

The plot shown here is quite ideal. It exhibits rapid up-and-down variation with no long-term trends or drifts. If we were to mentally break up this plot into a few horizontal sections, the trace within any section would not look much different from the trace in any other section. This indicates that the convergence in distribution takes place rapidly. Long-term trends or drifts in the plot indicate slower convergence. (Note that *long-term* is relative to the horizontal scale of this plot, which depends on the number of samples. As we take more samples, the trace plot gets squeezed together like an accordion, and slow drifts or trends eventually begin to look like rapid up-and-down variation.) The rapid up-and-down motion means that the sampled value at any iteration is unrelated to the sampled value k iterations later, for values of k that are small relative to the total number of samples.

To see how long it takes for the correlations among the samples to die down, we can examine a third plot, called an **autocorrelation plot**. This plot displays the estimated correlation between the sampled value at any iteration and the sampled value k iterations later for $k = 1, 2, 3,\ldots.$

▶ To display this plot, select Autocorrelation.

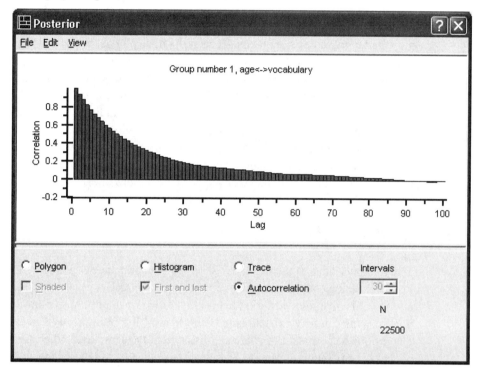

Lag, along the horizontal axis, refers to the spacing at which the correlation is estimated. In ordinary situations, we expect the autocorrelation coefficients to die down and become close to 0, and remain near 0, beyond a certain lag. In the autocorrelation plot shown above, the lag-10 correlation—the correlation between any sampled value and the value drawn 10 iterations later—is approximately 0.50. The lag-35 correlation lies below 0.20, and at lag 90 and beyond, the correlation is effectively 0. This indicates that by 90 iterations, the MCMC procedure has essentially forgotten its starting position, at least as far as this covariance parameter is concerned. Forgetting the starting position is equivalent to convergence in distribution. If we were to examine the autocorrelation plots for the other parameters in the model, we would find that they also effectively die down to 0 by 90 or so iterations. This fact gives us confidence that a burn-in period of 500 samples was more than enough to ensure that convergence in distribution was attained, and that the analysis samples are indeed samples from the true posterior distribution.

In certain pathological situations, the MCMC procedure may converge very slowly or not at all. This may happen in data sets with high proportions of missing values, when the missing values fall in a peculiar pattern, or in models with some parameters that are poorly estimated. If this should happen, the trace plots for one or more parameters in the model will have long-term drifts or trends that do not diminish as more and more samples are taken. Even as the trace plot gets squeezed together like an accordion, the drifts and trends will not go away. In that case, you will probably see that the range of sampled values for the parameter (as indicated by the vertical scale of the trace plot, or by the *S.D.* or the difference between *Min* and *Max* in the Bayesian SEM window) is huge. The autocorrelations may remain high for large lags or may appear to oscillate between positive and negative values for a long time. When this happens, it suggests that the model is too complicated to be supported by the data at hand, and we ought to consider either fitting a simpler model or introducing information about the parameters by specifying a more informative prior distribution.

Bivariate Marginal Posterior Plots

The summary table in the Bayesian SEM window and the frequency polygon in each Posterior dialog box describe the marginal posterior distributions of the estimands, one at a time. The marginal posterior distributions are very important, but they do not reveal relationships that may exist among the estimands. For example, two covariances or regression coefficients may share significance in the sense that either one could plausibly be 0, but both cannot. To help us visualize the relationships among pairs of estimands, Amos provides bivariate marginal posterior plots.

▶ To display the marginal posterior of two parameters, begin by displaying the posterior distribution of one of the parameters (for example, the variance of *age*).

▶ Hold down the control (Ctrl) key on the keyboard and select the second parameter in the summary table (for example, the variance of *vocabulary*).

Amos then displays a three-dimensional surface plot of the marginal posterior distribution of the variances of *age* and *vocabulary*.

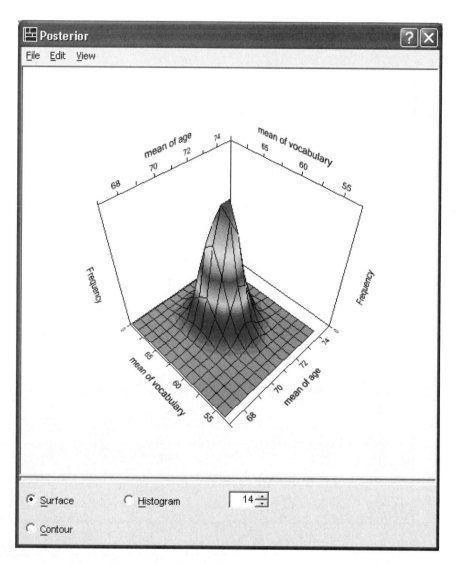

▶ Select Histogram to display a similar plot using vertical blocks.

▶ Select Contour to display a two-dimensional plot of the bivariate posterior density.

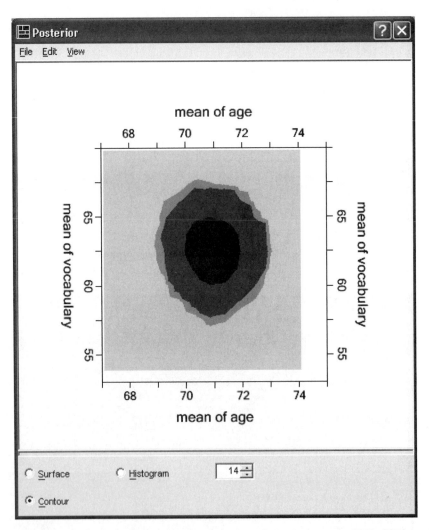

Ranging from dark to light, the three shades of gray represent 50%, 90%, and 95% **credible regions**, respectively. A credible region is conceptually similar to a bivariate confidence region that is familiar to most data analysts acquainted with classical statistical inference methods.

Credible Intervals

Recall that the summary table in the Bayesian SEM window displays the lower and upper endpoints of a Bayesian credible interval for each estimand. By default, Amos presents a 50% interval, which is similar to a conventional 50% confidence interval.

Researchers often report 95% confidence intervals, so you may want to change the boundaries to correspond to a posterior probability content of 95%.

Changing the Confidence Level

▶ Click the Display tab in the Options dialog box.

▶ Type 95 as the Confidence level value.

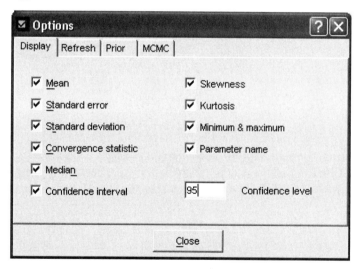

▶ Click the Close button. Amos now displays 95% credible intervals.

		Mean	S.E.	S.D.	C.S.	Median	95% Lower bound	95% Upper bound	Skewness	Kurtosis	Min	Max	Name
Means													
	age	70.969	0.024	0.811	1.000	70.972	69.355	72.561	-0.090	0.355	67.094	74.077	
	vocabulary	62.570	0.055	2.002	1.000	62.566	58.639	66.498	-0.032	0.252	53.845	69.860	
Covariances													
	age<->vocabulary	-6.462	0.334	10.902	1.000	-6.214	-29.046	14.673	-0.160	0.860	-70.086	43.096	
Variances													
	age	26.170	0.328	6.824	1.001	24.979	16.096	42.734	1.213	2.577	12.053	70.861	
	vocabulary	158.773	1.965	39.617	1.001	152.990	99.013	253.774	0.959	1.417	72.285	372.253	

Learning More about Bayesian Estimation

Gill (2004) provides a readable overview of Bayesian estimation and its advantages in a special issue of *Political Analysis*. Jackman (2000) offers a more technical treatment of the topic, with examples, in a journal article format. The book by Gelman, Carlin, Stern, and Rubin (2004) addresses a multitude of practical issues with numerous examples.

Example

27

Bayesian Estimation Using a Non-Diffuse Prior Distribution

Introduction

This example demonstrates using a non-diffuse prior distribution.

About the Example

Example 26 showed how to perform Bayesian estimation for a simple model with the uniform prior distribution that Amos uses by default. In the present example, we consider a more complex model and make use of a non-diffuse prior distribution. In particular, the example shows how to specify a prior distribution so that we avoid negative variance estimates and other improper estimates.

More about Bayesian Estimation

In the discussion of the previous example, we noted that Bayesian estimation depends on information supplied by the analyst in conjunction with data. Whereas maximum likelihood estimation maximizes the likelihood of an unknown parameter θ when given the observed data $\mathbf{y}$ through the relationship $L(\theta|y) \propto p(\mathbf{y}|\theta)$, Bayesian estimation approximates the *posterior density* of $\mathbf{y}$, $p(\theta|y) \propto p(\theta)L(\theta|y)$, where $p(\theta)$ is the *prior distribution* of θ, and $p(\theta|y)$ is the posterior density of θ given $\mathbf{y}$. Conceptually, this means that the posterior density of $\mathbf{y}$ given θ is the product of the prior distribution of θ and the likelihood of the observed data (Jackman, 2000, p. 377).

As the sample size increases, the likelihood function becomes more and more tightly concentrated about the ML estimate. In that case, a diffuse prior tends to be nearly flat or constant over the region where the likelihood is high; the shape of the posterior distribution is largely determined by the likelihood, that is by the data themselves.

Under a uniform prior distribution for θ, $p(\theta)$ is completely flat, and the posterior distribution is simply a re-normalized version of the likelihood. Even under a non-uniform prior distribution, the influence of the prior distribution diminishes as the sample size increases. Moreover, as the sample size increases, the joint posterior distribution for θ comes to resemble a normal distribution. For this reason, Bayesian and classical maximum likelihood analyses yield equivalent asymptotic results (Jackman, 2000). In smaller samples, if you can supply sensible prior information to the Bayesian procedure, the parameter estimates from a Bayesian analysis can be more precise. (The other side of the coin is that a bad prior can do harm by introducing bias.)

Bayesian Analysis and Improper Solutions

One familiar problem in the fitting of latent variable models is the occurrence of **improper solutions** (Chen, Bollen, Paxton, Curran, and Kirby, 2001). An improper solution occurs, for example, when a variance estimate is negative. Such a solution is called *improper* because it is impossible for a variance to be less than 0. An improper solution may indicate that the sample is too small or that the model is wrong. Bayesian estimation cannot help with a bad model, but it can be used to avoid improper solutions that result from the use of small samples. Martin and McDonald (1975), discussing Bayesian estimation for exploratory factor analysis, suggested that estimates can be improved and improper solutions can be avoided by choosing a prior distribution that assigns zero probability to improper solutions. The present example demonstrates Martin and McDonald's approach to avoiding improper solutions by a suitable choice of prior distribution.

About the Data

Jamison and Scogin (1995) conducted an experimental study of the effectiveness of a new treatment for depression in which participants were asked to read and complete the homework exercises in *Feeling Good: The New Mood Therapy* (Burns, 1999). Jamison and Scogin randomly assigned participants to a control condition or an experimental condition, measured their levels of depression, treated the experimental group, and then re-measured participants' depression. The researchers did not rely on a single measure of depression. Instead, they used two well-known depression scales, the Beck Depression Inventory (Beck, 1967) and the Hamilton Rating Scale for Depression (Hamilton, 1960). We will call them **BDI** and **HRSD** for short. The data are in the file *feelinggood.sav.*

Fitting a Model by Maximum Likelihood

The following figure shows the results of using maximum likelihood estimation to fit a model for the effect of treatment (COND) on depression at Time 2. Depression at Time 1 is used as a covariate. At Time 1 and then again at Time 2, *BDI* and *HRSD* are modeled as indicators of a single underlying variable, depression (*DEPR*).

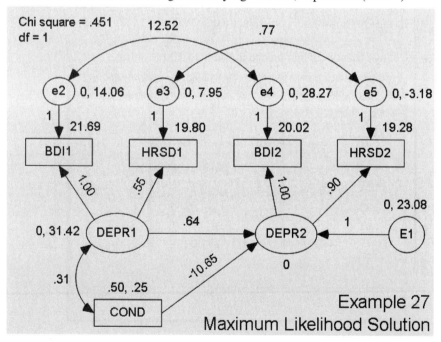

The path diagram for this model is in *Ex27.amw*. The chi-square statistic of 0.059 with one degree of freedom indicates a good fit, but the negative residual variance for post-therapy *HRSD* makes the solution improper.

Example 27

Bayesian Estimation with a Non-Informative (Diffuse) Prior

Does a Bayesian analysis with a diffuse prior distribution yield results similar to those of the maximum likelihood solution? To find out, we will do a Bayesian analysis of the same model. First, we will show how to increase the number of burn-in observations. This is just to show you how to do it. Nothing suggests that the default of 500 burn-in observations needs to be changed.

Changing the Number of Burn-In Observations

To change the number of burn-in observations to 1,000:

▶ From the menus, choose View → Options.

▶ In the Options dialog box, select the MCMC tab.

▶ Change Number of burn-in observations to 1000.

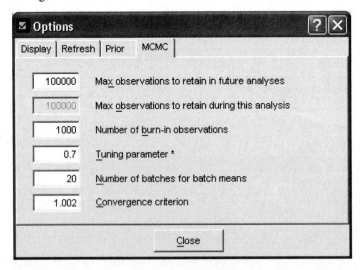

▶ Click Close and allow MCMC sampling to proceed until the unhappy face ☹ turns happy ☺.

The summary table should look something like this:

	Mean	S.E.	S.D.	C.S.	Median	95% Lower bound	95% Upper bound	Skewness	Kurtosis	Min	Max	Name
Regression weights												
HRSD1<--DEPR1	0.525	0.006	0.168	1.001	0.515	0.229	0.886	0.436	0.328	0.107	1.399	
HRSD2<--DEPR2	0.919	0.003	0.105	1.000	0.907	0.745	1.154	0.681	0.833	0.617	1.464	
DEPR2<--COND	-10.383	0.043	1.595	1.000	-10.390	-13.484	-7.241	0.010	0.010	-16.973	-4.704	
DEPR2<--DEPR1	0.599	0.007	0.197	1.001	0.593	0.238	1.010	0.285	0.083	0.045	1.409	
Means												
COND	0.502	0.001	0.058	1.000	0.502	0.388	0.613	-0.045	0.051	0.211	0.729	
Intercepts												
BDI1	21.705	0.013	0.784	1.000	21.696	20.189	23.280	0.062	0.034	18.846	24.966	
HRSD1	19.799	0.008	0.487	1.000	19.799	18.852	20.764	0.023	0.103	17.785	22.004	
BDI2	19.902	0.024	1.244	1.000	19.890	17.446	22.375	0.009	0.229	14.632	26.166	
HRSD2	19.192	0.015	0.820	1.000	19.177	17.587	20.801	-0.003	0.141	15.507	23.146	
Covariances												
COND<->DEPR1	0.344	0.009	0.406	1.000	0.335	-0.429	1.181	0.147	0.240	-1.212	2.203	
e2<->e4	14.123	0.146	5.250	1.000	13.738	4.805	25.660	0.487	0.688	-2.313	40.992	
e3<->e5	1.222	0.068	2.668	1.000	1.333	-4.247	6.063	-0.515	1.760	-15.785	11.580	
Variances												
DEPR1	39.024	0.851	14.328	1.002	36.571	18.194	72.086	1.243	2.972	7.660	120.018	
COND	0.275	0.001	0.046	1.000	0.271	0.200	0.377	0.594	0.554	0.146	0.544	
E1	27.067	0.103	6.706	1.000	26.260	16.333	42.591	0.787	1.145	8.732	71.053	
e2	12.180	0.783	13.675	1.002	14.405	-20.664	33.097	-1.205	3.036	-66.065	56.616	
e3	9.506	0.142	3.805	1.001	9.471	1.863	17.038	-0.048	0.335	-6.715	25.733	
e4	32.888	0.285	8.330	1.001	32.048	18.868	51.593	0.703	1.157	6.626	78.513	
e5	-3.880	0.219	5.256	1.001	-3.324	-15.421	4.898	-0.922	2.654	-36.545	14.380	

Window title: Bayesian SEM
Menu: File Edit View Analyze Help
Toolbar readout: 1.0018
(1,000+53,001) * 4   598   .142   (1,000+53,000) * 4
Group number 1

Example 27

In this analysis, we allowed Amos to reach its default limit of 100,000 MCMC samples. When Amos reaches this limit, it begins a process known as **thinning**. Thinning involves retaining an equally-spaced subset of samples rather than all samples. Amos begins the MCMC sampling process by retaining all samples until the limit of 100,000 samples is reached. At that point, if the data analyst has not halted the sampling process, Amos discards half of the samples by removing every alternate one, so that the lag-1 dependence in the remaining sequence is the same as the lag-2 dependence of the original unthinned sequence. From that point, Amos continues the sampling process, keeping one sample out of every two that are generated, until the upper limit of 100,000 is again reached. At that point, Amos thins the sample a second time and begins keeping one new sample out of every four...and so on.

Why does Amos perform thinning? Thinning reduces the autocorrelation between successive samples, so a thinned sequence of 100,000 samples provides more information than an unthinned sequence of the same length. In the current example, the displayed results are based on 53,000 samples that were collected after 1,000 burn-in samples, for a total of 54,000 samples. However, this is after the sequence of samples has been thinned three times, so that eight samples had to be generated for every one that was kept. If thinning had not been performed, there would have been $1,000 \times 8 = 8,000$ burn-in samples and $53,000 \times 8 = 424,000$ analysis samples.

The results of the Bayesian analysis are very similar to the maximum likelihood results. The posterior *Mean* for the residual variance of *e5* is negative, just as the maximum likelihood estimate is. The posterior distribution itself lies largely to the left of 0.

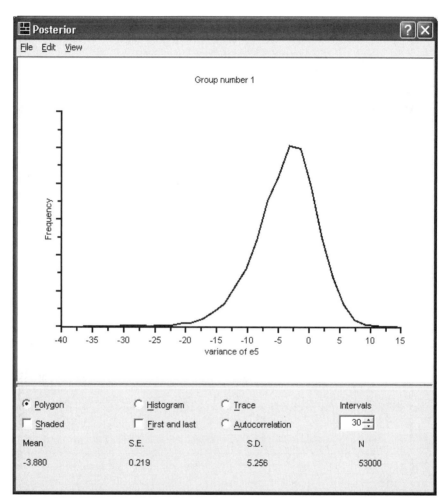

Fortunately, there is a remedy for this problem: Assign a prior density of 0 to any parameter vector for which the variance of *e5* is negative. To change the prior distribution of the variance of *e5*:

▶ From the menus, choose View → Prior.

Alternatively, click the Prior button 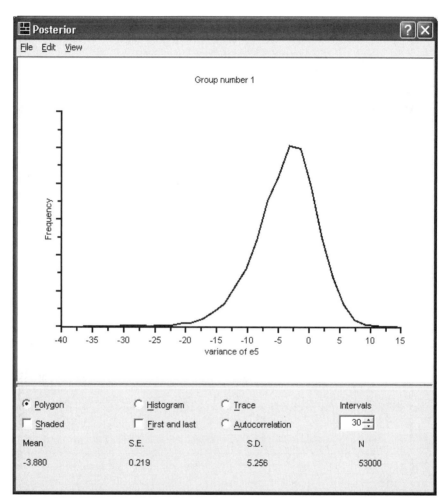 on the Bayesian SEM toolbar, or enter the keyboard combination Ctrl+R. Amos displays the Prior dialog box.

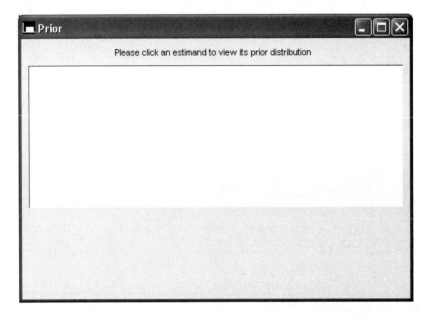

▶ Select the variance of *e5* in the Bayesian SEM window to display the default prior distribution for *e5*.

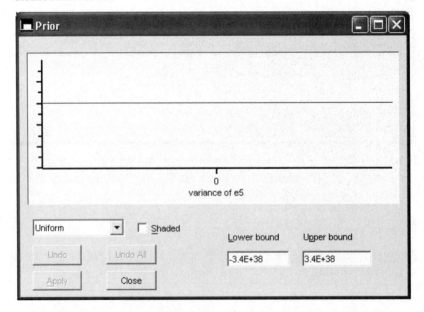

▶ Replace the default lower bound of -3.4×10^{-38} with 0.

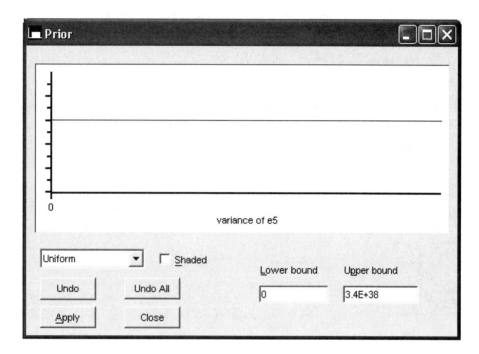

▶ Click Apply to save this change.

Amos immediately discards the accumulated MCMC samples and begins sampling all over again. After a while, the Bayesian SEM window should look something like this:

	Mean	S.E.	S.D.	C.S.	Median	95% Lower bound	95% Upper bound	Skewness	Kurtosis	Min	Max	Name
Regression weights												
HRSD1<--DEPR1	0.498	0.006	0.162	1.001	0.492	0.197	0.844	0.403	0.600	0.089	1.383	
HRSD2<--DEPR2	0.827	0.001	0.066	1.000	0.823	0.706	0.967	0.350	0.483	0.563	1.213	
DEPR2<--COND	-11.280	0.028	1.455	1.000	-11.256	-14.210	-8.506	-0.137	0.241	-17.719	-5.678	
DEPR2<--DEPR1	0.584	0.007	0.193	1.001	0.583	0.208	0.972	0.155	0.135	0.045	1.625	
Means												
COND	0.500	0.001	0.059	1.000	0.501	0.384	0.615	-0.038	0.045	0.244	0.746	
Intercepts												
BDI1	21.685	0.010	0.794	1.000	21.689	20.113	23.247	0.003	0.128	18.220	25.137	
HRSD1	19.799	0.007	0.495	1.000	19.803	18.825	20.760	-0.047	0.121	17.558	21.918	
BDI2	20.325	0.018	1.162	1.000	20.321	18.055	22.607	0.021	0.037	15.499	25.067	
HRSD2	19.110	0.013	0.809	1.000	19.118	17.521	20.667	-0.021	0.069	15.709	22.370	
Covariances												
COND<->DEPR1	0.272	0.006	0.414	1.000	0.260	-0.531	1.127	0.134	0.391	-1.496	2.400	
e2<->e4	10.331	0.099	4.434	1.000	10.105	2.249	19.714	0.316	0.692	-8.257	38.711	
e3<->e5	3.012	0.061	2.189	1.000	2.940	-1.139	7.557	0.194	0.425	-7.271	13.210	
Variances												
DEPR1	41.274	1.011	16.800	1.002	37.954	18.327	86.251	1.353	2.472	3.877	123.457	
COND	0.274	0.001	0.047	1.000	0.269	0.198	0.381	0.724	0.932	0.133	0.552	
E1	27.240	0.138	6.447	1.000	26.492	16.626	41.876	0.649	0.644	6.812	62.578	
e2	8.375	1.004	16.031	1.002	11.618	-37.763	30.435	-1.526	3.207	-74.182	50.045	
e3	10.372	0.133	3.625	1.001	10.286	3.341	17.530	0.070	0.614	-8.973	25.956	
e4	25.173	0.070	5.341	1.000	24.855	15.548	36.595	0.396	0.717	4.618	63.297	
e5	2.380	0.021	1.999	1.000	1.874	0.083	7.411	1.377	2.592	0.000	18.708	

The posterior mean of the variance of *e5* is now positive. Examining its posterior distribution confirms that no sampled values fall below 0.

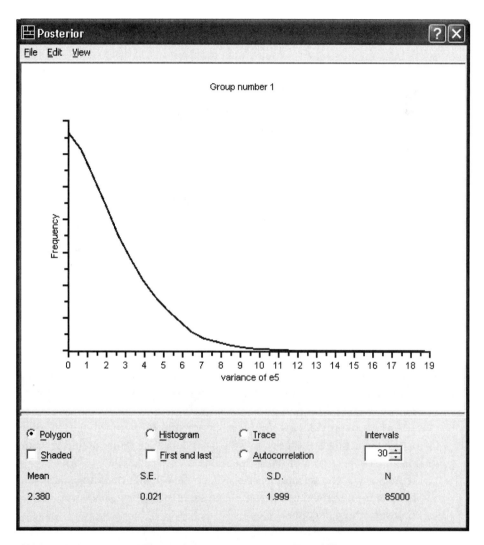

Is this solution proper? The posterior mean of each variance is positive, but a glance at the *Min* column shows that some of the sampled values for the variance of *e2* and the variance of *e3* are negative. To avoid negative variances for *e2* and *e3*, we can modify their prior distributions just as we did for *e5*.

It is not too difficult to impose such constraints on a parameter-by-parameter basis in small models like this one. However, there is also a way to automatically set the prior density to 0 for any parameter values that are improper. To use this feature:

Example 27

▶ From the menus, choose View → Options.

▶ In the Options dialog box, click the Prior tab.

▶ Select Admissibility test. (A check mark will appear next to it.)

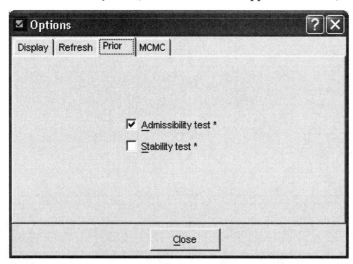

Selecting Admissibility test sets the prior density to 0 for parameter values that result in a model where any covariance matrix fails to be positive definite. In particular, the prior density is set to 0 for non-positive variances.

Amos also provides a stability test option that works much like the admissibility test option. Selecting Stability test sets the prior density to 0 for parameter values that result in an unstable system of linear equations.

As soon as you select Admissibility test, the MCMC sampling starts all over, discarding any previously accumulated samples. After a short time, the results should look something like this:

Bayesian SEM

File   Edit   View   Analyze   Help

1,000+73,001   592   .097   1,000+73,000

Group number 1

	Mean	S.E.	S.D.	C.S.	Median	95% Lower bound	95% Upper bound	Skewness	Kurtosis	Min	Max	Name
Regression weights												
HRSD1<--DEPR1	0.574	0.007	0.137	1.001	0.555	0.358	0.899	0.728	0.481	0.199	1.149	
HRSD2<--DEPR2	0.816	0.002	0.063	1.001	0.812	0.699	0.955	0.285	0.213	0.574	1.089	
DEPR2<--COND	-11.304	0.069	1.396	1.001	-11.261	-14.138	-8.588	-0.094	0.210	-18.362	-6.380	
DEPR2<--DEPR1	0.674	0.008	0.176	1.001	0.662	0.373	1.056	0.606	1.097	0.113	1.512	
Means												
COND	0.496	0.002	0.059	1.001	0.496	0.381	0.612	0.037	-0.065	0.302	0.711	
Intercepts												
BDI1	21.635	0.037	0.808	1.001	21.624	20.041	23.206	-0.085	0.032	18.378	24.665	
HRSD1	19.786	0.016	0.472	1.001	19.787	18.848	20.730	0.011	0.094	17.924	21.653	
BDI2	20.334	0.056	1.153	1.001	20.304	18.088	22.612	0.024	-0.123	16.207	24.285	
HRSD2	19.039	0.036	0.809	1.001	19.056	17.443	20.575	-0.063	-0.105	16.054	21.890	
Covariances												
COND<->DEPR1	0.262	0.021	0.382	1.001	0.260	-0.457	1.057	0.135	0.233	-1.210	1.726	
e2<->e4	11.139	0.213	4.354	1.001	10.854	3.393	20.485	0.383	0.529	-2.302	31.841	
e3<->e5	2.235	0.102	1.813	1.002	2.108	-1.028	6.195	0.364	0.248	-3.058	10.431	
Variances												
DEPR1	33.449	0.549	9.634	1.002	32.785	16.720	54.667	0.421	0.112	7.654	68.491	
COND	0.272	0.002	0.047	1.001	0.267	0.196	0.379	0.701	0.981	0.140	0.527	
E1	26.195	0.237	6.195	1.001	25.553	15.988	40.134	0.685	0.870	10.870	58.234	
e2	16.532	0.340	7.577	1.001	16.049	3.349	32.737	0.402	0.078	0.113	53.330	
e3	8.694	0.164	2.859	1.002	8.787	2.809	14.023	-0.049	0.395	0.004	23.794	
e4	24.459	0.217	5.286	1.001	24.232	14.846	36.060	0.420	0.935	3.736	55.246	
e5	2.755	0.105	2.025	1.001	2.323	0.282	7.964	1.467	3.069	0.006	15.824	

Notice that the analysis took only 73,000 observations to meet the convergence criterion for all estimands. Minimum values for all estimated variances are now positive.

Example
28

Bayesian Estimation of Values Other Than Model Parameters

Introduction

This example shows how to estimate other quantities besides model parameters in a Bayesian analyses.

About the Example

Examples 26 and 27 demonstrated Bayesian analysis. In both of those examples, we were concerned exclusively with estimating model parameters. We may also be interested in estimating other quantities that are functions of the model parameters. For instance, one of the most common uses of structural equation modeling is the simultaneous estimation of direct and indirect effects. In this example, we demonstrate how to estimate the posterior distribution of an indirect effect.

The Wheaton Data Revisited

In Example 6, we profiled the Wheaton et al. (1977) alienation data and described three alternative models for the data. Here, we re-examine Model C from Example 6. The following path diagram is in the file *Ex28.amw*:

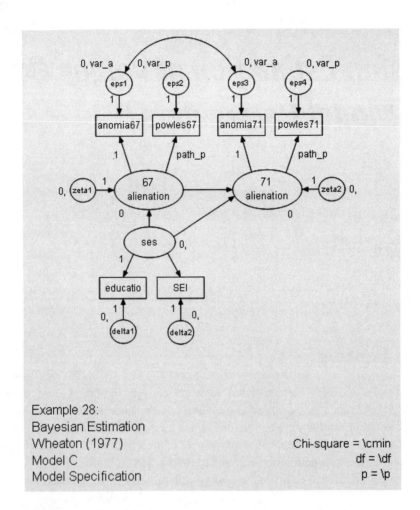

Example 28:
Bayesian Estimation
Wheaton (1977)
Model C
Model Specification

Chi-square = \cmin
df = \df
p = \p

Indirect Effects

Suppose we are interested in the indirect effect of *ses* on *71_alienation* through the mediation of *67_alienation*. In other words, we suspect that socioeconomic status exerts an impact on alienation in 1967, which in turn influences alienation in 1971.

Estimating Indirect Effects

▶ Before starting the Bayesian analysis, from the menus in Amos Graphics, choose View
→ Analysis Properties.

▶ In the Analysis Properties dialog box, click the Output tab.

▶ Select Indirect, direct & total effects and Standardized estimates to estimate standardized
indirect effects. (A check mark will appear next to these options.)

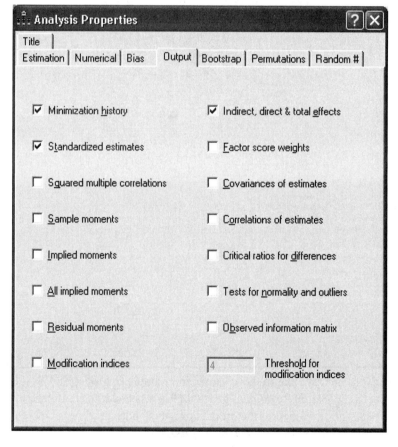

▶ Close the Analysis Properties dialog box.

▶ From the menus, choose Analyze → Calculate Estimates to obtain the maximum likelihood chi-square test of model fit and the parameter estimates.

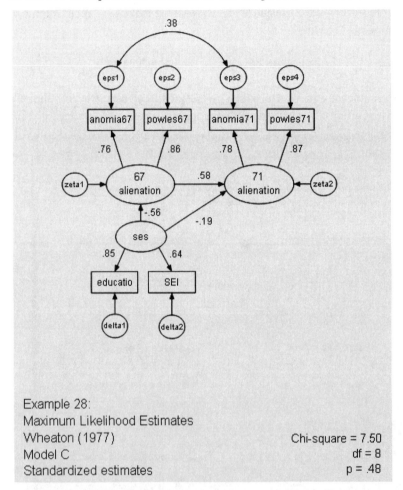

Example 28:
Maximum Likelihood Estimates
Wheaton (1977)
Model C
Standardized estimates

Chi-square = 7.50
df = 8
p = .48

The results are identical to those shown in Example 6, Model C. The standardized direct effect of *ses* on *71_alienation* is –0.19. The standardized indirect effect of *ses* on *71_alienation* is defined as the product of two standardized direct effects: the standardized direct effect of *ses* on *67_alienation* (–0.56) and the standardized direct effect of *67_alienation* on *71_alienation* (0.58). The product of these two standardized direct effects is $-0.56 \times 0.58 = -0.32$.

You do not have to work the standardized indirect effect out by hand. To view all the standardized indirect effects:

▶ From the menus, choose View → Text Output.

▶ In the upper left corner of the Amos Output window, select Estimates, then Matrices, and then Standardized Indirect Effects.

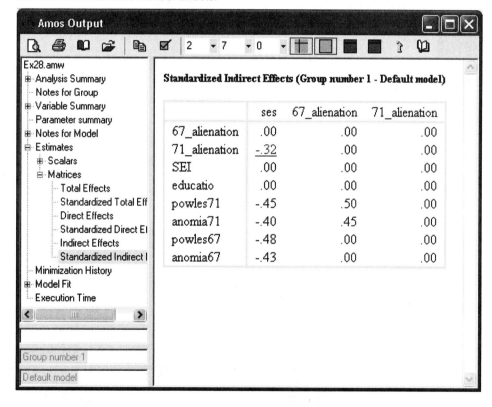

Bayesian Analysis of Model C

To begin Bayesian estimation for Model C:

▶ From the menus, choose Analyze → Bayesian Estimation.

Example 28

The MCMC algorithm converges quite rapidly within 22,000 MCMC samples.

Additional Estimands

The summary table displays results for model parameters only. To estimate the posterior of quantities derived from the model parameters, such as indirect effects:

▶ From the menus, choose View → Additional Estimands.

Estimating the marginal posterior distribution of the additional estimands may take a while. A status window keeps you informed of progress.

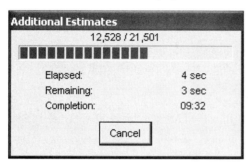

Results are displayed in the Additional Estimands window. To display the posterior mean for each standardized indirect effect:

▶ Select Standardized Indirect Effects and Mean in the panel at the left side of the window.

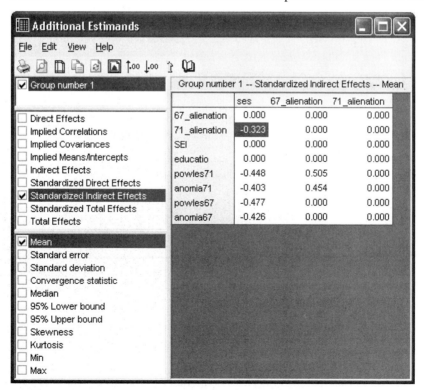

Example 28

▶ To print the results, select the items you want to print. (A check mark will appear next to them).

▶ From the menus, choose File → Print.

Be careful because it is possible to generate a lot of printed output. If you put a check mark in every check box in this example, the program will print $1 \times 8 \times 11 = 88$ matrices.

▶ To view the posterior means of the standardized direct effects, select Standardized Direct Effects and Mean in the panel at the left.

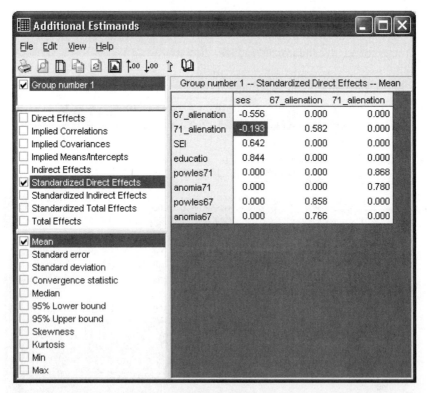

The posterior means of the standardized direct and indirect effects of socioeconomic status on alienation in 1971 are almost identical to the maximum likelihood estimates.

Inferences about Indirect Effects

There are two methods for finding a confidence interval for an indirect effect or for testing an indirect effect for significance. Sobel (1982, 1986) gives a method that assumes that the indirect effect is normally distributed. A growing body of statistical simulation literature calls into question this assumption, however, and advocates the use of the bootstrap to construct better, typically asymmetric, confidence intervals (MacKinnon, Lockwood, and Williams, 2004; Shrout and Bolger, 2002). These studies have found that the bias-corrected bootstrap confidence intervals available in Amos produce reliable inferences for indirect effects.

As an alternative to the Sobel method and the bootstrap for finding confidence intervals, Amos can provide (typically asymmetric) credible intervals for standardized or unstandardized indirect effects. The next figure shows the lower boundary of a 95% credible interval for each standardized indirect effect in the model. Notice that 95% Lower bound is selected in the panel at the left of the Additional Estimands window. (You can specify a value other than 95% in the Bayesian Sem Options dialog box.)

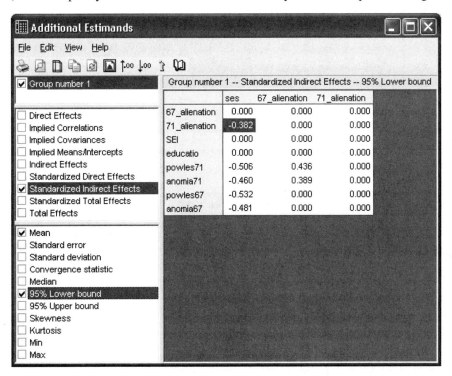

Example 28

The lower boundary of the 95% credible interval for the indirect effect of socioeconomic status on alienation in 1971 is –0.382. The corresponding upper boundary value is –0.270, as shown below:

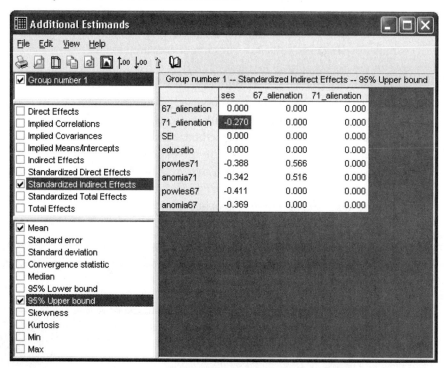

We are now 95% certain that the true value of this standardized indirect effect lies between –0.382 and –0.270. To view the posterior distribution:

▶ From the menus in the Additional Estimands window, choose View → Posterior.

At first, Amos displays an empty posterior window.

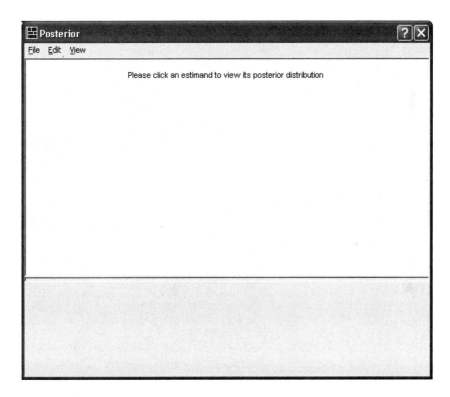

▶ Select Mean and Standardized Indirect Effect in the Additional Estimands window.

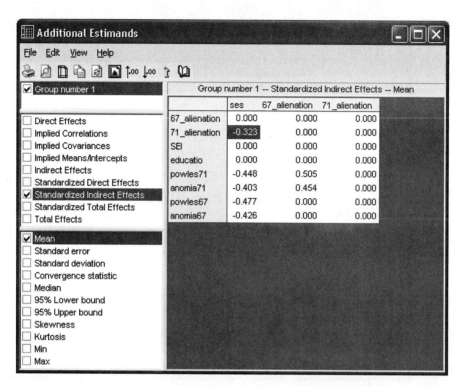

Amos then displays the posterior distribution of the indirect effect of socioeconomic status on alienation in 1971. The distribution of the indirect effect is approximately, but not exactly, normal.

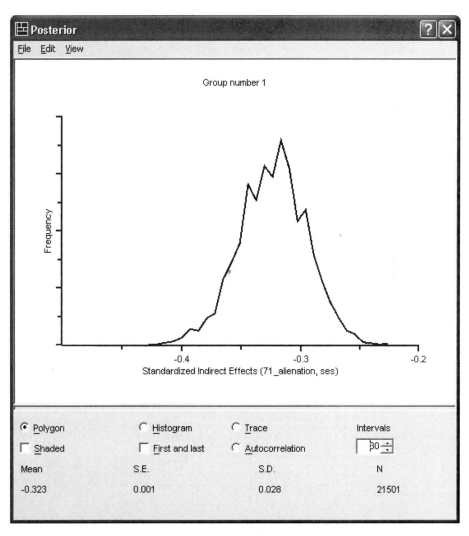

The skewness of the mean of the indirect effect values is –0.13; the kurtosis is 0.02. These values indicate very mild non-normality of the distribution of the mean indirect effect values.

Example

29

Estimating a User-Defined Quantity in Bayesian SEM

Introduction

This example shows how to estimate a user-defined quantity: in this case, the difference between a direct effect and an indirect effect.

About the Example

In the previous example, we showed how to use the Additional Estimands feature of Amos Bayesian analysis to estimate an indirect effect. Suppose you wanted to carry the analysis a step further and address a commonly asked research question: How does an indirect effect compare to the corresponding direct effect?

The Stability of the Alienation Model

You can use the Custom Estimands feature of Amos to estimate and draw inferences about an arbitrary function of the model parameters. To illustrate the Custom Estimands feature, let us revisit the previous example. The path diagram for the model is shown on p. 442 and can be found in the file *Ex29.amw*. The model allows socioeconomic status to exert a direct effect on alienation experienced in 1971. It also allows an indirect effect that is mediated by alienation experienced in 1967.

The remainder of this example focuses on the direct effect, the indirect effect, and a comparison of the two. Notice that we supplied parameter labels for the direct effect ("*c*") and the two components of the indirect effect ("*a*" and "*b*"). Although not required, parameter labels make it easier to specify custom estimands.

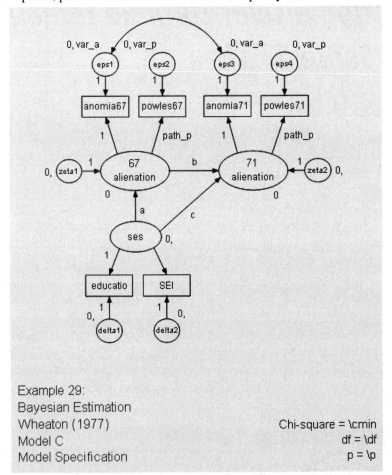

Example 29:
Bayesian Estimation
Wheaton (1977)   Chi-square = \cmin
Model C   df = \df
Model Specification   p = \p

To begin a Bayesian analysis of this model:

▶ From the menus, choose Analyze → Bayesian Estimation.

After a while, the Bayesian SEM window should look something like this:

Bayesian SEM

File   Edit   View   Analyze   Help

1.0016

500+29,501   1422   .146   500+29,500

Group number 1

	Mean	S.E.	S.D.	C.S.	Median	95% Lower bound	95% Upper bound	Skewness	Kurtosis	Min	Max	Name
Regression weights												
powles71<--71_alienation	1.000	0.002	0.041	1.001	0.998	0.926	1.086	0.229	-0.103	0.869	1.165	path_p
71_alienation<--67_alienation	0.604	0.002	0.046	1.001	0.603	0.516	0.693	0.063	-0.091	0.445	0.761	b
71_alienation<--ses	-0.206	0.002	0.049	1.001	-0.204	-0.306	-0.117	-0.245	0.181	-0.414	-0.070	c
67_alienation<--ses	-0.561	0.002	0.054	1.001	-0.560	-0.671	-0.460	-0.066	-0.053	-0.766	-0.374	a
SEI<--ses	5.201	0.020	0.433	1.001	5.194	4.377	6.061	0.129	0.175	3.735	7.053	
Intercepts												
anomia67	13.610	0.006	0.113	1.001	13.613	13.373	13.827	-0.122	-0.121	13.233	13.972	
powles67	14.760	0.004	0.106	1.001	14.760	14.549	14.965	-0.060	-0.269	14.431	15.110	
anomia71	14.132	0.005	0.118	1.001	14.135	13.896	14.361	-0.105	-0.229	13.683	14.522	
powles71	14.896	0.004	0.104	1.001	14.899	14.687	15.099	-0.039	-0.155	14.517	15.277	
educatio	10.898	0.005	0.100	1.001	10.900	10.700	11.093	-0.020	-0.018	10.438	11.250	
SEI	37.486	0.034	0.690	1.001	37.492	36.145	38.820	-0.024	-0.147	35.112	39.925	
Covariances												
eps1<->eps3	1.889	0.012	0.253	1.001	1.888	1.392	2.378	-0.002	0.164	1.015	2.911	
Variances												
eps1	4.976	0.015	0.299	1.001	4.964	4.403	5.605	0.127	0.156	3.962	6.082	var_a
eps2	2.454	0.010	0.228	1.001	2.453	1.997	2.898	-0.006	-0.035	1.586	3.339	var_p
ses	6.857	0.030	0.676	1.001	6.825	5.587	8.285	0.200	-0.113	4.534	9.483	
zeta1	4.847	0.024	0.432	1.002	4.827	4.052	5.751	0.178	-0.150	3.445	6.307	
zeta2	3.833	0.018	0.328	1.002	3.818	3.233	4.527	0.281	0.263	2.811	5.443	
delta1	2.775	0.024	0.518	1.001	2.788	1.729	3.763	-0.149	-0.052	1.016	4.610	
delta2	267.467	0.807	17.530	1.001	267.373	235.028	301.055	0.066	-0.134	209.770	325.935	

Example 29

▶ From the menus, choose View → Additional Estimands.

▶ In the Additional Estimands window, select Standardized Direct Effects and Mean.

The posterior mean for the direct effect of *ses* on *71_alienation* is –0.195.

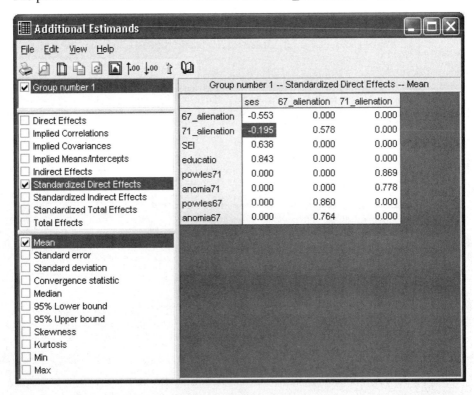

▶ Select Standardized Indirect Effects and Mean.

The indirect effect of socioeconomic status on alienation in 1971 is –0.320.

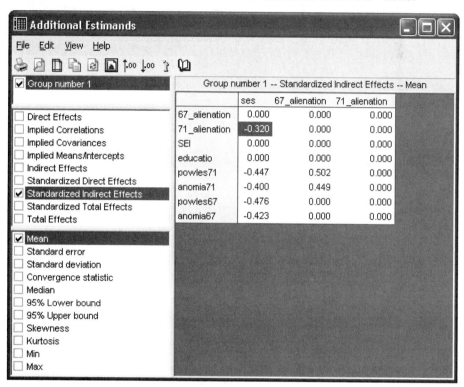

The posterior distribution of the indirect effect lies entirely to the left of 0, so we are practically certain that the indirect effect is less than 0.

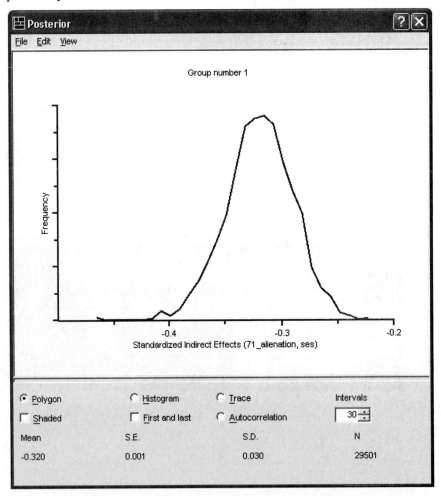

You can also display the posterior distribution of the direct effect. The program does not, however, have any built-in way to examine the posterior distribution of the difference between the indirect effect and the direct effect (or perhaps their ratio). This is a case of wanting to estimate and draw inferences about a quantity that the developers of the program did not anticipate. For this, you need to extend the capabilities of Amos by defining your own **custom estimand**.

Numeric Custom Estimands

In this section, we show how to write a Visual Basic program for estimating the numeric difference between a direct effect and an indirect effect. (You can use C# instead of Visual Basic.) The final Visual Basic program is in the file *Ex29.vb*.

The first step in writing a program to define a custom estimand is to open the custom estimands window.

▶ From the menus on the Bayesian SEM window, choose View → Custom estimands.

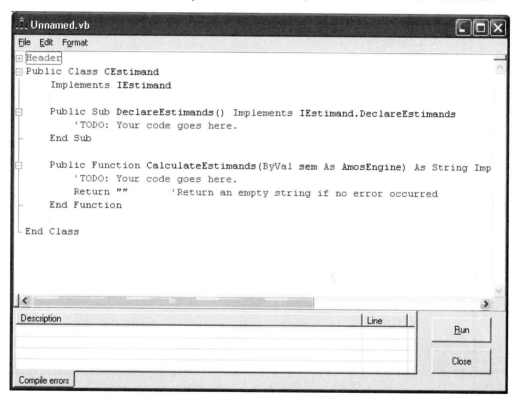

This window displays a skeleton Visual Basic program to which we will add lines to define the new quantities that we want Amos to estimate.

Note: If you want to use C# instead of Visual Basic, from the menus, choose File → New C# plug-in.

The skeleton program contains a subroutine and a function. You have no control over when the subroutine and the function are called. They are called by Amos.

■ Amos calls your DeclareEstimands subroutine once to find out how many new quantities (estimands) you want to estimate and what you want to call them.

■ Amos calls your CalculateEstimands function repeatedly. Each time your CalculateEstimands function is called, Amos has to calculate the value of your custom estimands for a given set of parameter values.

Only the first line of the DeclareEstimands subroutine is shown initially.

▶ To display all of the lines, double-click Sub DeclareEstimands or click the + sign in the little box at the beginning of the line.

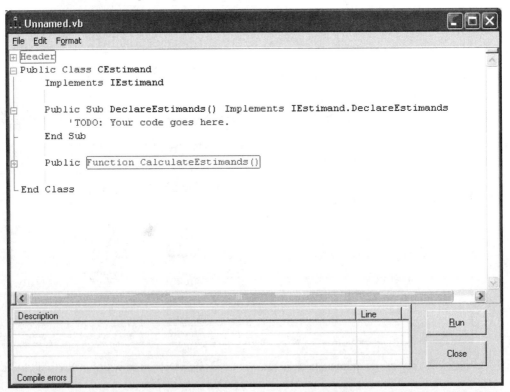

You need to replace the placeholder 'TODO: Your code goes here with lines that specify how many new quantities you want to estimate and what you want to call them. For this example, we want to estimate the difference between the direct effect of *ses* on *71_alienation* and the corresponding indirect effect. We will also write code for computing the direct effect and the indirect individually, but this is only to show how to do it. The direct effect and the indirect effect individually can be estimated without defining them as custom estimands. To define each estimand, we use the keyword newestimand, as shown below:

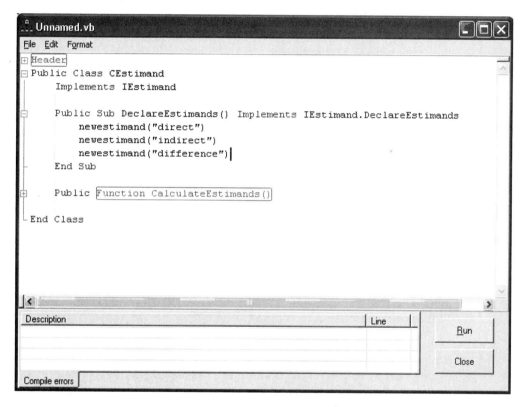

The words "direct", "indirect", and "difference" are estimand labels. You can use different labels.

The function CalculateEstimands computes the values of the estimands defined in the DeclareEstimands subroutine. Only the first line of the function is shown.

▶ To display all of the lines, double-click Function CalculateEstimands or click the + sign in the little box at the beginning of the line.

Example 29

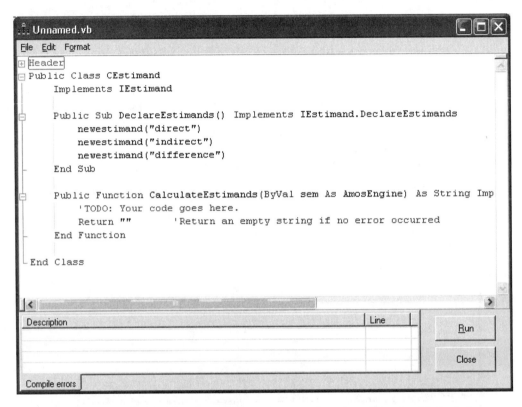

The placeholder 'TODO: Your code goes here needs to be replaced with lines for evaluating the estimands called "direct", "indirect" and "difference".

We start by writing Visual Basic code for computing the direct effect. In the following figure, we have already typed part of a Visual Basic statement: estimand("direct") .value =.

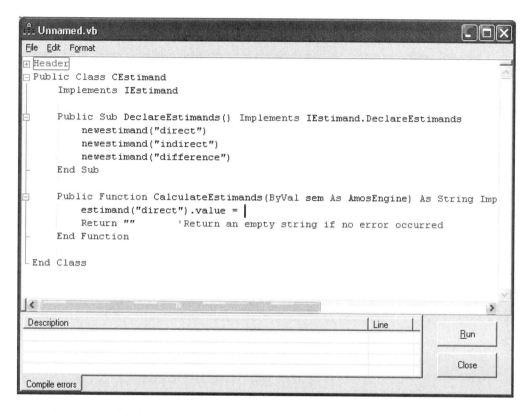

We need to finish the statement by adding additional code to the right of the equals (=) sign, describing how to compute the direct effect. The direct effect is to be calculated for a set of parameter values that are accessible through the AmosEngine object that is supplied as an argument to the CalculateEstimands function. Unless you are an expert Amos programmer, you would not know how to use the AmosEngine object; however, there is an easy way to get the needed Visual Basic syntax by dragging and dropping.

Dragging and Dropping

▶ Find the direct effect in the Bayesian SEM window and click to select its row. (Its row is highlighted in the following figure.)

▶ Move the mouse pointer to an edge of the selected row. Either the top edge or the bottom edge will do.

Tip: When you get the mouse pointer on the right spot, a plus (+) symbol will appear next to the mouse pointer.

	Mean	S.E.	S.D.	C.S.	Median	95% Lower bound	95% Upper bound	Skewness	Kurtosis	Min	Max	Name
Regression weights												
powles71<--71_alienation	1.000	0.002	0.041	1.001	0.998	0.926	1.086	0.229	-0.103	0.869	1.165	path_p
71_alienation<--67_alienation	0.604	0.002	0.046	1.001	0.603	0.516	0.693	0.063	-0.091	0.445	0.761	b
71_alienation<--ses	-0.206	0.002	0.049	1.001	-0.204	-0.306	-0.117	-0.245	0.181	-0.414	-0.070	c
67_alienation<--ses	-0.561	0.002	0.054	1.001	-0.560	-0.671	-0.460	-0.066	-0.053	-0.766	-0.374	a
SEI<--ses	5.201	0.020	0.433	1.001	5.194	4.377	6.061	0.129	0.175	3.735	7.053	
Intercepts												
anomia67	13.610	0.006	0.113	1.001	13.613	13.373	13.827	-0.122	-0.121	13.233	13.972	
powles67	14.760	0.004	0.106	1.001	14.760	14.549	14.965	-0.060	-0.269	14.431	15.110	
anomia71	14.132	0.005	0.118	1.001	14.135	13.896	14.361	-0.105	-0.229	13.683	14.522	
powles71	14.896	0.004	0.104	1.001	14.899	14.687	15.099	-0.039	-0.155	14.517	15.277	
educatio	10.898	0.005	0.100	1.001	10.900	10.700	11.093	-0.020	-0.018	10.438	11.250	
SEI	37.486	0.034	0.690	1.001	37.492	36.145	38.820	-0.024	-0.147	35.112	39.925	
Covariances												
eps1<->eps3	1.889	0.012	0.253	1.001	1.888	1.392	2.378	-0.002	0.164	1.015	2.911	
Variances												
eps1	4.976	0.015	0.299	1.001	4.964	4.403	5.605	0.127	0.156	3.962	6.082	var_a
eps2	2.454	0.010	0.228	1.001	2.453	1.997	2.898	-0.006	-0.035	1.586	3.339	var_p
ses	6.857	0.030	0.676	1.001	6.825	5.587	8.285	0.200	-0.113	4.534	9.483	
zeta1	4.847	0.024	0.432	1.002	4.827	4.052	5.751	0.178	-0.150	3.445	6.307	
zeta2	3.833	0.018	0.328	1.002	3.818	3.233	4.527	0.281	0.263	2.811	5.443	
delta1	2.775	0.024	0.518	1.001	2.788	1.729	3.763	-0.149	-0.052	1.016	4.610	
delta2	267.467	0.807	17.530	1.001	267.373	235.028	301.055	0.066	-0.134	209.770	325.935	

▶ Hold down the left mouse button, drag the mouse pointer into the Visual Basic window to the spot where you want the expression for the direct effect to go, and release the mouse button.

When you complete this operation, Amos fills in the appropriate parameter expression, as shown in the next figure:

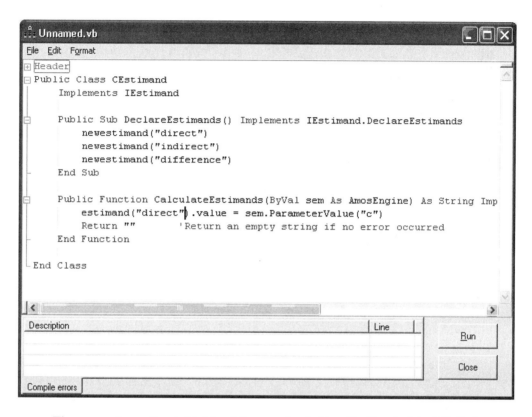

The parameter on the right side of the equation is identified by the label (*"c"*) that was used in the path diagram shown earlier.

We next turn our attention to calculating the indirect effect of socioeconomic status on alienation in 1971. This indirect effect is defined as the product of its two direct effects, the direct effect of socioeconomic status on alienation in 1967 (parameter *a*) and the direct effect of alienation in 1967 on alienation in 1971 (parameter *b*).

▶ On the left side of the Visual Basic assignment statement for computing the indirect effect, type estimand("indirect") .value =.

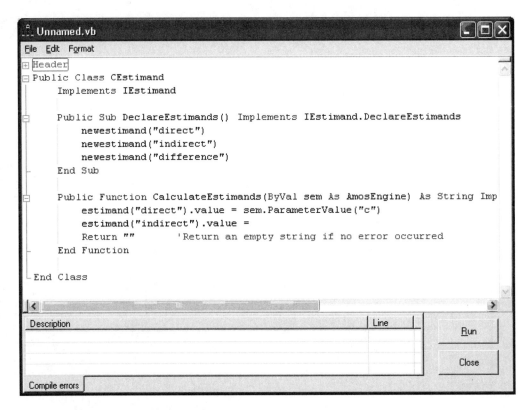

Using the same drag-and-drop process as previously described, start dragging things from the Bayesian SEM window to the Unnamed.vb window.

▶ First, drag the direct effect of socioeconomic status on alienation in 1967 to the right side of the equals sign in the unfinished statement.

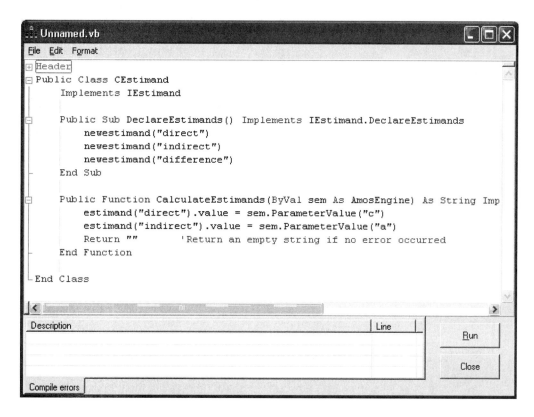

▶ Next, drag and drop the direct effect of 1967 alienation on 1971alienation.

This second direct effect appears in the Unnamed.vb window as sem.ParameterValue("b").

Example 29

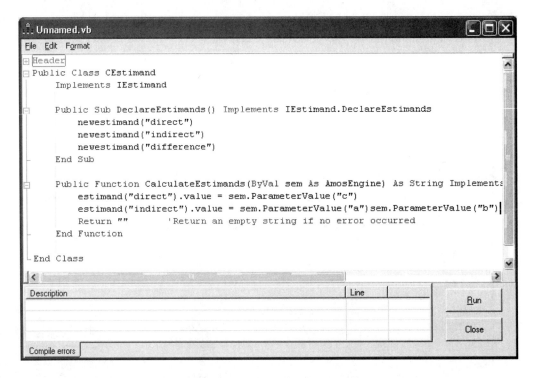

▶ Finally, use the keyboard to insert an asterisk (*) between the two parameter values.

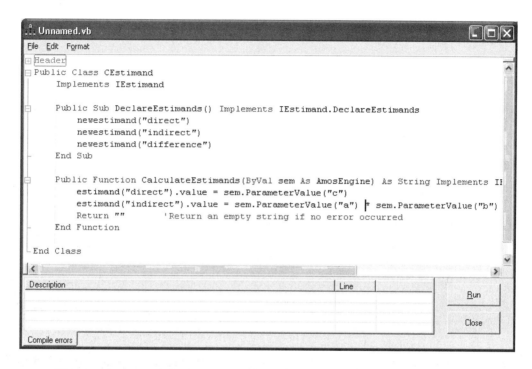

Hint: For complicated custom estimands, you can also drag and drop from the Additional Estimands window to the Custom Estimands window.

To compute the difference between the direct and indirect effects, add a third line of Visual Basic syntax, as seen in the following figure:

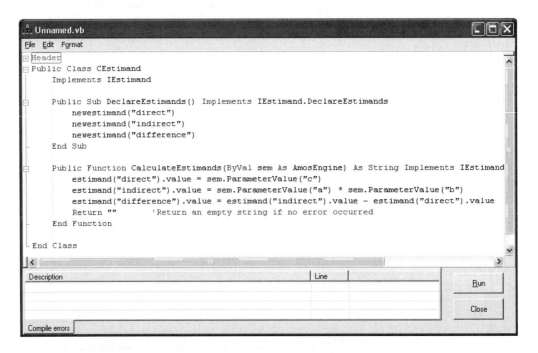

▶ To find the posterior distribution of all three custom estimands, click Run.

The results will take a few seconds. A status window keeps you informed of progress.

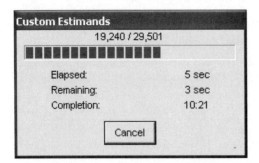

The marginal posterior distributions of the three custom estimands are summarized in the following table:

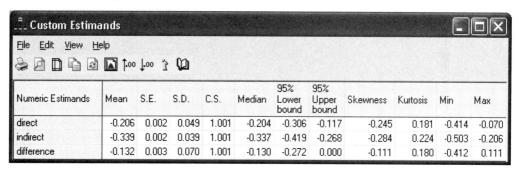

Numeric Estimands	Mean	S.E.	S.D.	C.S.	Median	95% Lower bound	95% Upper bound	Skewness	Kurtosis	Min	Max
direct	-0.206	0.002	0.049	1.001	-0.204	-0.306	-0.117	-0.245	0.181	-0.414	-0.070
indirect	-0.339	0.002	0.039	1.001	-0.337	-0.419	-0.268	-0.284	0.224	-0.503	-0.206
difference	-0.132	0.003	0.070	1.001	-0.130	-0.272	0.000	-0.111	0.180	-0.412	0.111

The results for *direct* can also be found in the Bayesian SEM summary table, and the results for *indirect* can be found in the Additional Estimands table. We are really interested in *difference*. Its posterior mean is –0.132. Its minimum is –0.412, and its maximum is 0.111.

▶ To see its marginal posterior, from the menus, choose View → Posterior.

▶ Select the *difference* row in the Custom Estimands table.

Example 29

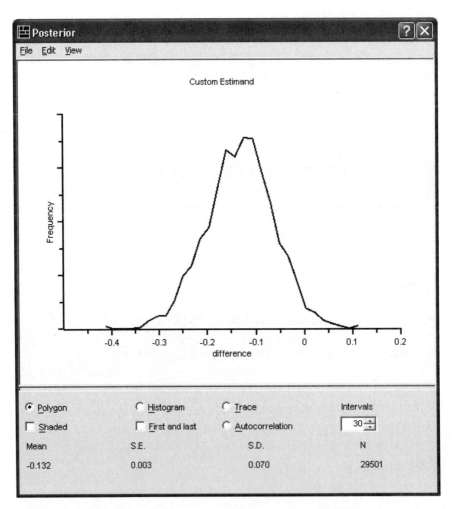

Most of the area lies to the left of 0, meaning that the difference is almost sure to be negative. In other words, it is almost certain that the indirect effect is more negative than the direct effect. Eyeballing the posterior, perhaps 95% or so of the area lies to the left of 0, so there is about a 95% chance that the indirect effect is larger than the direct effect. It is not necessary to rely on *eyeballing* the posterior, however. There is a way to find any area under a marginal posterior or, more generally, to estimate the probability that any proposition about the parameters is true.

Dichotomous Custom Estimands

Visual inspection of the frequency polygon reveals that the majority of *difference* values are negative, but it does not tell us exactly what proportion of values are negative. That proportion is our estimate of the probability that the indirect effect exceeds the direct effect. To estimate probabilities like these, we can use **dichotomous estimands.** In Visual Basic (or C#) programs, dichotomous estimands are just like numeric estimands except that dichotomous estimands take on only two values: true and false. In order to estimate the probability that the indirect effect is more negative than the direct effect, we need to define a function of the model parameters that is true when the indirect effect is more negative than the direct effect and is false otherwise.

Defining a Dichotomous Estimand

▶ Name each dichotomous estimand in the DeclareEstimands subroutine. For purposes of illustration, we will declare two dichotomous estimands, calling them "indirect is less than zero" and "indirect is smaller than direct".

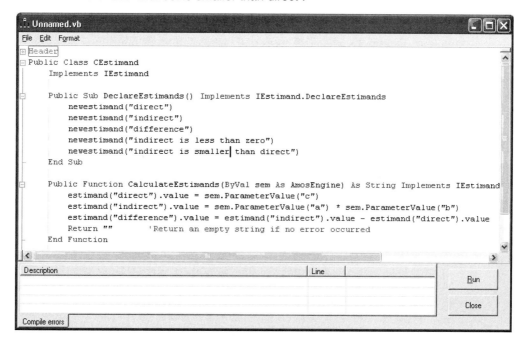

▶ Add lines to the CalculateEstimates function specifying how to compute them.

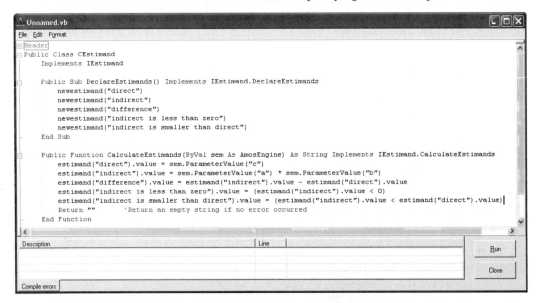

```
Unnamed.vb
File   Edit   Format
 Header
Public Class CEstimand
    Implements IEstimand

    Public Sub DeclareEstimands() Implements IEstimand.DeclareEstimands
        newestimand("direct")
        newestimand("indirect")
        newestimand("difference")
        newestimand("indirect is less than zero")
        newestimand("indirect is smaller than direct")
    End Sub

    Public Function CalculateEstimands(ByVal sem As AmosEngine) As String Implements IEstimand.CalculateEstimands
        estimand("direct").value = sem.ParameterValue("c")
        estimand("indirect").value = sem.ParameterValue("a") * sem.ParameterValue("b")
        estimand("difference").value = estimand("indirect").value - estimand("direct").value
        estimand("indirect is less than zero").value = (estimand("indirect").value < 0)
        estimand("indirect is smaller than direct").value = (estimand("indirect").value < estimand("direct").value)
        Return ""        'Return an empty string if no error occurred
    End Function
```

Description	Line	
		Run
		Close

Compile errors

In this example, the first dichotomous custom estimand is true when the value of the indirect effect is less than 0. The second dichotomous custom estimand is true when the indirect effect is smaller than the direct effect.

▶ Click the Run button.

Amos evaluates the truth of each logical expression for each MCMC sample drawn. When the analysis finishes, Amos reports the proportion of MCMC samples in which each expression was found to be true. These proportions appear in the *Dichotomous Estimands* section of the Custom Estimands summary table.

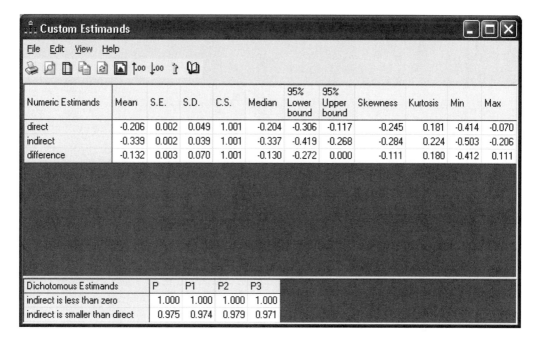

The *P* column shows the proportion of times that each evaluated expression was true in the whole series of MCMC samples. In this example, the number of MCMC samples was 29,501, so *P* is based on approximately 30,000 samples. The *P1*, *P2*, and *P3* columns show the proportion of times each logical expression was true in the first third, the middle third, and the final third of the MCMC samples. In this illustration, each of these proportions is based upon approximately 10,000 MCMC samples.

Based on the proportions in the *Dichotomous Estimands* area of the Custom Estimands window, we can say with near certainty that the indirect effect is negative. This is consistent with the frequency polygon on p. 446 that showed no MCMC samples with an indirect effect value greater than or equal to 0.

Similarly, the probability is about 0.975 that the indirect effect is larger (more negative) than the direct effect. The 0.975 is only an estimate of the probability. It is a proportion based on 29,501 correlated observations. However it appears to be a good estimate because the proportions from the first third (0.974), middle third (0.979) and final third (0.971) are so close together.

Example

30

Data Imputation

Introduction

This example demonstrates multiple imputation in a factor analysis model.

About the Example

Example 17 showed how to fit a model using maximum likelihood when the data contain missing values. Amos can also *impute* values for those that are missing. In data imputation, each missing value is replaced by some numeric guess. Once each missing value has been replaced by an imputed value, the resulting completed dataset can be analyzed by data analysis methods that are designed for complete data. Amos provides three methods of data imputation.

- In **regression imputation**, the model is first fitted using maximum likelihood. After that, model parameters are set equal to their maximum likelihood estimates, and linear regression is used to predict the unobserved values for each case as a linear combination of the observed values for that same case. Predicted values are then plugged in for the missing values.

- **Stochastic regression imputation** (Little and Rubin, 2002) imputes values for each case by drawing, at random, from the conditional distribution of the missing values given the observed values, with the unknown model parameters set equal to their maximum likelihood estimates. Because of the random element in stochastic regression imputation, repeating the imputation process many times will produce a different completed dataset each time.

■ **Bayesian imputation** is like stochastic regression imputation except that it takes into account the fact that the parameter values are only estimated and not known.

Multiple Imputation

In **multiple imputation** (Schafer, 1997), a nondeterministic imputation method (either stochastic regression imputation or Bayesian imputation) is used to create multiple completed datasets. While the observed values never change, the imputed values vary from one completed dataset to the next. Once the completed datasets have been created, each completed dataset is analyzed alone. For example, if there are *m* completed datasets, then there will be *m* separate sets of results, each containing estimates of various quantities along with estimated standard errors. Because the *m* completed datasets are different from each other, the *m* sets of results will also differ from one to the next.

After each of the *m* completed datasets has been analyzed alone, the data analyst has *m* sets of estimates and standard errors that must be combined into a single set of results. Well-known formulas attributed to Rubin (1987) are available for combining the results from multiple completed datasets. Those formulas will be used in Example 31.

Model-Based Imputation

In this example, imputation is performed using a factor analysis model. Model-based imputation has two advantages. First, you can impute values for any latent variables in the model. Second, if the model is correct and has positive degrees of freedom, the implied covariance matrix and implied means will be estimated more accurately than with a saturated model. (Imputation is based on the implied covariance matrix and means.) However, a saturated model like the model in Example 1 can be used for imputation when no other model is appropriate.

Performing Multiple Data Imputation Using Amos Graphics

For this example, we will perform Bayesian multiple imputation using the confirmatory factor analysis model from Example 17. The dataset is the incomplete Holzinger and Swineford (1939) dataset in the file *grant_x.sav*. The imputation of missing values is only the first step in obtaining useful results from multiple imputation. Eventually, all three of the following steps need to be carried out.

- Step 1: Use the Data Imputation feature of Amos to create *m* complete data files.
- Step 2: Perform an analysis of each of the *m* completed data files separately.

  Performing this analysis is up to you. You can perform the analysis in Amos but, typically, you would use some other program. For purposes of this example and the next, we will use SPSS to carry out a regression analysis in which one variable (*sentence*) is used to predict another variable (*wordmean*). Specifically, we will focus on the estimation of the regression weight and its standard error.

- Step 3: Combine the results from the analyses of the *m* data files.

  This example covers the first step. Steps 2 and 3 will be covered in Example 31.

▶ To generate the completed data files, open the Amos Graphics file *Ex30.amw*.

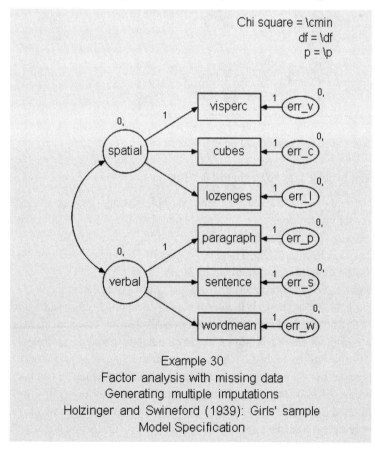

Example 30
Factor analysis with missing data
Generating multiple imputations
Holzinger and Swineford (1939): Girls' sample
Model Specification

Example 30

▶ From the menus, choose Analyze → Data Imputation.

Amos displays the Amos Data Imputation window.

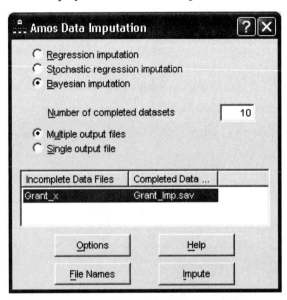

▶ Make sure that Bayesian imputation is selected.

▶ Set Number of completed datasets to 10. (This sets $m = 10$.)

You might suppose that a large number of completed data files are needed. It turns out that, in most applications, very few completed data files are needed. Five to 10 completed data files are generally sufficient to obtain accurate parameter estimates and standard errors (Rubin, 1987). There is no penalty for using more than 10 imputations except for the clerical effort involved in Steps 2 and 3.

Amos can save the completed datasets in a single file (Single output file) with the completed datasets stacked, or it can save each completed dataset in a separate file (Multiple output files). In a single-group analysis, selecting Single output file yields one output data file, whereas selecting Multiple output files yields m separate data files.

In a multiple-group analysis, when you select the Single output file option, you get a separate output file for each analysis group; if you select the Multiple output files option, you get m output files per group. For instance, if you had four groups and requested five completed datasets, then selecting Single output file would give you four output files, and selecting Multiple output files would give you 20. Since we are going to use

SPSS to analyze the completed datasets, the simplest thing would be to select Single output file. Then, the *split file* capability of SPSS could be used in Step 2 to analyze each completed dataset separately. However, to make it easy to replicate this example using any regression program:

▶ Select Multiple output files.

You can save imputed data in two file formats: plain text or SPSS.

▶ Click File Names to display a Save As dialog box.

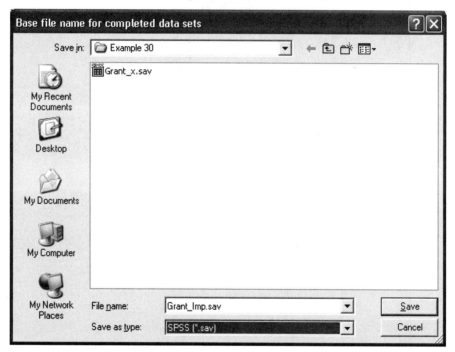

▶ In the File name text box, you can specify a prefix name for the imputed datasets. Here, we have specified *Grant_Imp*.

Amos will name the imputed data files *Grant_Imp1*, *Grant_Imp2*, and so on through *Grant_Imp10*.

▶ Use the Save as type drop-down list to select plain text (*.txt*) or SPSS data file format (*.sav*).

▶ Click Save.

▶ Click Options in the Data Imputation window to display the available imputation options.

The online Help explains these options. To get an explanation of an option, place your mouse pointer over the option in question and press the F1 key. The figure below shows how the number of observations can be changed from 10,000 (the default) to 30,000.

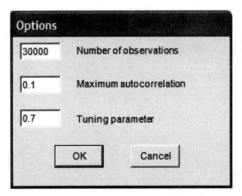

▶ Close the Options dialog box and click the Impute button in the Data Imputation window. After a short time, the following message appears:

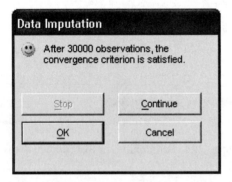

▶ Click OK.

Amos lists the names of the completed data files.

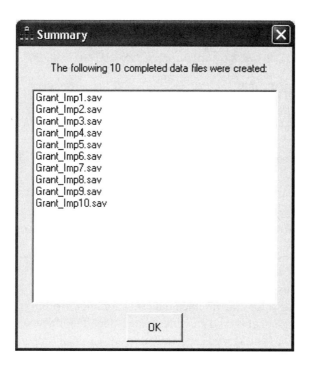

Each completed data file contains 73 complete cases. Here is a view of the first few records of the first completed data file, *Grant_Imp1.sav*:

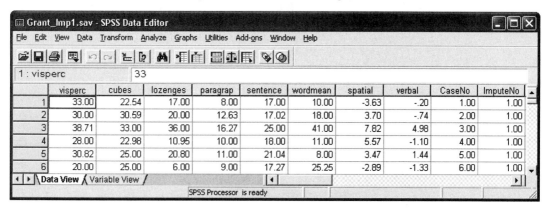

Example 30

Here is an identical view of the second completed data file, *Grant_Imp2.sav*:

	visperc	cubes	lozenges	paragrap	sentence	wordmean	spatial	verbal	CaseNo	ImputeNo
1	33.00	25.34	17.00	8.00	17.00	10.00	-.86	-3.05	1.00	2.00
2	30.00	33.61	20.00	9.67	19.98	18.00	.50	-2.97	2.00	2.00
3	40.84	33.00	36.00	19.57	25.00	41.00	14.18	10.10	3.00	2.00
4	28.00	24.06	22.37	10.00	18.00	11.00	-1.07	-1.59	4.00	2.00
5	28.04	25.00	11.10	11.00	24.08	8.00	3.77	.06	5.00	2.00
6	20.00	25.00	6.00	9.00	23.24	28.68	-2.84	1.13	6.00	2.00

The values in the first two cases for *visperc* were observed in the original data file and therefore do not change across the imputed data files. By contrast, the values for these cases for *cubes* were missing in the original data file, *Grant_x.sav*, so Amos has imputed different values across the imputed data files for *cubes* for these two cases.

In addition to the original observed variables, Amos added four new variables to the imputed data files. *Spatial* and *verbal* are imputed latent variable scores. *Caseno* and *imputeno* are the case number and completed dataset number, respectively.

Example
31

Analyzing Multiply Imputed Datasets

Introduction

This example demonstrates the analysis of multiply (pronounced *multiplee*) imputed datasets.

Analyzing the Imputed Data Files Using SPSS

Ten completed datasets were created in Example 30. That was Step 1 in a three-step process: Use the Data Imputation feature of Amos to impute *m* complete data files. (Here, *m* = 10.) The next two steps are:

■ Step 2: Perform an analysis of each of the *m* completed data files separately.

■ Step 3: Combine the results from the analyses of the *m* data files.

The analysis in Step 2 can be performed using Amos, SPSS, or any other program. Without knowing ahead of time what program will be used to analyze the completed datasets, it is not possible to automate Steps 2 and 3.

To walk through Steps 2 and 3 for a specific problem, we will analyze the completed datasets by using SPSS to carry out a regression analysis in which one variable (*sentence*) is used to predict another variable (*wordmean*). We will focus specifically on the estimation of the regression weight and its standard error.

Step 2: Ten Separate Analyses

For each of the 10 completed datasets from Example 30, we need to perform a regression analysis in which *sentence* is used to predict *wordmean*. We start by opening the first completed dataset, *Grant_Imp1.sav*, in SPSS.

	visperc	cubes	lozenges	paragrap	sentence	wordmean	spatial	verbal	CaseNo	ImputeNo
1	33.00	22.54	17.00	8.00	17.00	10.00	-3.63	-.20	1.00	1.00
2	30.00	30.59	20.00	12.63	17.02	18.00	3.70	-.74	2.00	1.00
3	38.71	33.00	36.00	16.27	25.00	41.00	7.82	4.98	3.00	1.00
4	28.00	22.98	10.95	10.00	18.00	11.00	5.57	-1.10	4.00	1.00
5	30.82	25.00	20.80	11.00	21.04	8.00	3.47	1.44	5.00	1.00
6	20.00	25.00	6.00	9.00	17.27	25.25	-2.89	-1.33	6.00	1.00

▶ From the SPSS menus, choose Analyze → Regression → Linear and perform the regression analysis. (We assume you do not need detailed instructions for this step.)

The results are as follows:

Coefficients[a]

Model		Unstandardized Coefficients B	Unstandardized Coefficients Std. Error	Standardized Coefficients Beta	t	Sig.
1	(Constant)	-2.712	3.110		-.872	.386
	sentence	1.106	.160	.634	6.908	.000

a. Dependent Variable: wordmean

We are going to focus on the regression weight estimate (1.106) and its estimated standard error (0.160). Repeating the analysis that was just performed for each of the other nine completed datasets gives nine more estimates for the regression weight and for its standard error. All 10 estimates and standard errors are shown in the following table:

Imputation	ML Estimate	ML Standard Error
1	1.106	0.160
2	1.080	0.160
3	1.118	0.151
4	1.273	0.155
5	1.102	0.154
6	1.286	0.152
7	1.121	0.139
8	1.283	0.140
9	1.270	0.156
10	1.081	0.157

Step 3: Combining Results of Multiply Imputed Data Files

The standard errors from an analysis of any single completed dataset are not accurate because they do not take into account the uncertainty arising from imputing missing data values. The estimates and standard errors must be gathered from the separate analyses of the completed data files and combined into single summary values, one summary value for the parameter estimate and another summary value for the standard error of the parameter estimate. Formulas for doing this (Rubin, 1987) can be found in many places. The formulas below were taken from Schafer (1997, p. 109). The remainder of this section applies those formulas to the table of 10 estimates and 10 standard errors shown above. In what follows:

Let m be the number of completed datasets ($m = 10$ in this case).

Let $\hat{Q}^{(t)}$ be the estimate from sample t, so $\hat{Q}^{(1)} = 1.106$, $\hat{Q}^{(2)} = 1.080$, and so on.

Let $\sqrt{U^{(t)}}$ be the estimated standard error from sample t, so $\sqrt{U^{(1)}} = 0.160$, $\sqrt{U^{(2)}} = 0.160$, and so on.

Then the multiple-imputation estimate of the regression weight is simply the mean of the 10 estimates from the 10 completed datasets:

$$\overline{Q} = \frac{1}{m} \sum_{t=1}^{m} \hat{Q}^{(t)} = 1.172$$

Example 31

To obtain a standard error for the combined parameter estimate, go through the following steps:

▶ Compute the average within-imputation variance.

$$\bar{U} = \frac{1}{m}\sum_{t=1}^{m} U^{(t)} = 0.0233$$

▶ Compute the between-imputation variance.

$$B = \frac{1}{m-1}\sum_{t=1}^{m}(\hat{Q}^{(t)} - \bar{Q})^2 = 0.0085$$

▶ Compute the total variance.

$$T = \bar{U} + \left(1 + \frac{1}{m}\right)B = 0.0233 + \left(1 + \frac{1}{10}\right)0.0085 = 0.0326$$

The multiple-group standard error is then

$$\sqrt{T} = \sqrt{0.0326} = 0.1807$$

A test of the null hypothesis that the regression weight is 0 in the population can be based on the statistic

$$\frac{\bar{Q}}{\sqrt{T}} = \frac{1.172}{0.1807} = 6.49$$

which, if the regression weight is 0, has a t distribution with degrees of freedom given by

$$v = (m-1)\left[1 + \frac{\bar{U}}{\left(1+\frac{1}{m}\right)B}\right]^2 = (10-1)\left[1 + \frac{0.0233}{\left(1+\frac{1}{10}\right)0.0085}\right]^2 = 109$$

A calculator that implements these formulas and also provides multiple-imputation confidence intervals can be downloaded from *http://www.amosdevelopment.com/bayes/calculator*.

Joseph Schafer's NORM program also performs these calculations. NORM can be downloaded from *http://www.stat.psu.edu/~jls/misoftwa.html#win*.

Further Reading

Amos provides several advanced methods of handling missing data, including FIML (described in Example 17), multiple imputation, and Bayesian estimation. To learn more about each method, consult Schafer and Graham (2002) for an overview of the strengths of FIML and multiple imputation. Allison has a concise, readable monograph that covers both FIML and multiple imputation, including a number of worked examples and an excellent discussion of how to handle non-normal and categorical variables within the context of multiple imputation methods that assume multivariate normality (Allison, 2002). Schafer (1997) provides an in-depth, technical treatment of multiple imputation. Schafer and Olsen (1998) provide a readable, step-by-step guide to performing multiple imputation.

A SEM-specific study comparing the statistical performance of FIML and multiple imputation in structural equation models is also available (Olinsky, Chen, and Harlow, 2003). Lastly, it is worth noting that the Bayesian estimation approach discussed in Examples 26 through 29 is similar to FIML in its handling of missing data. Ibrahim and colleagues recently compared the performance of FIML, Bayesian estimation, probability weighting, and multiple imputation approaches to address incomplete data problems and concluded that these four approaches were generally similar in their satisfactory performance for handling incomplete data problems in which the missing data arose from a missing-at-random (MAR) process (Ibrahim, Chen, Lipsitz, and Herring, 2005). While their review considered generalized linear models rather than SEM, their results and conclusions should be generally applicable to a wide range of statistical models and data analysis scenarios, including those featuring SEM.

Example
32

Censored Data

Introduction

This example demonstrates parameter estimation, estimation of posterior predictive distributions, and data imputation with censored data.

About the Data

For this example, we use the censored data from 103 patients who were accepted into the Stanford Heart Transplantation Program during the years 1967 through 1974. The data were collected by Crowley and Hu (1977) and have been reanalyzed by Kalbfleisch and Prentice (2002), among others. The dataset is saved in the file *transplant-a.sav*.

Example 32

	acceptyr	age	time	timesqr	status
17	1968	20.33	35	5.916	uncensored
18	1968	56.85	42	6.481	uncensored
19	1968	59.12	36	6.000	uncensored
20	1969	55.28	27	5.196	uncensored
21	1969	43.34	1031	32.109	uncensored
22	1969	42.78	50	7.071	uncensored
23	1969	58.36	732	27.055	uncensored
24	1969	51.80	218	14.765	uncensored
25	1969	33.22	1799	42.415	censored
26	1969	30.54	1400	37.417	censored
27	1969	8.79	262	16.186	uncensored

Reading across the first visible row in the figure above, Patient 17 was accepted into the program in 1968. The patient at that time was 20.33 years old. The patient died 35 days later. The next number, 5.916, is the square root of 35. Amos assumes that censored variables are normally distributed. The square root of survival time will be used in this example in the belief that it is probably more nearly normally distributed than is survival time itself. Uncensored simply means that we know how long the patient lived. In other words, the patient has already died, and that is how we are able to tell that he lived for 35 days after being admitted into the program.

Some patients were still alive when last seen. For example, Patient 25 entered the program in 1969 at the age of 33.22 years. The patient was last seen 1,799 days later. The number 42.415 is the square root of 1,799. The word censored in the Status column means that the patient was still alive 1,799 days after being accepted into the program, and that is the last time the patient was seen. So, we can't say that the patient survived for 1,799 days. In fact, he survived for longer than that; we just don't know how much longer. There are more cases like that. Patient number 26 was last seen 1,400 days after acceptance into the program and, at that time, was still alive, so we know that that patient lived for at least 1,400 days.

It is not clear what is to be done with a censored value like Patient 25's survival time of 1,799 days. You can't just discard the 1,799 and all the other censored values because that amounts to discarding the patients who lived a long time. On the other hand, you can't keep the 1,799 and treat it as an ordinary score because you know the patient really lived for more than 1,799 days.

In Amos, you can use the information that Patient 25 lived for more than 1,799 days, neither discarding the information nor pretending that the patient's survival time is known more precisely than it is. Of course, wherever the data provide an exact numeric value, as in the case of Patient 24 who is known to have survived for 218 days, that exact numeric value is used.

Recoding the Data

The data file needs to be recoded before Amos reads it. The next figure shows a portion of the dataset after recoding. (This complete dataset is in the file *transplant-b.sav.*)

	acceptyr	age	time	timesqr
17	1968	20.33	35	5.916
18	1968	56.85	42	6.481
19	1968	59.12	36	6.000
20	1969	55.28	27	5.196
21	1969	43.34	1031	32.109
22	1969	42.78	50	7.071
23	1969	58.36	732	27.055
24	1969	51.80	218	14.765
25	1969	33.22	> 1799	> 42.415
26	1969	30.54	> 1400	> 37.417
27	1969	8.79	262	16.186

Every uncensored observation appears in the new data file just the way it did in the original data file. Censored values, however, are coded differently. For example, Patient 25's survival time, which is known only to be greater than 1,799, is coded as > 1799 in the new data file. (Spaces in a string like > 1799 are optional.) The square root of survival time is known to be greater than 42.415, so the timesqr column of the data file contains > 42.415 for Patient 25. For data file formats (like SPSS) that make a distinction between numeric and string variables, *time* and *timesqr* need to be coded as string variables.

Analyzing the Data

To specify the data file in Amos Graphics:

▶ From the menus, choose File → Data Files.

▶ Then in the Data Files dialog box, click the File Name button.

▶ Select the data file *transplant-b.sav*.

▶ Select Allow non-numeric data (a check mark appears next to it).

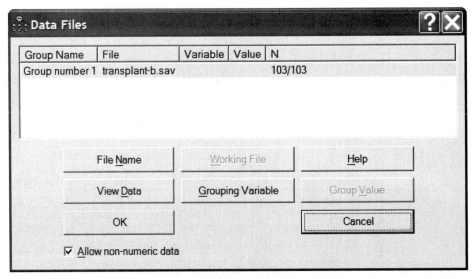

Recoding the data as shown above and selecting Allow non-numeric data are the only extra steps that are required for analyzing censored data. In all other respects, fitting a model with censored data and interpreting the results is exactly the same as if the data were purely numeric.

Performing a Regression Analysis

Let's try predicting *timesqr* using *age* and year of acceptance (*acceptyr*) as predictors. Begin by drawing the following path diagram:

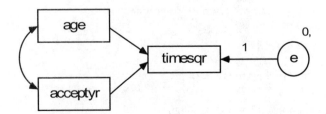

To fit the model:

▶ Click ▲ on the toolbar.

or

▶ From the menus, choose Analyze → Bayesian Estimation.

Note: The ▦ button is disabled because, with non-numeric data, you can perform only Bayesian estimation.

After the Bayesian SEM window opens, wait until the unhappy face ● changes into a happy face ☺. The table of estimates in the Bayesian SEM window should look something like this:

	Mean	S.E.	S.D.	C.S.	Median	Skewness	Kurtosis	Min	Max
Regression weights									
timesqr<--age	-0.29	0.00	0.15	1.00	-0.29	-0.05	0.13	-0.94	0.38
timesqr<--acceptyr	1.45	0.00	0.81	1.00	1.43	0.10	0.09	-1.55	4.93
Means									
age	45.17	0.00	1.00	1.00	45.18	-0.01	0.05	40.93	49.76
acceptyr	1970.61	0.00	0.19	1.00	1970.61	0.00	0.08	1969.73	1971.43

(Only a portion of the table is shown in the figure.) The Mean column contains point estimates for the parameters. The regression weight for using *acceptyr* to predict *timesqr* is 1.45, so that each time the calendar advances by one year, you predict an increase of 1.45 in the square root of survival time. This suggests that the transplant program may have been improving over the period covered by the study. The regression weight for using *age* to predict *timesqr* is –0.29, so for every year older a patient is when admitted into the transplant program, you expect a decrease of 0.29 in the square root of survival time. The regression weight estimate of –0.29 is actually the mean of the posterior distribution of the regression weight.

▶ To see the entire posterior distribution, right-click the row that contains the –0.29 estimate and choose Show Posterior from the pop-up menu.

Example 32

	Mean	S.E.	S.D.	C.S.	Median	Skewness	Kurtosis	Min	Max
Regression weights									
timesqr<--age	-0.29	0.00	0.15	1.00	-0.29	-0.05	0.13	-0.94	0.38
timesqr<--acceptyr	1.45	Show Posterior			1.43	0.10	0.09	-1.55	4.93
		Show Prior							
Means									
age	45.17	0.00	1.00	1.00	45.18	-0.01	0.05	40.93	49.76
acceptyr	1970.61	0.00	0.19	1.00	1970.61	0.00	0.08	1969.73	1971.43

The Posterior dialog box opens, displaying the posterior distribution of the regression weight.

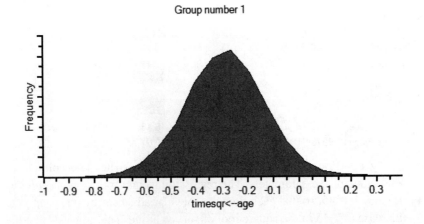

Group number 1

The posterior distribution of the regression weight is indeed centered around –0.29. The distribution lies almost entirely between –0.75 and 0.25, so it is practically guaranteed that the regression weight lies in that range. Most of the distribution lies between –0.5 and 0, so we are pretty sure that the regression weight lies between –0.5 and 0.

Posterior Predictive Distributions

Recall that the dataset contains some censored values like Patient 25's survival time. All we really know about Patient 25's survival time is that it is longer than 1,799 days or, equivalently, that the square root of survival time exceeds 42.415. Even though we do not know the amount by which this patient's *timesqr* exceeds 42.415, we can ask for its posterior distribution. Taking into account the fact that *timesqr* exceeds 42.415, assuming that the model is correct, and taking the patient's *age* and *acceptyr* into account, what can be said about Patient 25's survival time? To find out:

▶ Click the Posterior Predictive button 🔡.

or

▶ From the menus, choose View → Posterior Predictive.

	timesqr	age	acceptyr	
17	5.916	20.33127995	1968	
18	6.481	56.84873374	1968	
19	6	59.12388775	1968	
20	5.196	55.27994524	1969	
21	32.109	43.34291581	1969	
22	7.071	42.78439425	1969	
23	27.055	58.35728953	1969	
24	14.765	51.80013689	1969	
25	<<	33.2238193	1969	
26	<<	30.53524983	1969	
27	16.186	8.785763176	1969	

The Posterior Predictive Distributions window shows a table with a row for every person and a column for every observed variable in the model. Looking in the 25th row, we see Patient 25's *age* and *acceptyr* scores. For Patient 25's *timesqr*, all we see is the symbol <<, which indicates that the data provide an inequality constraint on the *timesqr* score and not an actual numeric value.

To see the posterior distribution of Patient 25's *timesqr*:

▶ Click <<. The posterior distribution appears in the Posterior window.

Example 32

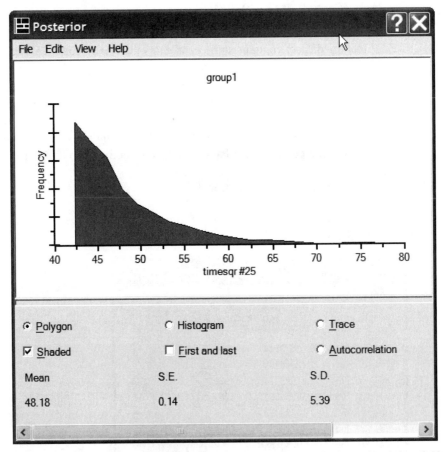

The posterior distribution for Patient 25's *timesqr* lies entirely to the right of 42.415. Of course, we knew from the data alone that *timesqr* exceeds 42.415, but now we also know that there is practically no chance that Patient 25's *timesqr* exceeds 70. For that matter, there is only a slim chance that *timesqr* exceeds even 55.

To see a posterior predictive distribution that looks very different from Patient 25's:

▶ Click the << symbol in the 100th row of the Posterior Predictive Distributions table.

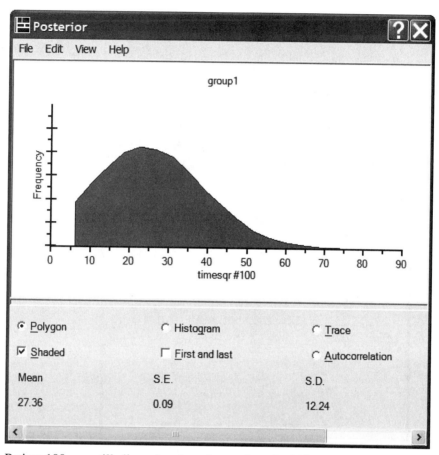

Patient 100 was still alive when last observed on the 38th day after acceptance into the program, so that his *timesqr* is known to exceed 6.164. The posterior distribution of that patient's *timesqr* shows that it is practically guaranteed to be between 6.164 and 70, and almost certain to be between, 6.164 and 50. The mean is 27.36, providing a point estimate of *timesqr* if one is needed. Squaring 27.36 gives 748, an estimate of Patient 100's survival time in days.

Example 32

Imputation

You can use this model to impute values for the censored values.

▶ Close the Bayesian SEM window if it is open.

▶ From the Amos Graphics menu, choose Analyze → Data Imputation.

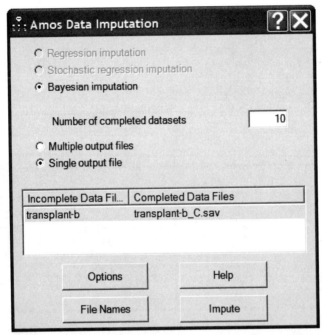

Notice that Regression imputation and Stochastic regression imputation are disabled. When you have non-numeric data such as censored data, Bayesian imputation is the only choice.

We will accept the options shown in the preceding figure, creating 10 completed datasets and saving all 10 in a single SPSS data file called *transplant-b_C.sav*. To start the imputation:

▶ Click the Impute button.

The Bayesian SEM window opens along with the Data Imputation dialog box.

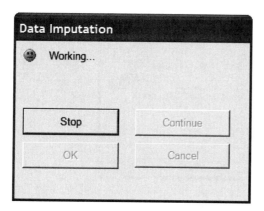

▶ Wait until the Data Imputation dialog box displays a happy face 😊 to indicate that each of the 10 completed datasets is effectively uncorrelated with the others.

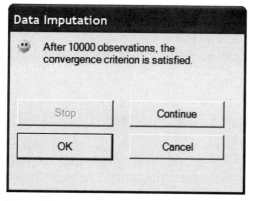

Note: After you see a happy face but before you click OK, you may optionally choose to right-click a parameter in the Bayesian SEM window and choose Show Posterior from the pop-up menu. This will allow you to examine the Trace and Autocorrelation plots.

▶ Click OK in the Data Imputation dialog box.

The Summary window shows a list of the completed data files that were created. In this case, only one completed data file was created.

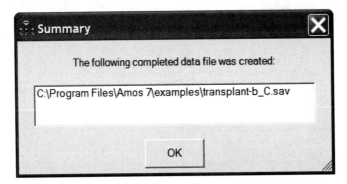

▶ Double-click the file name to display the contents of the single completed data file, which contains 10 completed datasets.

The file contains 1,030 cases because each of the 10 completed datasets contains 103 cases. The first 103 rows of the new data file contain the first completed dataset. The *imputeno* variable is equal to 1 for each row in the first completed dataset, and the *caseno* variable runs from 1 through 103.

	timesqr	age	acceptyr	caseno	imputeno
1	7.00	30.84	1967.00	1.00	1.00
2	2.24	51.84	1968.00	2.00	1.00
3	3.87	54.30	1968.00	3.00	1.00
4	6.16	40.26	1968.00	4.00	1.00
5	4.12	20.79	1968.00	5.00	1.00
6	1.41	54.60	1968.00	6.00	1.00
7	25.96	50.87	1968.00	7.00	1.00
8	6.25	45.35	1968.00	8.00	1.00
9	9.16	47.16	1968.00	9.00	1.00
10	7.55	42.50	1968.00	10.00	1.00
11	12.33	47.98	1968.00	11.00	1.00
12	2.65	53.19	1968.00	12.00	1.00
13	8.94	54.57	1968.00	13.00	1.00
14	37.23	54.01	1968.00	14.00	1.00
15	.00	53.82	1968.00	15.00	1.00
16	17.52	49.45	1968.00	16.00	1.00
17	5.92	20.33	1968.00	17.00	1.00
18	6.48	56.85	1968.00	18.00	1.00
19	6.00	59.12	1968.00	19.00	1.00
20	5.20	55.28	1969.00	20.00	1.00
21	32.11	43.34	1969.00	21.00	1.00
22	7.07	42.78	1969.00	22.00	1.00
23	27.06	58.36	1969.00	23.00	1.00
24	14.77	51.80	1969.00	24.00	1.00
25	49.66	33.22	1969.00	25.00	1.00
26	41.67	30.54	1969.00	26.00	1.00

The first row of the completed data file contains a *timesqr* value of 7. Because that was not a censored value, 7 is not an imputed value. It is just an ordinary numeric value that was present in the original data file. On the other hand, Patient 25's *timesqr was* censored, so that patient has an imputed *timesqr* (in this case, 49.66.) The value of 49.66 is a value drawn randomly from the posterior predictive distribution in the figure on p. 486.

Normally, the next step would be to use the 10 completed datasets in *transplant-b_C.sav* as input to some other program that cannot accept censored data. You would use that other program to perform 10 separate analyses, using each one of the 10 completed datasets in turn. Then you would do further computations to combine the results of those 10 separate analyses into a single set of results, as was done in Example 31. Those steps will not be carried out here.

General Inequality Constraints on Data Values

This example employed only inequality constraints like *> 1799*. Here are some other examples of string values that can be used in a data file to place inequality constraints on the value of an underlying numeric variable:

- The string value *< 5* means that the underlying numeric value is less than 5.
- The string value *4<<5* means that the underlying numeric value is between 4 and 5.

Example
33

Ordered-Categorical Data

Introduction

This example shows how to fit a factor analysis model to ordered-categorical data. It also shows how to find the posterior predictive distribution for the numeric variable that underlies a categorical response and how to impute a numeric value for a categorical response.

About the Data

This example uses data on attitudes toward environment issues obtained from a questionnaire administered to 1,017 respondents in the Netherlands. The data come from the European Values Study Group (see the bibliography for a citation). The data file *environment-nl-string.sav* contains responses to six questionnaire items with categorical responses *strongly disagree* (*SD*), *disagree* (*D*), *agree* (*A*), and *strongly agree* (*SA*).

	item1	item2	item3	item4	item5	item6
1	A		SA	SD	A	A
2	A		A	SA	SA	SA
3		A	A	A	A	A
4	A	A	A			
5	D	SD			D	
6	SA	SA	A		A	A
7	A	D		A	A	A
8	D	D		SD		SD
9	SA	SA	SA	A		A
10	SA	A	A	SA	SA	
11	A	A	A	A		A
12	SA	SA	A	A		A

One way to analyze these data is to assign numbers to the four categorical responses; for example, using the assignment $1 = SD$, $2 = D$, $3 = A$, $4 = SA$. If you assign numbers to categories in that way, you get the dataset in *environment-nl-numeric.sav*.

	item1	item2	item3	item4	item5	item6
1	3	.	4	1	3	3
2	3	.	3	4	4	4
3	.	3	3	3	3	3
4	3	3	3	.	.	.
5	2	1	.	.	2	.
6	4	4	3	.	3	3
7	3	2	.	3	3	3
8	2	2	.	1	.	1
9	4	4	4	3	.	3
10	4	3	3	4	4	.
11	3	3	3	3	.	3
12	4	4	3	3	.	3

In an Amos analysis, it is not necessary to assign numbers to categories in the way just shown. It is possible to use only the ordinal properties of the four categorical responses. If you want to use only the ordinal properties of the data, you can use either dataset, *environment-nl-string.sav* or *environment-nl-numeric.sav*.

It may be slightly easier to use *environment-nl-numeric.sav* because Amos will assume by default that the numbered categories go in the order 1, 2, 3, 4, with 1 being the lowest category. That happens to be the correct order. With *environment-nl-string.sav*, by contrast, Amos will assume by default that the categories are arranged alphabetically in the order A, D, SA, SD, with A being the lowest category. That is the wrong order, so the default ordering of the categories by Amos has to be overridden.

The data file *environment-nl-string.sav* will be used for this example because then it will be clear that only the ordinal properties of the data are employed, and also you can see how to specify the correct ordering of the categories.

Specifying the Data File

▶ From the Amos Graphics menus , choose File → Data Files.

▶ In the Data Files window, click the File Name button.

▶ Select the data file environment-nl-string.sav.

▶ Select Allow non-numeric data (a check mark appears next to it).

▶ Click OK.

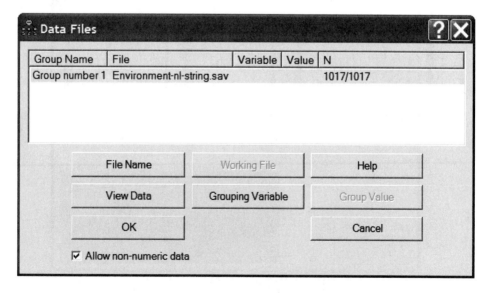

Recoding the Data within Amos

The ordinal properties of the data cannot be inferred from the data file alone. To give Amos the additional information it needs so that it can interpret the data values *SD*, *D*, *A*, and *SA*:

▶ From the Amos Graphics menus, choose Tools → Data Recode.

▶ Select item1 in the list of variables in the upper-left corner of the Data Recode window.

This displays a frequency distribution of the responses to *item1* at the bottom of the window.

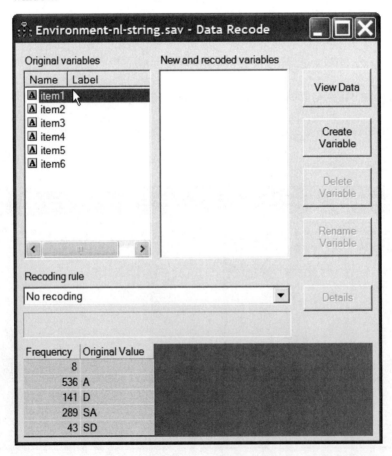

In the box labeled Recoding rule, the notation No recoding means that Amos will read the responses to *item1* as is. In other words, it will read either *SD*, *D*, *A*, *SA*, or an empty string. We can't leave things that way because Amos doesn't know what to do with *SD*, *D*, and so on.

▶ Click No recoding and select Ordered-categorical from the drop-down list.

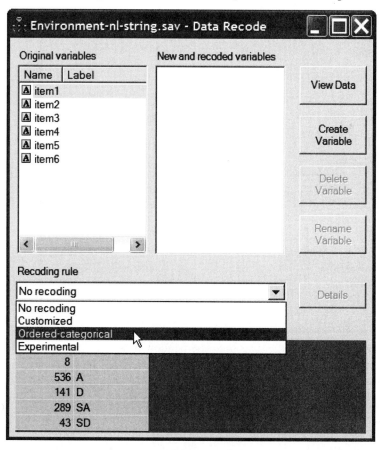

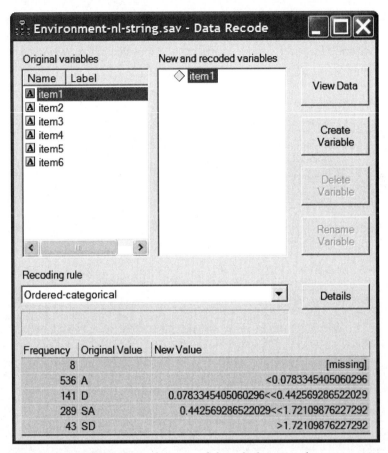

The frequency table at the bottom of the window now has a New Value column that shows how the *item1* values in the data file will be recoded before Amos reads the data. The first row of the frequency table shows that empty strings in the original data file will be treated as missing values. The second row shows that the *A* response will be translated into the string <0.0783345405060296. Amos will interpret this to mean that there is a continuous numeric variable that underlies responses to *item1*, and that a person who gives the *A* response has a score that is less than 0.0783345405060296 on that underlying variable. Similarly, the third row shows that the *D* response will be translated into the string 0.0783345405060296<<0.442569286522029 and interpreted by Amos to mean that the score on the underlying numeric variable is between 0.0783345405060296 and 0.442569286522029. The numbers, 0.0783345405060296, 0.442569286522029, and so on, are derived from the frequencies in the Frequency column, based on the assumption that scores on the underlying numeric variable are normally distributed with a mean of 0 and a standard deviation of 1.

The ordering of the categories in the Original Value column needs to be changed. To change the ordering:

▶ Click the Details button. The Ordered-Categorical Details dialog box opens.

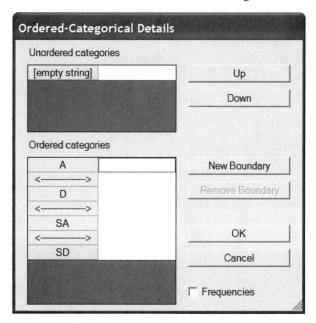

The Ordered categories list box shows four response categories arranged in the order *A, D, SA, SD*, and separated from each other by dashed lines, <----->. The dashed lines represent three boundaries that divide the real numbers into four intervals, with the four intervals being associated with the four categorical responses. The assumption is made that a person who scores below the lowest boundary on some unobserved numeric variable gives the *A* response. A person who scores between the lowest boundary and the middle boundary gives the *D* response. A person who scores between the middle boundary and the highest boundary gives the *SA* response. Finally, a person who scores above the highest boundary gives the *SD* response.

The program is correct about there being four categories (intervals) and three boundaries, but it has the ordering of the categories wrong. The program arbitrarily alphabetized the categories. We need to keep the four categories and the three boundaries but rearrange them. We want *SD* to fall in the lowest interval (below the lowest boundary), and so on.

You can rearrange the categories and the boundaries. To do this:

▶ Drag and drop with the mouse.

or

▶ Select a category or boundary with the mouse and then click the **Up** or **Down** button.

After putting the categories and boundaries in the correct order, the Ordered-Categorical Details dialog box looks like this:

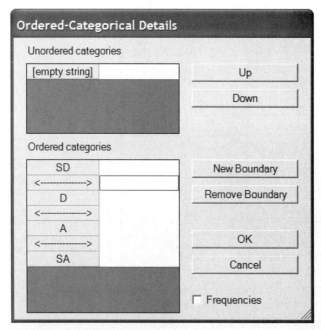

The Unordered categories list box contains a list of values that Amos will treat as missing. At the moment, the list contains one entry, [empty string], so that Amos will treat an empty string as a missing value. If a response coded as an *empty string* was actually a response that could be meaningfully compared to *SD*, *D*, *A*, and *SA*, then you would select [empty string] in the Unordered categories list box and click the **Down** button to move [empty string] into the Ordered categories list box.

Similarly, if a response in the Ordered categories list box, for example *SD*, was not comparable to the other responses, you would select it with the mouse and click the **Up** button to move it into the Unordered categories list box. Then *SD* would be treated as a missing value.

Note: You can't drag and drop between the Ordered categories list box and the Unordered categories list box. You have to use the Up and Down buttons to move a category from one box to the other.

We could stop here and close the Ordered-Categorical Details dialog box because we have the right number of boundaries and categories and we have the categories going in the right order. However, we will make a further change based on a suggestion by Croon (2002), who also worked with this dataset and concluded that the *SD* category occurred so seldom that it should be combined with the *D* category. To merge those two categories into a single category:

▶ Select the boundary between the two categories you want to merge.

▶ Click the Remove Boundary button. The Ordered categories list now looks like this:

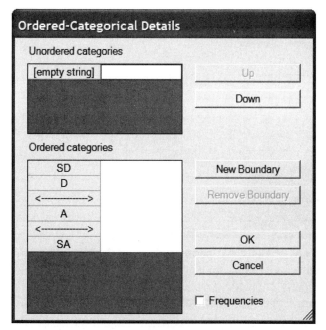

Now the *SD* response and the *D* response are indistinguishable. Either response means that the person who gave the response has a score that lies in the lowest interval on the underlying numeric variable.

There remains the question of the values of the two boundaries that separate the three intervals. If you do not specify values for the boundaries, Amos will estimate the boundaries by assuming that scores on the underlying numeric variable are normally distributed with a mean of 0 and a standard deviation of 1. Alternatively, you can assign a value to a boundary instead of letting Amos estimate it. To assign a value:

▶ Select the boundary with the mouse.

▶ Type a numeric value in the text box.

The following figure shows the result of assigning values 0 and 1 to the two boundaries.

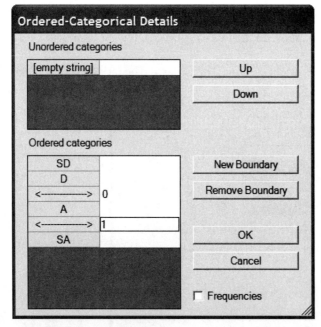

Although it may not be obvious, it is permissible to assign 0 and 1, or any pair of numbers, to the two boundaries, as long as the higher boundary is assigned a larger value than the lower one. No matter how many boundaries there are (as long as there are at least two), assigning values to two of the boundaries amounts to choosing a zero point and a unit of measurement for the underlying numeric variable. The scaling of the underlying numeric variable is discussed further in the Help file under the topic "Choosing boundaries when there are three categories."

▶ Click OK to close the Ordered-Categorical Details dialog box.

The changes that were just made to the categories and the interval boundaries are now reflected in the frequency table at the bottom of the Data Recode window.

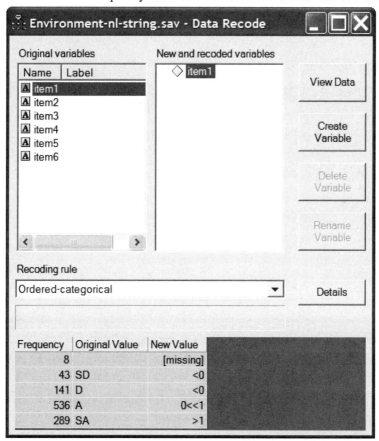

The frequency table shows how the values that appear in the data file will be recoded before Amos reads them. Reading the frequency table from top to bottom:

■ An empty string will be treated as a missing value.

■ The strings *SD* and *D* will be recoded as <0, meaning that the underlying numeric score is less than 0.

■ *A* will be recoded as 0<<1, meaning that the underlying numeric score is between 0 and 1.

■ *SA* will be recoded as >1, meaning that the underlying numeric score is greater than 1.

That takes care of *item1*. What was just done for *item1* has to be repeated for each of the five remaining observed variables. After specifying the recoding for all six observed variables, you can view the original dataset along with the recoded variables. To do this:

▶ Click the View Data button.

Data

Original variables

	item1	item2	item3	item4	item5	item6
1	A		SA	SD	A	A
2	A		A	SA	SA	SA
3		A	A	A	A	A
4	A	A	A			
5	D	SD			D	
6	SA	SA	A		A	A
7	A	D		A	A	A
8	D	D		SD		SD
9	SA	SA	SA	A		A
10	SA	A	A	SA	SA	

New and recoded variables

	item1	item2	item3	item4	item5	item6
1	0<;<1	*	>1	<0	0<;<1	0<;<1
2	0<;<1	*	0<;<1	>1	>1	>1
3	*	0<;<1	0<;<1	0<;<1	0<;<1	0<;<1
4	0<;<1	0<;<1	0<;<1	*	*	*
5	<0	<0	*	*	<0	*
6	>1	>1	0<;<1	*	0<;<1	0<;<1
7	0<;<1	<0	*	0<;<1	0<;<1	0<;<1
8	<0	<0	*	<0	*	<0
9	>1	>1	>1	0<;<1	*	0<;<1
10	>1	0<;<1	0<;<1	>1	>1	*

The table on the left shows the contents of the original data file before recoding. The table on the right shows the recoded variables after recoding. When Amos performs an analysis, it reads the recoded values, not the original values.

Note: You can create a raw data file in which the data recoding has already been performed. In other words, you can create a raw data file that contains the inequalities on the right-hand side of the figure above. In that case, you wouldn't need to use the Data Recode window in Amos. Indeed, that approach was used in Chapter 32.

▶ Finally, close the Data Recode window before specifying the model.

Specifying the Model

After you have specified the rules for data recoding as shown above, the analysis proceeds just like any Bayesian analysis. For this example, a factor analysis model will be fitted to the six questionnaire items in the environment dataset. The first three items were designed to be measures of willingness to spend money to take care of the environment. The other three items were designed to be measures of awareness of environmental issues. This design of the questionnaire is reflected in the following factor analysis model, which is saved in the file *Ex33-a.amw*.

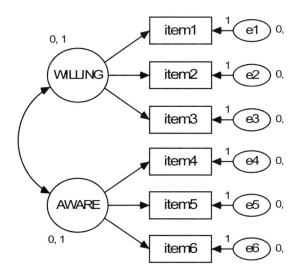

The path diagram is drawn exactly as it would be drawn for numeric data. This is one of the good things about having at least three categories for each ordered-categorical variable: You can specify a model in the way that you are used to, just as though all the variables were numeric, and the model will work for any combination of numeric and ordered-categorical variables. If variables are dichotomous, you will need to impose additional parameter constraints in order to make the model identified. This issue is discussed further in the online Help under the topic "Parameter identification with dichotomous variables."

Fitting the Model

▶ Click ▣ on the toolbar.

or

▶ From the menus, choose Analyze → Bayesian Estimation.

Note: The ▦ button is disabled because, with non-numeric data, you can perform only Bayesian estimation.

After the Bayesian SEM window opens, wait until the unhappy face changes into a happy face. The Bayesian SEM window should then look something like this:

	Mean	S.E.	S.D.	C.S.	Median	Skewness	Kurtosis	Min	Max	Name
Regression weights										
item1<--WILLING	0.59	0.00	0.03	1.00	0.59	0.09	-0.01	0.47	0.71	
item2<--WILLING	0.61	0.00	0.03	1.00	0.61	0.11	0.02	0.48	0.74	
item3<--WILLING	0.41	0.00	0.02	1.00	0.41	0.06	0.03	0.32	0.52	
item4<--AWARE	0.56	0.00	0.03	1.00	0.56	0.11	0.03	0.43	0.70	
item5<--AWARE	0.41	0.00	0.03	1.00	0.40	0.09	-0.02	0.30	0.52	
item6<--AWARE	0.55	0.00	0.03	1.00	0.55	0.08	0.02	0.43	0.68	
Intercepts										
item1	0.62	0.00	0.02	1.00	0.62	0.02	0.04	0.52	0.72	
item2	0.35	0.00	0.03	1.00	0.35	-0.01	0.01	0.25	0.45	
item3	0.52	0.00	0.02	1.00	0.52	0.00	-0.01	0.43	0.61	
item6	0.62	0.00	0.02	1.00	0.62	0.02	0.08	0.53	0.72	
item4	0.35	0.00	0.03	1.00	0.35	-0.07	0.10	0.23	0.47	
item5	0.48	0.00	0.02	1.00	0.48	-0.02	-0.03	0.39	0.57	
Covariances										
AWARE<->WILLING	0.55	0.00	0.04	1.00	0.56	-0.11	0.04	0.39	0.69	

(The figure above shows some, but not all, of the parameter estimates.) The Mean column provides a point estimate for each parameter. For example, the regression weight for using *WILLING* to predict *item1* is estimated to be 0.59. The skewness (0.09) and kurtosis (–0.01) of the posterior distribution are close to 0, which is compatible with the posterior distribution being nearly normal. The standard deviation (S.D.) is 0.03, so there is about a 67% chance that the regression weight is within 0.03 of 0.59. Doubling the standard deviation gives 0.06, so there is about a 95% chance that the regression weight is within 0.06 of 0.59.

To view the posterior distribution of the regression weight:

▶ Right-click its row and choose Show Posterior from the pop-up menu.

	Mean	S.E.	S.D.	C.S.	Median	Skewness	Kurtosis	Min	Max	Name
Regression weights										
item1<--WILLING	0.59	0.00	0.03	1.00	0.59	0.09	-0.01	0.47	0.71	
item2<--WILLING	0.61	0.00	0.03	1.00	Show Posterior			0.02	0.48	0.74
item3<--WILLING	0.41	0.00	0.02	1.00	Show Prior			0.03	0.32	0.52
item4<--AWARE	0.56	0.00	0.03	1.00	0.56	0.11		0.03	0.43	0.70

The Posterior window displays the posterior distribution. The appearance of the
distribution confirms what was concluded above from the mean, standard deviation,
skewness, and kurtosis of the distribution. The shape of the distribution is nearly
normal, and it looks like roughly 95% of the area lies between 0.53 and 0.65 (that is,
within 0.06 of 0.59).

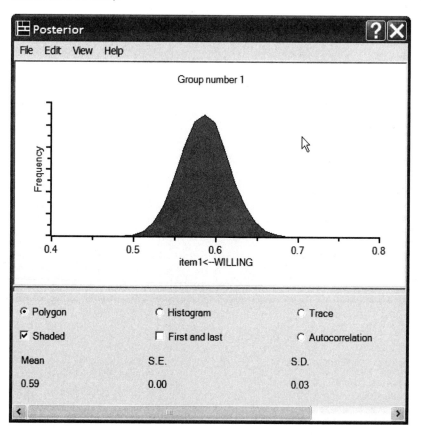

Example 33

MCMC Diagnostics

If you know how to interpret the diagnostic output from MCMC algorithms (for example, see Gelman, et al, 2004), you might want to view the Trace plot and the Autocorrelation plot.

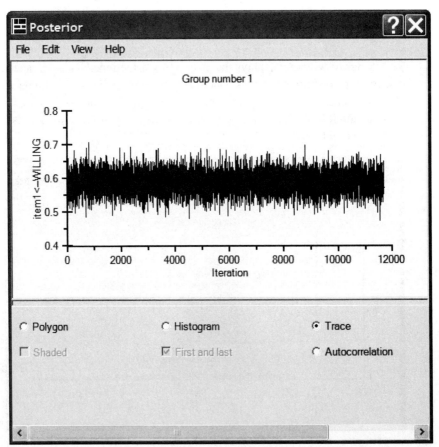

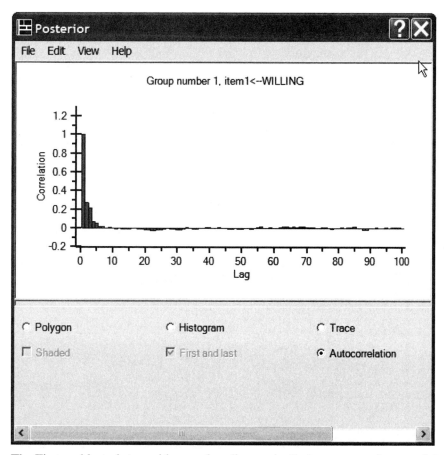

The First and last plot provides another diagnostic. It shows two estimates of the posterior distribution (two superimposed plots), one estimate from the first third of the MCMC sample and another estimate from the last third of the MCMC sample.

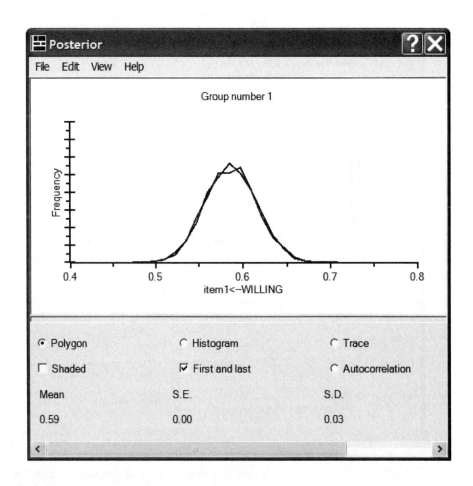

Posterior Predictive Distributions

When you think of estimation, you normally think of estimating model parameters or some function of the model parameters such as a standardized regression weight or an indirect effect. However, there are other unknown quantities in the present analysis. Each entry in the data table on p. 494 represents a numeric value that is either unknown or partially known. For example, Person 1 did not respond to *item2,* so we can only guess at (estimate) that person's score on the underlying numeric variable. On the other hand, it seems like we ought to be able to make a fairly educated guess about the underlying numeric value, considering that we know how the person responded to the other items, and that we can also make use of the assumption that the model is correct.

We are in an even better position to guess at Person 1's score on the numeric variable that underlies *item1* because Person 1 gave a response to *item1*. This person's response places his or her score in the middle interval, between the two boundaries. Since the two boundaries were arbitrarily fixed at 0 and 1, we know that the score is somewhere between 0 and 1, but it seems like we should be able to say more than that by using the person's responses on the other variables along with the assumption that the model is correct.

In Bayesian estimation, all unknown quantities are treated in the same way. Just as unknown parameter values are estimated by giving their posterior distribution, so are unknown data values. A posterior distribution for an unknown data value is called a **posterior predictive distribution**, but it is interpreted just like any posterior distribution. To view posterior predictive distributions for unknown data values:

▶ Click the Posterior Predictive button [icon].

or

▶ From the menus, choose View → Posterior Predictive.

The Posterior Predictive Distributions window appears.

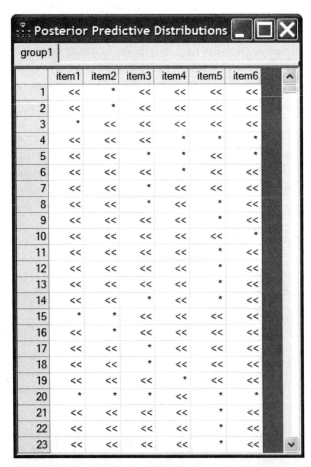

The Posterior Predictive Distributions window contains a table with a row for every person and a column for every observed variable in the model. An asterisk (*) indicates a missing value, while << indicates a response that places inequality constraints on the underlying numeric variable. To display the posterior distribution for an item:

▶ Click on the table entry in the upper-left corner (Person 1's response to *item1*).

The Posterior window opens, displaying the posterior distribution of Person 1's underlying numeric score. At first, the posterior distribution looks jagged and random.

group1

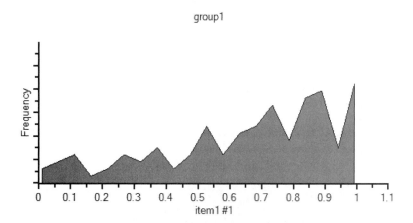

That is because the program is building up an estimate of the posterior distribution as MCMC sampling proceeds. The longer you wait, the better the estimate of the posterior distribution will be. After a while, the estimate of the posterior distribution stabilizes and looks something like this:

group1

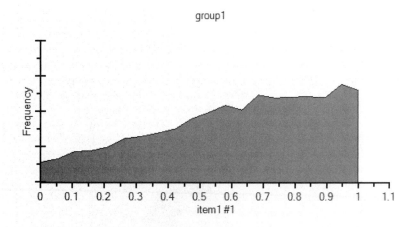

The posterior distribution shows that Person 1's score on the numeric variable that underlies his or her response to *item1* is between 0 and 1 (which we knew already), and that the score is more likely to be close to 1 than close to 0.

Example 33

▶ Next, click the table entry in the first column of the 22nd row to estimate Person 22's score on the numeric variable that underlies his or her response to *item1*.

After you wait a while to get a good estimate of the posterior distribution, you see this:

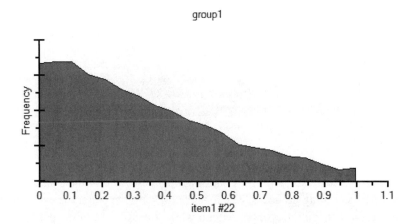

Both Person 1 and Person 22 gave the *agree* response to *item1*, so both people have scores between 0 and 1 on the underlying numeric variable; however, their posterior distributions are very different

For another example of a posterior predictive distribution, select a missing value like Person 1's response to *item2*. After allowing MCMC sampling to proceed long enough to get a good estimate of the posterior distribution, it looks like this:

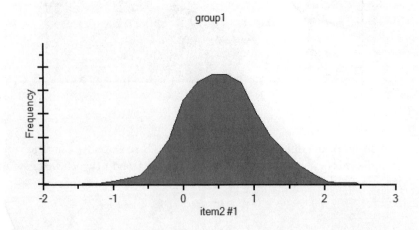

The mean of the posterior distribution (0.52) can be taken as an estimate of Person 1's score on the underlying variable if a point estimate is required. Looking at the plot of the posterior distribution, we can be nearly 100% sure that the score is between −1 and 2. The score is probably between 0 and 1 because most of the area under the posterior distribution lies between 0 and 1.

Posterior Predictive Distributions for Latent Variables

Suppose you want to estimate Person 1's score on the *WILLING* factor. Amos can estimate posterior predictive distributions for unknown scores only for observed variables. It cannot estimate a posterior predictive distribution of a score on a latent variable. However, there is a trick that you can use to estimate the posterior predictive distribution of a score on *WILLING*. You can change *WILLING* to an observed variable, treating it not as a latent variable but as an observed variable that has a missing value for every case. That requires two changes – a change to the path diagram and a change to the data.

In the path diagram, the *WILLING* ellipse has to be changed into a rectangle. To accomplish this:

▶ Right-click the WILLING ellipse and choose Toggle Observed/Unobserved from the pop-up menu.

▶ Click the WILLING ellipse.

The **WILLING** ellipse changes to a rectangle so that the path diagram looks like this:

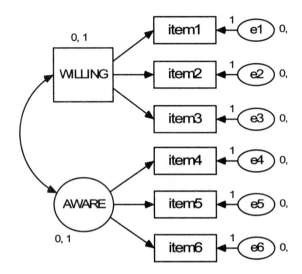

That takes care of the path diagram. It is also necessary to make a change to the data because if *WILLING* is an observed variable, then there has to be a *WILLING* column in the data file. You can directly modify the data file. Since this is an SPSS data file, you would use SPSS to add a *WILLING* variable to the data file, making sure that all the scores on *WILLING* are missing.

To avoid changing the original data file:

▶ Right-click the WILLING variable in the path diagram

▶ Choose Data Recode from the pop-up menu to open the Data Recode window.

▶ In the Data Recode window, click Create Variable. A new variable with the default name *V1*, appears in the New and recoded variables list box.

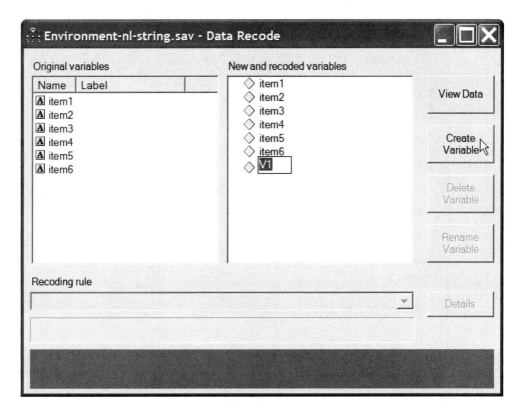

▶ Change V1 to WILLING. (If necessary, click the Rename Variable button.)

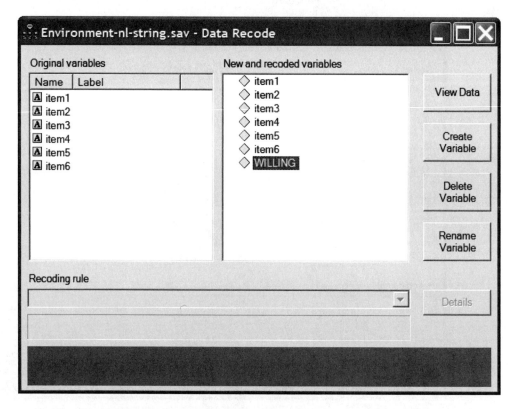

▶ You can optionally view the recoded dataset that includes the new *WILLING* variable by clicking the View Data button.

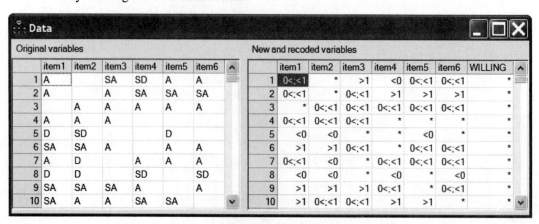

The table on the left shows the original dataset. The table on the right shows the recoded dataset as read by Amos. It includes *item1* through *item6* after recoding, and also the new *WILLING* variable.

▶ Close the Data Recode window.

▶ Start the Bayesian analysis by clicking ▲ on the Amos Graphics toolbar.

▶ In the Bayesian SEM window, wait until the unhappy face ☻ changes into a happy face ☺ and then click the Posterior Predictive button ▦.

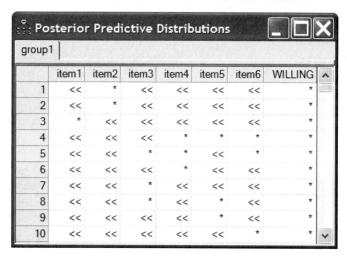

▶ Click the entry in the upper-right corner of the table to display the posterior distribution of Person 1's score on the *WILLING* factor.

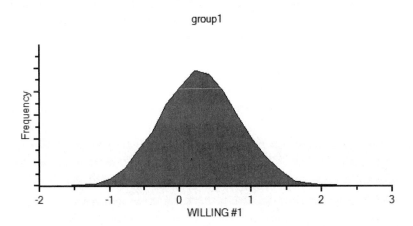

Imputation

Data imputation works the same way for ordered-categorical data as it does for numeric data. With ordered-categorical data, you can impute numeric values for missing values, for scores on latent variables, and for scores on the unobserved numeric variables that underlie observed ordered-categorical measurements.

You need a model in order to perform imputation. You could use the factor analysis model that was used earlier. There are several advantages and one disadvantage to using the factor analysis model for imputation. One advantage is that, if the model is correct, you can impute values for the factors. That is, you can create a new data set in which *WILLING* and *AWARE* are observed variables. The other advantage is that, if the factor analysis model is correct, it can be expected to give more accurate imputations for *item1* through *item6* than would be obtained from a less restrictive model. The disadvantage of using the factor analysis model is that it may be wrong. To be on the safe side, the present example will use the model that has the biggest chance of being correct, the saturated model shown in the following figure. (See the file *Ex33-c.amw*.)

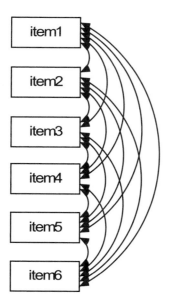

After drawing the path diagram for the saturated model, you can begin the imputation.

▶ From the Amos Graphics menu, choose Analyze → Data Imputation.

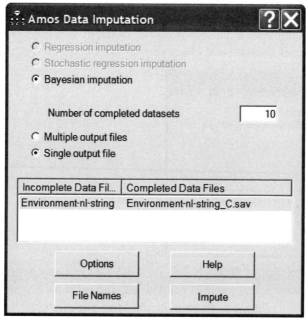

In the Amos Data Imputation window, notice that Regression imputation and Stochastic regression imputation are disabled. When you have non-numeric data, Bayesian imputation is the only choice.

We will accept the options shown in the preceding figure, creating 10 completed datasets and saving all 10 in a single SPSS data file called *environment-nl-string_C.sav*. To start the imputation:

▶ Click the Impute button.

The Bayesian SEM window opens along with the Data Imputation dialog box.

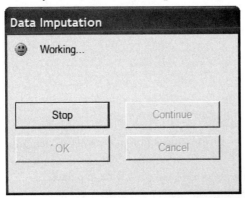

▶ Wait until the Data Imputation dialog box displays a happy face 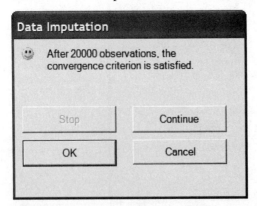 to indicate that each of the 10 completed data sets is effectively uncorrelated with the others.

Note: After you see a happy face but before you click OK, you may optionally right-click a parameter in the Bayesian SEM window and choose Show Posterior from the pop-up menu. This will allow you to examine the Trace and Autocorrelation plots.

▶ Click OK in the Data Imputation dialog box.

The Summary window shows a list of the completed data files that were created. In this case, only one completed data file was created.

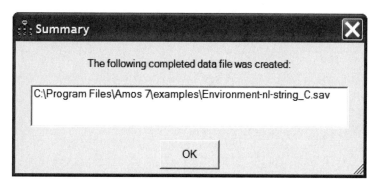

▶ Double-click the file name in the Summary window to display the contents of the single completed data file, which contains 10 completed data sets.

The file contains 10,170 cases because each of the 10 completed data sets contains 1,017 cases. The first 1,017 rows of the new data file contain the first completed data set. The *imputeno* variable is equal to 1 for each row in the first completed data set, and the *caseno* variable runs from 1 through 1,017 before starting over again at 1.

	item1	item2	item3	item4	item5	item6	caseno	imputeno
1	.82	.57	1.01	-.45	.78	.10	1.00	1.00
2	.64	-.25	.30	1.22	1.56	1.91	2.00	1.00
3	1.32	.61	.53	.35	.17	.74	3.00	1.00
4	.00	.39	.79	1.50	.84	1.73	4.00	1.00
5	-.32	-.69	-.46	-.90	-.47	.13	5.00	1.00
6	1.63	1.26	.61	.73	.74	.44	6.00	1.00
7	.75	-.13	.61	.25	.41	.78	7.00	1.00
8	-.98	-.09	.13	-.63	.52	-.12	8.00	1.00
9	2.69	2.45	1.22	.34	.99	.95	9.00	1.00
10	1.35	.10	.78	1.55	1.03	1.29	10.00	1.00
11	.18	.37	.78	.24	.53	.95	11.00	1.00
12	1.34	1.05	.29	.05	.53	.82	12.00	1.00

Normally, the next step would be to use the 10 completed data sets in *environment-nl-string_C.sav* as input to some other program that requires numeric (not ordered-categorical) data. You would use that other program to perform 10 separate analyses using each one of the 10 completed data sets in turn. Then, you would do further computations to combine the results of those 10 separate analyses into a single set of results, as was done in Example 31. Those steps will not be carried out here.

Notation

q = the number of parameters

γ = the vector of parameters (of order q)

G = the number of groups

$N^{(g)}$ = the number of observations in group g

$$N = \sum_{g=1}^{G} N^{(g)} = \text{the total number of observations in all groups combined}$$

$p^{(g)}$ = the number of observed variables in group g

$p^{*(g)}$ = the number of sample moments in group g. When means and intercepts are explicit model parameters, the relevant sample moments are means, variances, and covariances, so that $p^{*(g)} = p^{(g)}(p^{(g)} + 3)/2$. Otherwise, only sample variances and covariances are counted so that $p^{*(g)} = p^{(g)}(p^{(g)} + 1)/2$.

$$p = \sum_{g=1}^{G} p^{*(g)} = \text{the number of sample moments in all groups combined}$$

$d = p - q$ = the number of degrees of freedom for testing the model

$x_{ir}^{(g)}$ = the r-th observation on the i-th variable in group g

$\mathbf{x}_r^{(g)}$ = the r-th observation in group g

$\mathbf{S}^{(g)}$ = the sample covariance matrix for group g

$\Sigma^{(g)}(\gamma)$ = the covariance matrix for group g, according to the model

$\mu^{(g)}(\gamma)$ = the mean vector for group g, according to the model

$\Sigma_0^{(g)}$ = the population covariance matrix for group g

$\mu_0^{(g)}$ = the population mean vector for group g

$\mathbf{s}^{(g)} = \text{vec}(\mathbf{S}^{(g)})$ = the $p^{*(g)}$ distinct elements of $\mathbf{S}^{(g)}$ arranged in a single column vector

$\sigma^{(g)}(\gamma) = \text{vec}(\Sigma^{(g)}(\gamma))$

r = the non-negative integer specified by the ChiCorrect method. By default $r = G$. When the Emulisrel6 method is used, $r = G$ and cannot be changed by using ChiCorrect.

$n = N - r$

$\mathbf{a}$ = the vector of order p containing the sample moments for all groups; that is, $\mathbf{a}$ contains the elements of $\mathbf{S}^{(1)}, ..., \mathbf{S}^{(G)}$ and also (if means and intercepts are explicit model parameters) $\bar{\mathbf{x}}^{(1)}, ..., \bar{\mathbf{x}}^{(G)}$.

α_0 = the vector of order p containing the population moments for all groups; that is, α_0 contains the elements of $\Sigma_0^{(1)}, ..., \Sigma_0^{(G)}$ and also (if means and intercepts are explicit model parameters) $\mu_0^{(1)}, ..., \mu_0^{(G)}$. The ordering of the elements of $\alpha(\gamma)$ must match the ordering of the elements of $\mathbf{a}$.

$\alpha(\gamma)$ = the vector of order p containing the population moments for all groups according to the model; that is, $\alpha(\gamma)$ contains the elements of $\Sigma^{(1)}(\gamma), ..., \Sigma^{(G)}(\gamma)$ and also (if means and intercepts are explicit model parameters) $\mu^{(1)}(\gamma), ..., \mu^{(G)}(\gamma)$. The ordering of the elements of $\alpha(\gamma)$ must match the ordering of the elements of $\mathbf{a}$.

$F(\alpha(\gamma), \mathbf{a})$ = the function (of γ) that is minimized in fitting the model to the sample

$\hat{\gamma}$ = the value of γ that minimizes $F(\alpha(\gamma), \mathbf{a})$

$\hat{\Sigma}^{(g)} = \Sigma^{(g)}(\hat{\gamma})$

$\hat{\mu}^{(g)} = \mu^{(g)}(\hat{\gamma})$

$\hat{\alpha} = \alpha(\hat{\gamma})$

Discrepancy Functions

Amos minimizes discrepancy functions (Browne, 1982, 1984) of the form:

(D1)

$$
C(\alpha,\mathbf{a}) = [N-r]\left(\frac{\sum\limits_{g=1}^{G} N^{(g)} f\!\left(\mu^{(g)},\Sigma^{(g)};\overline{\mathbf{x}}^{(g)},\mathbf{S}^{(g)}\right)}{N}\right) = [N-r]F(\alpha,\mathbf{a})
$$

Different discrepancy functions are obtained by changing the way f is defined. If means and intercepts are unconstrained and do not appear as explicit model parameters, $\overline{\mathbf{x}}^{(g)}$ and $\mu^{(g)}$ will be omitted and f will be written $f(\Sigma^{(g)}; \mathbf{S}^{(g)})$.

The discrepancy functions C_{KL} and F_{KL} are obtained by taking f to be:

$$
f_{KL}\!\left(\mu^{(g)},\Sigma^{(g)};\overline{\mathbf{x}}^{(g)},\mathbf{S}^{(g)}\right) = \log\!\left|\Sigma^{(g)}\right| + \mathrm{tr}\!\left(\mathbf{S}^{(g)}\Sigma^{(g)^{-1}}\right) + \left(\overline{\mathbf{x}}^{(g)} - \mu^{(g)}\right)'\Sigma^{(g)^{-1}}\!\left(\overline{\mathbf{x}}^{(g)} - \mu^{(g)}\right)
$$

Except for an additive constant that depends only on the sample size, f_{KL} is -2 times the Kullback-Leibler information quantity (Kullback and Leibler, 1951). Strictly speaking, C_{KL} and F_{KL} do not qualify as discrepancy functions according to Browne's definition because $F_{KL}(\mathbf{a}, \mathbf{a}) \neq 0$.

For *maximum likelihood* estimation (*ML*), C_{ML}, and F_{ML} are obtained by taking f to be:

(D2)

$$f_{ML}\left(\mu^{(g)},\Sigma^{(g)};\bar{\mathbf{x}}^{(g)},\mathbf{S}^{(g)}\right)=f_{KL}\left(\mu^{(g)},\Sigma^{(g)};\bar{\mathbf{x}}^{(g)},\mathbf{S}^{(g)}\right)-f_{KL}\left(\bar{\mathbf{x}}^{(g)},\mathbf{S}^{(g)};\bar{\mathbf{x}}^{(g)},\mathbf{S}^{(g)}\right)$$

$$=\log\left|\Sigma^{(g)}\right|+\mathrm{tr}\left(\mathbf{S}^{(g)}\Sigma^{(g)^{-1}}\right)-\log\left|\mathbf{S}^{(g)}\right|-p^{(g)}+\left(\bar{\mathbf{x}}^{(g)}-\mu^{(g)}\right)'\Sigma^{(g)^{-1}}\left(\bar{\mathbf{x}}^{(g)}-\mu^{(g)}\right)$$

For *generalized least squares* estimation (*GLS*), C_{GLS}, and F_{GLS} are obtained by taking f to be:

(D3)

$$f_{GLS}\left(\Sigma^{(g)};\mathbf{S}^{(g)}\right)=\tfrac{1}{2}\,\mathrm{tr}\left[\mathbf{S}^{(g)^{-1}}\left(\mathbf{S}^{(g)}-\Sigma^{(g)}\right)\right]^2$$

For *asymptotically distribution-free* estimation (*ADF*), C_{ADF}, and F_{ADF} are obtained by taking f to be:

(D4)

$$f_{ADF}\left(\Sigma^{(g)};\mathbf{S}^{(g)}\right)=\sum_{g=1}^{G}\left[\mathbf{s}^{(g)}-\sigma^{(g)}(\gamma)\right]'\mathbf{U}^{(g)^{-1}}\left[\mathbf{s}^{(g)}-\sigma^{(g)}(\gamma)\right]$$

where the elements of $\mathbf{U}^{(g)}$ are given by Browne (1984, Equations 3.1–3.4):

$$\bar{x}_i^{(g)}=\frac{1}{N_g}\sum_{r=1}^{N_g}x_{ir}^{(g)}$$

$$w_{ij}^{(g)}=\frac{1}{N_g}\sum_{r=1}^{N_g}\left(x_{ir}^{(g)}-\bar{x}_i^{(g)}\right)\left(x_{jr}^{(g)}-\bar{x}_j^{(g)}\right)$$

$$w_{ij,kl}^{(g)}=\frac{1}{N_g}\sum_{r=1}^{N_g}\left(x_{ir}^{(g)}-\bar{x}_i^{(g)}\right)\left(x_{jr}^{(g)}-\bar{x}_j^{(g)}\right)\left(x_{kr}^{(g)}-\bar{x}_k^{(g)}\right)\left(x_{lr}^{(g)}-\bar{x}_l^{(g)}\right)$$

$$\left[\mathbf{U}^{(g)}\right]_{ij,kl}=w_{ij,kl}^{(g)}-w_{ij}^{(g)}w_{kl}^{(g)}$$

For *scale-free least squares* estimation *(SLS)*, C_{SLS}, and F_{SLS} are obtained by taking f to be:

(D5)

$$f_{SLS}\left(\Sigma^{(g)};\mathbf{S}^{(g)}\right)=\tfrac{1}{2}\mathrm{tr}\left[\mathbf{D}^{(g)^{-1}}\left(\mathbf{S}^{(g)}-\Sigma^{(g)}\right)\right]^2$$

where $\mathbf{D}^{(g)} = \mathrm{diag}(\mathbf{S}^{(g)})$.

For *unweighted least squares* estimation *(ULS)*, C_{ULS}, and F_{ULS} are obtained by taking f to be:

(D6)

$$f_{ULS}\left(\Sigma^{(g)};\mathbf{S}^{(g)}\right)=\tfrac{1}{2}\mathrm{tr}\left[\mathbf{S}^{(g)}-\Sigma^{(g)}\right]^2$$

The Emulisrel6 method in Amos can be used to replace (D1) with:

(D1a)

$$C=\sum_{g=1}^{G}\left(N^{(g)}-1\right)F^{(g)}$$

F is then calculated as $F = C/(N-G)$.

When $G = 1$ and $r = 1$, (D1) and (D1a) are equivalent, giving:

$$C=\left(N^{(1)}-1\right)F^{(1)}=(N-1)F$$

For maximum likelihood, asymptotically distribution-free, and generalized least squares estimation, both (D1) and (D1a) have a chi-square distribution for correctly specified models under appropriate distributional assumptions. Asymptotically, (D1) and (D1a) are equivalent; however, both formulas can exhibit some inconsistencies in finite samples.

Suppose you have two independent samples and a model for each. Furthermore, suppose that you analyze the two samples simultaneously, but that, in doing so, you impose no constraints requiring any parameter in one model to equal any parameter in the other model. Then, if you minimize (D1a), the parameter estimates obtained from the simultaneous analysis of both groups will be the same as from separate analyses of each group alone.

Furthermore, the discrepancy function (D1a) obtained from the simultaneous analysis will be the sum of the discrepancy functions from the two separate analyses. Formula (D1) does not have this property when *r* is nonzero. Using formula (D1) to do a simultaneous analysis of the two groups will give the same parameter estimates as two separate analyses, but the discrepancy function from the simultaneous analysis will not be the sum of the individual discrepancy functions.

On the other hand, suppose you have a single sample to which you have fitted some model using Amos. Now suppose that you arbitrarily split the sample into two groups of unequal size and perform a simultaneous analysis of both groups, employing the original model for both groups and constraining each parameter in the first group to be equal to the corresponding parameter in the second group. If you have minimized (D1) in both analyses, you will get the same results in both. However, if you use (D1a) in both analyses, the two analyses will produce different estimates and a different minimum value for *F*.

All of the inconsistencies just pointed out can be avoided by using (D1) with the choice *r* = 0, so that (D1) becomes:

$$C = \sum_{g=1}^{G} N^{(g)} F^{(g)} = NF$$

Measures of Fit

Model evaluation is one of the most unsettled and difficult issues connected with structural modeling. Bollen and Long (1993), MacCallum (1990), Mulaik, et al. (1989), and Steiger (1990) present a variety of viewpoints and recommendations on this topic. Dozens of statistics, besides the value of the discrepancy function at its minimum, have been proposed as measures of the merit of a model. Amos calculates most of them.

Fit measures are reported for each model specified by the user and for two additional models called the *saturated* model and the *independence* model.

■ In the **saturated model**, no constraints are placed on the population moments. The saturated model is the most general model possible. It is a vacuous model in the sense that it is guaranteed to fit any set of data perfectly. Any Amos model is a constrained version of the saturated model.

■ The **independence model** goes to the opposite extreme. In the independence model, the observed variables are assumed to be uncorrelated with each other. When means are being estimated or constrained, the means of all observed variables are fixed at 0. The independence model is so severely and implausibly constrained that you would expect it to provide a poor fit to any interesting set of data.

It frequently happens that each one of the models that you have specified can be so constrained as to be equivalent to the independence model. If this is the case, the saturated model and the independence model can be viewed as two extremes between which your proposed models lie.

For every estimation method except maximum likelihood, Amos also reports fit measures for a **zero model**, in which every parameter is fixed at 0.

Measures of Parsimony

Models with relatively few parameters (and relatively many degrees of freedom) are sometimes said to be high in parsimony, or **simplicity**. Models with many parameters (and few degrees of freedom) are said to be **complex**, or lacking in parsimony. This use of the terms *simplicity* and *complexity* does not always conform to everyday usage. For example, the saturated model would be called *complex*, while a model with an elaborate pattern of linear dependencies but with highly constrained parameter values would be called *simple*.

While one can inquire into the grounds for preferring simple, parsimonious models (such as Mulaik, et al., 1989), there does not appear to be any disagreement that parsimonious models are preferable to complex ones. When it comes to parameters, all other things being equal, less is more. At the same time, well-fitting models are preferable to poorly fitting ones. Many fit measures represent an attempt to balance these two conflicting objectives—simplicity and goodness of fit.

> In the final analysis, it may be, in a sense, impossible to define one *best* way to combine measures of complexity and measures of badness-of-fit in a single numerical index, because the precise nature of the *best* numerical trade-off between complexity and fit is, to some extent, a matter of personal taste. The choice of a model is a classic problem in the two-dimensional analysis of preference. (Steiger, 1990, p. 179)

NPAR

NPAR is the number of distinct parameters (q) being estimated. For example, two regression weights that are required to be equal to each other count as one parameter, not two.

Note: Use the \npar text macro to display the number of parameters in the output path diagram.

DF

DF is the number of degrees of freedom for testing the model

$$\mathrm{df} = d = p - q$$

where p is the number of sample moments and q is the number of distinct parameters. Rigdon (1994a) gives a detailed explanation of the calculation and interpretation of degrees of freedom.

Note: Use the \df text macro to display the degrees of freedom in the output path diagram.

PRATIO

The parsimony ratio (James, Mulaik, and Brett, 1982; Mulaik, et al., 1989) expresses the number of constraints in the model being evaluated as a fraction of the number of constraints in the independence model

$$\textbf{PRATIO} = \frac{d}{d_i}$$

where d is the degrees of freedom of the model being evaluated and d_i is the degrees of freedom of the independence model. The parsimony ratio is used in the calculation of *PNFI* and *PCFI* (see "Parsimony Adjusted Measures" on p. 546).

Note: Use the \pratio text macro to display the parsimony ratio in the output path diagram.

Minimum Sample Discrepancy Function

The following fit measures are based on the minimum value of the discrepancy.

CMIN

CMIN is the minimum value, $\hat{C}$, of the discrepancy, C (see Appendix B).

Note: Use the \cmin text macro to display the minimum value $\hat{C}$ of the discrepancy function C in the output path diagram.

P

P is the probability of getting as large a discrepancy as occurred with the present sample (under appropriate distributional assumptions and assuming a correctly specified model). That is, **P** is a "*p* value" for testing the hypothesis that the model fits perfectly in the population.

One approach to model selection employs statistical hypothesis testing to eliminate from consideration those models that are inconsistent with the available data. Hypothesis testing is a widely accepted procedure, and there is a lot of experience in its use. However, its unsuitability as a device for model selection was pointed out early in the development of analysis of moment structures (Jöreskog, 1969). It is generally acknowledged that most models are useful approximations that do not fit perfectly in the population. In other words, the null hypothesis of perfect fit is not credible to begin with and will, in the end, be accepted only if the sample is not allowed to get too big.

If you encounter resistance to the foregoing view of the role of hypothesis testing in model fitting, the following quotations may come in handy. The first two predate the development of structural modeling and refer to other model fitting problems.

> The power of the test to detect an underlying disagreement between theory and data is controlled largely by the size of the sample. With a small sample an alternative hypothesis which departs violently from the null hypothesis may still have a small probability of yielding a significant value of χ^2. In a very large sample, small and unimportant departures from the null hypothesis are almost certain to be detected. (Cochran, 1952)

> If the sample is *small*, then the χ^2 test will show that the data are '*not* significantly different from' quite a wide range of very different theories, while if the sample is *large*, the χ^2 test will show that the data are *significantly* different from those expected on a given theory even though the difference may be so very slight as to be negligible or unimportant on other criteria. (Gulliksen and Tukey, 1958, pp. 95–96)

> Such a hypothesis [of perfect fit] may be quite unrealistic in most empirical work with test data. If a sufficiently large sample were obtained this χ^2 statistic would, no doubt, indicate that any such non-trivial hypothesis is statistically untenable. (Jöreskog, 1969, p. 200)

> ...in very large samples virtually all models that one might consider would have to be rejected as statistically untenable.... In effect, a nonsignificant chi-square value is desired, and one attempts to infer the validity of the hypothesis of no difference between model and data. Such logic is well-known in various statistical guises as attempting to prove the null hypothesis. This procedure cannot generally be justified, since the chi-square variate v can be made small by simply reducing sample size. (Bentler and Bonett, 1980, p. 591)

Our opinion...is that this null hypothesis [of perfect fit] is implausible and that it does not help much to know whether or not the statistical test has been able to detect that it is false. (Browne and Mels, 1992, p. 78).

See also "PCLOSE" on p. 539.

Note: Use the \p text macro for displaying this *p* value in the output path diagram.

CMIN/DF

CMIN/DF is the minimum discrepancy, $\hat{C}$, (see Appendix B) divided by its degrees of freedom.

$$\frac{\hat{C}}{d}$$

Several writers have suggested the use of this ratio as a measure of fit. For every estimation criterion except for ULS and SLS, the ratio should be close to 1 for correct models. The trouble is that it isn't clear how far from 1 you should let the ratio get before concluding that a model is unsatisfactory.

Rules of Thumb

...Wheaton et al. (1977) suggest that the researcher also compute a *relative* chi-square (χ^2/df).... They suggest a ratio of approximately five or less 'as beginning to be reasonable.' In our experience, however, χ^2 to degrees of freedom ratios in the range of 2 to 1 or 3 to 1 are indicative of an acceptable fit between the hypothetical model and the sample data. (Carmines and McIver, 1981, p. 80)

...different researchers have recommended using ratios as low as 2 or as high as 5 to indicate a reasonable fit. (Marsh and Hocevar, 1985).

...it seems clear that a χ^2/df ratio > 2.00 represents an inadequate fit. (Byrne, 1989, p. 55).

Note: Use the \cmindf text macro to display the value of CMIN/DF in the output path diagram.

FMIN

FMIN is the minimum value, $\hat{F}$, of the discrepancy, F (see Appendix B).

Note: Use the \fmin text macro to display the minimum value $\hat{F}$ of the discrepancy function F in the output path diagram.

Measures Based On the Population Discrepancy

Steiger and Lind (1980) introduced the use of the population discrepancy function as a measure of model adequacy. The population discrepancy function, F_0, is the value of the discrepancy function obtained by fitting a model to the population moments rather than to sample moments. That is,

$$F_0 = \min_{\gamma}[F(\alpha(\gamma),\alpha_0)]$$

in contrast to

$$\hat{F} = \min_{\gamma}[F(\alpha(\gamma),\mathbf{a})]$$

Steiger, Shapiro, and Browne (1985) showed that, under certain conditions, $\hat{C} = n\hat{F}$ has a noncentral chi-square distribution with d degrees of freedom and noncentrality parameter $\delta = C = nF$. The Steiger-Lind approach to model evaluation centers around the estimation of F_0 and related quantities.

   This section of the User's Guide relies mainly on Steiger and Lind (1980) and Steiger, Shapiro, and Browne (1985). The notation is primarily that of Browne and Mels (1992).

NCP

$NCP = \max(\hat{C} - d, 0)$ is an estimate of the noncentrality parameter, $\delta = C_0 = nF_0$.

The columns labeled *LO 90* and *HI 90* contain the lower limit (δ_L) and upper limit (δ_U) of a 90% confidence interval, on δ. δ_L is obtained by solving

$$\Phi\left(\hat{C}\,\middle|\,\delta, d\right) = .95$$

for δ, and δ_U is obtained by solving

$$\Phi\left(\hat{C}\mid \delta, d\right) = .05$$

for δ, where $\Phi(x\mid \delta, d)$ is the distribution function of the noncentral chi-squared distribution with noncentrality parameter δ and d degrees of freedom.

Note: Use the \ncp text macro to display the value of the noncentrality parameter estimate in the path diagram, \ncplo to display the lower 90% confidence limit, and \ncphi for the upper 90% confidence limit.

F0

$$\text{F0} = \hat{F}_0 = \max\left(\frac{\hat{C}-d}{n}, 0\right) = \frac{\text{NCP}}{n} \text{ is an estimate of } \frac{\delta}{n} = F_0.$$

The columns labeled *LO 90* and *HI 90* contain the lower limit and upper limit of a 90% confidence interval for F_0.

$$\text{LO } 90 = \sqrt{\frac{\delta_L}{n}}$$

$$\text{HI } 90 = \sqrt{\frac{\delta_U}{n}}$$

Note: Use the \f0 text macro to display the value of $\hat{F}_0$ in the output path diagram, \f0lo to display its lower 90% confidence estimate, and \f0hi to display the upper 90% confidence estimate.

RMSEA

F_0 incorporates no penalty for model complexity and will tend to favor models with many parameters. In comparing two nested models, F_0 will never favor the simpler model. Steiger and Lind (1980) suggested compensating for the effect of model complexity by dividing F_0 by the number of degrees of freedom for testing the model. Taking the square root of the resulting ratio gives the population *root mean square error of approximation*, called **RMS** by Steiger and Lind, and **RMSEA** by Browne and Cudeck (1993).

$$\text{population RMSEA} = \sqrt{\frac{F_0}{d}}$$

$$\text{estimated RMSEA} = \sqrt{\frac{\hat{F}_0}{d}}$$

The columns labeled *LO 90* and *HI 90* contain the lower limit and upper limit of a 90% confidence interval on the population value of *RMSEA*. The limits are given by

$$\text{LO } 90 = \sqrt{\frac{\delta_L/n}{d}}$$

$$\text{HI } 90 = \sqrt{\frac{\delta_U/n}{d}}$$

Rule of Thumb

Practical experience has made us feel that a value of the *RMSEA* of about 0.05 or less would indicate a close fit of the model in relation to the degrees of freedom. This figure is based on subjective judgment. It cannot be regarded as infallible or correct, but it is more reasonable than the requirement of exact fit with the *RMSEA* = 0.0. We are also of the opinion that a value of about 0.08 or less for the *RMSEA* would indicate a reasonable error of approximation and would not want to employ a model with a *RMSEA* greater than 0.1. (Browne and Cudeck, 1993)

Note: Use the \rmsea text macro to display the estimated root mean square error of approximation in the output path diagram, \rmsealo for its lower 90% confidence estimate, and \rmseahi for its upper 90% confidence estimate.

PCLOSE

PCLOSE $= 1 - \Phi(\hat{C}|.05^2 nd, d)$ is a p value for testing the null hypothesis that the population *RMSEA* is no greater than 0.05.

$$H_0 : \text{RMSEA} \leq .05$$

By contrast, the p value in the P column (see "P" on p. 533) is for testing the hypothesis that the population *RMSEA* is 0.

$$H_0 : \text{RMSEA} = 0$$

Based on their experience with *RMSEA*, Browne and Cudeck (1993) suggest that a *RMSEA* of 0.05 or less indicates a **close fit**. Employing this definition of close fit, *PCLOSE* gives a test of close fit while P gives a test of exact fit.

Note: Use the \pclose text macro to display the p value for close fit of the population *RMSEA* in the output path diagram.

Information-Theoretic Measures

Amos reports several statistics of the form $\hat{C} + kq$ or $\hat{F} + kq$, where k is some positive constant. Each of these statistics creates a composite measure of badness of fit ($\hat{C}$ or $\hat{F}$) and complexity (q) by forming a weighted sum of the two. Simple models that fit well receive low scores according to such a criterion. Complicated, poorly fitting models get high scores. The constant k determines the relative penalties to be attached to badness of fit and to complexity.

The statistics described in this section are intended for model comparisons and not for the evaluation of an isolated model.

All of these statistics were developed for use with maximum likelihood estimation. Amos reports them for *GLS* and *ADF* estimation as well, although it is not clear that their use is appropriate there.

AIC

The Akaike information criterion (Akaike, 1973, 1987) is given by

$$\text{AIC} = \hat{C} + 2q$$

See also "ECVI" on p. 541.

Note: Use the \aic text macro to display the value of the Akaike information criterion in the output path diagram.

BCC

The Browne-Cudeck (1989) criterion is given by

$$BCC = \hat{C} + 2q \frac{\displaystyle\sum_{g=1}^{G} b^{(g)} \frac{p^{(g)}\left(p^{(g)}+3\right)}{N^{(g)}-p^{(g)}-2}}{\displaystyle\sum_{g=1}^{G} p^{(g)}\left(p^{(g)}+3\right)}$$

where $b^{(g)} = N^{(g)} - 1$ if the Emulisrel6 command has been used, or $b^{(g)} = n\frac{N^{(g)}}{N}$ if it has not.

BCC imposes a slightly greater penalty for model complexity than does *AIC*. *BCC* is the only measure in this section that was developed specifically for analysis of moment structures. Browne and Cudeck provided some empirical evidence suggesting that *BCC* may be superior to more generally applicable measures. Arbuckle (in preparation) gives an alternative justification for *BCC* and derives the above formula for multiple groups.

See also "MECVI" on p. 542.

Note: Use the \bcc text macro to display the value of the Browne-Cudeck criterion in the output path diagram.

BIC

The Bayes information criterion (Schwarz, 1978; Raftery, 1993) is given by the formula

$$BIC = \hat{C} + q\ln(N^{(1)})$$

In comparison to the *AIC*, *BCC*, and *CAIC*, the *BIC* assigns a greater penalty to model complexity and, therefore, has a greater tendency to pick parsimonious models. The *BIC* is reported only for the case of a single group where means and intercepts are not explicit model parameters.

Note: Use the \bic text macro to display the value of the Bayes information criterion in the output path diagram.

CAIC

Bozdogan's (1987) *CAIC* (consistent *AIC*) is given by the formula

$$\text{CAIC} = \hat{C} + q\left(\ln N^{(1)} + 1\right)$$

CAIC assigns a greater penalty to model complexity than either *AIC* or *BCC* but not as great a penalty as does *BIC*. *CAIC* is reported only for the case of a single group where means and intercepts are not explicit model parameters.

Note: Use the \caic text macro to display the value of the consistent *AIC* statistic in the output path diagram.

ECVI

Except for a constant scale factor, *ECVI* is the same as *AIC*.

$$\text{ECVI} = \frac{1}{n}(\text{AIC}) = \hat{F} + \frac{2q}{n}$$

The columns labeled *LO 90* and *HI 90* give the lower limit and upper limit of a 90% confidence interval on the population *ECVI*:

$$\text{LO } 90 = \frac{\delta_L + d + 2q}{n}$$

$$\text{HI } 90 = \frac{\delta_U + d + 2q}{n}$$

See also "AIC" on p. 539.

Note: Use the \ecvi text macro to display the value of the expected cross-validation index in the output path diagram, \ecvilo to display its lower 90% confidence estimate, and \ecvihi for its upper 90% confidence estimate.

MECVI

Except for a scale factor, *MECVI* is identical to *BCC*.

$$
\mathbf{MECVI} = \frac{1}{n}(\mathbf{BCC}) = \hat{F} + 2q \frac{\displaystyle\sum_{g=1}^{G} a^{(g)} \frac{p^{(g)}\left(p^{(g)}+3\right)}{N^{(g)} - p^{(g)} - 2}}{\displaystyle\sum_{g=1}^{G} p^{(g)}\left(p^{(g)}+3\right)}
$$

where $a^{(g)} = \dfrac{N^{(g)} - 1}{N - G}$ if the Emulisrel6 command has been used, or $a^{(g)} = \dfrac{N^{(g)}}{N}$ if it has not.

See also "BCC" on p. 540.

Note: Use the \mecvi text macro to display the modified *ECVI* statistic in the output path diagram.

Comparisons to a Baseline Model

Several fit measures encourage you to reflect on the fact that, no matter how badly your model fits, things could always be worse.

Bentler and Bonett (1980) and Tucker and Lewis (1973) suggested fitting the independence model or some other very badly fitting baseline model as an exercise to see how large the discrepancy function becomes. The object of the exercise is to put the fit of your own model(s) into some perspective. If none of your models fit very well, it may cheer you up to see a *really* bad model. For example, as the following output shows, Model A from Example 6 has a rather large discrepancy ($\hat{C} = 71.544$) in relation to its degrees of freedom. On the other hand, 71.544 does not look so bad compared to 2131.790 (the discrepancy for the independence model).

Model	NPAR	CMIN	DF	P	CMIN/DF
Model A: No Autocorrelation	15	71.544	6	0.000	11.924
Model B: Most General	16	6.383	5	0.271	1.277
Model C: Time-Invariance	13	7.501	8	0.484	0.938
Model D: A and C Combined	12	73.077	9	0.000	8.120
Saturated model	21	0.000	0		
Independence model	6	2131.790	15	0.000	142.119

This things-could-be-much-worse philosophy of model evaluation is incorporated into a number of fit measures. All of the measures tend to range between 0 and 1, with values close to 1 indicating a good fit. Only *NFI* (described below) is guaranteed to be between 0 and 1, with 1 indicating a perfect fit. (*CFI* is also guaranteed to be between 0 and 1, but this is because values bigger than 1 are reported as 1, while values less than 0 are reported as 0.)

The independence model is only one example of a model that can be chosen as the baseline model, although it is the one most often used and the one that Amos uses. Sobel and Bohrnstedt (1985) contend that the choice of the independence model as a baseline model is often inappropriate. They suggest alternatives, as did Bentler and Bonett (1980), and give some examples to demonstrate the sensitivity of *NFI* to the choice of baseline model.

NFI

The Bentler-Bonett (1980) normed fit index (*NFI*), or Δ_1 in the notation of Bollen (1989b) can be written

$$\text{NFI} = \Delta_1 = 1 - \frac{\hat{C}}{\hat{C}_b} = 1 - \frac{\hat{F}}{\hat{F}_b}$$

where $\hat{C} = n\hat{F}$ is the minimum discrepancy of the model being evaluated and $\hat{C}_b = n\hat{F}_b$ is the minimum discrepancy of the baseline model.

In Example 6, the independence model can be obtained by adding constraints to any of the other models. Any model can be obtained by constraining the saturated model. So Model A, for instance, with $\chi^2 = 71.544$, is unambiguously *in between* the perfectly fitting saturated model ($\chi^2 = 0$) and the independence model ($\chi^2 = 2131.790$).

Model	NPAR	CMIN	DF	P	CMIN/DF
Model A: No Autocorrelation	15	71.544	6	0.000	11.924
Model B: Most General	16	6.383	5	0.271	1.277
Model C: Time-Invariance	13	7.501	8	0.484	0.938
Model D: A and C Combined	12	73.077	9	0.000	8.120
Saturated model	21	0.000	0		
Independence model	6	2131.790	15	0.000	142.119

Looked at in this way, the fit of Model A is a lot closer to the fit of the saturated model than it is to the fit of the independence model. In fact, you might say that Model A has a discrepancy that is 96.6% of the way between the (terribly fitting) independence model and the (perfectly fitting) saturated model.

$$\text{NFI} = \frac{2131.790 - 71.54}{2131.790} = 1 - \frac{71.54}{2131.790} = .966$$

Rule of Thumb

Since the scale of the fit indices is not necessarily easy to interpret (*e.g.*, the indices are not squared multiple correlations), experience will be required to establish values of the indices that are associated with various degrees of meaningfulness of results. In our experience, models with overall fit indices of less than 0.9 can usually be improved substantially. These indices, and the general hierarchical comparisons described previously, are best understood by examples. (Bentler and Bonett, 1980, p. 600, referring to both the *NFI* and the *TLI*)

Note: Use the \nfi text macro to display the normed fit index value in the output path diagram.

RFI

Bollen's (1986) relative fit index (*RFI*) is given by

$$\text{RFI} = \rho_1 = 1 - \frac{\hat{C}/d}{\hat{C}_b/d_b} = 1 - \frac{\hat{F}/d}{\hat{F}_b/d_b}$$

where $\hat{C}$ and d are the discrepancy and the degrees of freedom for the model being evaluated, and $\hat{C}_b$ and d_b are the discrepancy and the degrees of freedom for the baseline model.

The *RFI* is obtained from the *NFI* by substituting F/d for F. *RFI* values close to 1 indicate a very good fit.

Note: Use the \rfi text macro to display the relative fit index value in the output path diagram.

IFI

Bollen's (1989b) incremental fit index (*IFI*) is given by:

$$\text{IFI} = \Delta_2 = \frac{\hat{C}_b - \hat{C}}{\hat{C}_b - d}$$

where $\hat{C}$ and d are the discrepancy and the degrees of freedom for the model being evaluated, and $\hat{C}_b$ and d_b are the discrepancy and the degrees of freedom for the baseline model. *IFI* values close to 1 indicate a very good fit.

Note: Use the \ifi text macro to display the incremental fit index value in the output path diagram.

TLI

The Tucker-Lewis coefficient (ρ_2 in the notation of Bollen, 1989b) was discussed by Bentler and Bonett (1980) in the context of analysis of moment structures and is also known as the Bentler-Bonett non-normed fit index (*NNFI*).

$$\text{TLI} = \rho_2 = \frac{\dfrac{\hat{C}_b}{d_b} - \dfrac{\hat{C}}{d}}{\dfrac{\hat{C}_b}{d_b} - 1}$$

The typical range for *TLI* lies between 0 and 1, but it is not limited to that range. *TLI* values close to 1 indicate a very good fit.

Note: Use the \tli text macro to display the value of the Tucker-Lewis index in the output path diagram.

CFI

The comparative fit index (*CFI*; Bentler, 1990) is given by

$$\text{CFI} = 1 - \frac{\max\left(\hat{C} - d, 0\right)}{\max\left(\hat{C}_b - d_b, 0\right)} = 1 - \frac{\text{NCP}}{\text{NCP}_b}$$

where $\hat{C}$, d, and *NCP* are the discrepancy, the degrees of freedom, and the noncentrality parameter estimate for the model being evaluated, and $\hat{C}_b$, d_b, and NCP_b are the discrepancy, the degrees of freedom, and the noncentrality parameter estimate for the baseline model.

The *CFI* is identical to McDonald and Marsh's (1990) relative noncentrality index (*RNI*)

$$\text{RNI} = 1 - \frac{\hat{C} - d}{\hat{C}_b - d_b}$$

except that the *CFI* is truncated to fall in the range from 0 to 1. *CFI* values close to 1 indicate a very good fit.

Note: Use the \cfi text macro to display the value of the comparative fit index in the output path diagram.

Parsimony Adjusted Measures

James, et al. (1982) suggested multiplying the *NFI* by a *parsimony index* so as to take into account the number of degrees of freedom for testing both the model being evaluated and the baseline model. Mulaik, et al. (1989) suggested applying the same adjustment to the *GFI*. Amos also applies a parsimony adjustment to the *CFI*.

See also "PGFI" on p. 549.

PNFI

The **PNFI** is the result of applying James, et al.'s (1982) parsimony adjustment to the *NFI*

$$\mathrm{PNFI} = (\mathrm{NFI})(\mathrm{PRATIO}) = \mathrm{NFI}\frac{d}{d_b}$$

where d is the degrees of freedom for the model being evaluated, and d_b is the degrees of freedom for the baseline model.

Note: Use the \pnfi text macro to display the value of the parsimonious normed fit index in the output path diagram.

PCFI

The **PCFI** is the result of applying James, et al.'s (1982) parsimony adjustment to the *CFI*:

$$\mathrm{PCFI} = (\mathrm{CFI})(\mathrm{PRATIO}) = \mathrm{CFI}\frac{d}{d_b}$$

where d is the degrees of freedom for the model being evaluated, and d_b is the degrees of freedom for the baseline model.

Note: Use the \pcfi text macro to display the value of the parsimonious comparative fit index in the output path diagram.

GFI and Related Measures

The *GFI* and related fit measures are described here.

GFI

The **GFI** (goodness-of-fit index) was devised by Jöreskog and Sörbom (1984) for *ML* and *ULS* estimation, and generalized to other estimation criteria by Tanaka and Huba (1985).

The *GFI* is given by

$$\text{GFI} = 1 - \frac{\hat{F}}{\hat{F}_b}$$

where $\hat{F}$ is the minimum value of the discrepancy function defined in Appendix B and $\hat{F}_b$ is obtained by evaluating F with $\Sigma^{(g)} = \mathbf{0}$, $g = 1, 2,...,G$. An exception has to be made for maximum likelihood estimation, since (D2) in Appendix B is not defined for $\Sigma^{(g)} = \mathbf{0}$. For the purpose of computing *GFI* in the case of maximum likelihood estimation, $f(\Sigma^{(g)}; \mathbf{S}^{(g)})$ in Appendix B is calculated as

$$f\left(\Sigma^{(g)}; \mathbf{S}^{(g)}\right) = \tfrac{1}{2}\text{tr}\left[\mathbf{K}^{(g)^{-1}}\left(\mathbf{S}^{(g)} - \Sigma^{(g)}\right)\right]^2$$

with $\mathbf{K}^{(g)} = \Sigma^{(g)}(\hat{\gamma}_{ML})$, where $\hat{\gamma}_{ML}$ is the maximum likelihood estimate of γ. *GFI* is always less than or equal to 1. *GFI* = 1 indicates a perfect fit.

Note: Use the \gfi text macro to display the value of the goodness-of-fit index in the output path diagram.

AGFI

The **AGFI** (adjusted goodness-of-fit index) takes into account the degrees of freedom available for testing the model. It is given by

$$\text{AGFI} = 1 - (1 - \text{GFI})\frac{d_b}{d}$$

where

$$d_b = \sum_{g=1}^{G} p^{*(g)}$$

The *AGFI* is bounded above by 1, which indicates a perfect fit. It is not, however, bounded below by 0, as the *GFI* is.

Note: Use the \agfi text macro to display the value of the adjusted *GFI* in the output path diagram.

PGFI

The **PGFI** (parsimony goodness-of-fit index), suggested by Mulaik, et al. (1989), is a modification of the *GFI* that takes into account the degrees of freedom available for testing the model

$$PGFI = GFI \frac{d}{d_b}$$

where d is the degrees of freedom for the model being evaluated, and

$$d_b = \sum_{g=1}^{G} p^{*(g)}$$

is the degrees of freedom for the baseline zero model.

Note: Use the \pgfi text macro to display the value of the parsimonious *GFI* in the output path diagram.

Miscellaneous Measures

Miscellaneous fit measures are described here.

HI 90

Amos reports a 90% confidence interval for the population value of several statistics. The upper and lower boundaries are given in columns labeled *HI 90* and *LO 90*.

HOELTER

Hoelter's (1983) *critical N* is the largest sample size for which one would accept the hypothesis that a model is correct. Hoelter does not specify a significance level to be used in determining the critical *N*, although he uses 0.05 in his examples. Amos reports a critical *N* for significance levels of 0.05 and 0.01.

Here are the critical N's displayed by Amos for each of the models in Example 6:

Model	HOELTER 0.05	HOELTER 0.01
Model A: No Autocorrelation	164	219
Model B: Most General	1615	2201
Model C: Time-Invariance	1925	2494
Model D: A and C Combined	216	277
Independence model	11	14

Model A, for instance, would have been accepted at the 0.05 level if the sample moments had been exactly as they were found to be in the Wheaton study but with a sample size of 164. With a sample size of 165, Model A would have been rejected. Hoelter argues that a critical N of 200 or better indicates a satisfactory fit. In an analysis of multiple groups, he suggests a threshold of 200 times the number of groups. Presumably this threshold is to be used in conjunction with a significance level of 0.05. This standard eliminates Model A and the independence model in Example 6. Model B is satisfactory according to the Hoelter criterion. I am not myself convinced by Hoelter's arguments in favor of the 200 standard. Unfortunately, the use of critical N as a practical aid to model selection requires some such standard. Bollen and Liang (1988) report some studies of the critical N statistic.

Note: Use the \hfive text macro to display Hoelter's critical N in the output path diagram for $\alpha = 0.05$, or the \hone text macro for $\alpha = 0.01$.

LO 90

Amos reports a 90% confidence interval for the population value of several statistics. The upper and lower boundaries are given in columns labeled *HI 90* and *LO 90*.

RMR

The **RMR** (root mean square residual) is the square root of the average squared amount by which the sample variances and covariances differ from their estimates obtained under the assumption that your model is correct.

$$\text{RMR} = \sqrt{\sum_{g=1}^{G}\left\{\sum_{i=1}^{p_g}\sum_{j=1}^{j\le i}\left(\hat{s}_{ij}^{(g)} - \sigma_{ij}^{(g)}\right)\right\} \bigg/ \sum_{g=1}^{G} p *^{(g)}}$$

The smaller the *RMR* is, the better. An *RMR* of 0 indicates a perfect fit.

The following output from Example 6 shows that, according to the *RMR*, Model A is the best among the models considered except for the saturated model:

Model	RMR	GFI	AGFI	PGFI
Model A: No Autocorrelation	0.284	0.975	0.913	0.279
Model B: Most General	0.757	0.998	0.990	0.238
Model C: Time-Invariance	0.749	0.997	0.993	0.380
Model D: A and C Combined	0.263	0.975	0.941	0.418
Saturated model	0.000	1.000		
Independence model	12.342	0.494	0.292	0.353

Note: Use the \rmr text macro to display the value of the root mean square residual in the output path diagram.

Selected List of Fit Measures

If you want to focus on a few fit measures, you might consider the implicit recommendation of Browne and Mels (1992), who elect to report only the following fit measures:

"CMIN" on p. 533

"P" on p. 533

"FMIN" on p. 536

"F0" on p. 537, with 90% confidence interval

"PCLOSE" on p. 539

"RMSEA" on p. 537, with 90% confidence interval

"ECVI" on p. 541, with 90% confidence interval (See also "AIC" on p. 539)

For the case of maximum likelihood estimation, Browne and Cudeck (1989, 1993) suggest substituting *MECVI* (p. 542) for *ECVI*.

Numeric Diagnosis of Non-Identifiability

In order to decide whether a parameter is identified or an entire model is identified, Amos examines the rank of the matrix of approximate second derivatives and of some related matrices. The method used is similar to that of McDonald and Krane (1977). There are objections to this approach in principle (Bentler and Weeks, 1980; McDonald, 1982). There are also practical problems in determining the rank of a matrix in borderline cases. Because of these difficulties, you should judge the identifiability of a model on *a priori* grounds if you can. With complex models, this may be impossible, so you will have to rely on the numeric determination of Amos. Fortunately, Amos is pretty good at assessing identifiability in practice.

Using Fit Measures to Rank Models

In general, it is hard to pick a fit measure because there are so many from which to choose. The choice gets easier when the purpose of the fit measure is to compare models to each other rather than to judge the merit of models by an absolute standard. For example, it turns out that it does not matter whether you use *RMSEA*, *RFI*, or *TLI* when rank ordering a collection of models. Each of those three measures depends on $\hat{C}$ and d only through $\hat{C}/d$, and each depends monotonically on $\hat{C}/d$. Thus, each measure gives the same rank ordering of models. For this reason, the specification search procedure reports only *RMSEA*.

$$\text{RMSEA} = \sqrt{\frac{\hat{C}-d}{nd}} = \sqrt{\frac{1}{n}\left(\frac{\hat{C}}{d}-1\right)}$$

$$\text{RFI} = \rho_1 = 1 - \frac{\hat{C}/d}{\hat{C}_b/d_b}$$

$$\text{TLI} = \rho_2 = \frac{\dfrac{\hat{C}_b}{d_b} - \dfrac{\hat{C}}{d}}{\dfrac{\hat{C}_b}{d_b} - 1}$$

The following fit measures depend on $\hat{C}$ and d only through $\hat{C}-d$, and they depend monotonically on $\hat{C}-d$. The specification search procedure reports only *CFI* as representative of them all.

$$\text{NCP} = \max(\hat{C} - d, 0)$$

$$\text{F0} = \hat{F}_0 = \max\left(\frac{\hat{C} - d}{n}, 0\right)$$

$$\text{CFI} = 1 - \frac{\max(\hat{C} - d, 0)}{\max(\hat{C}_b - d_b, \hat{C} - d, 0)}$$

$$\text{RNI} = 1 - \frac{\hat{C} - d}{\hat{C}_b - d_b} \quad \text{(not reported by Amos)}$$

The following fit measures depend monotonically on $\hat{C}$ and not at all on d. The specification search procedure reports only $\hat{C}$ as representative of them all.

$$\text{CMIN} = \hat{C}$$

$$\text{FMIN} = \frac{\hat{C}}{n}$$

$$\text{NFI} = 1 - \frac{\hat{C}}{\hat{C}_b}$$

Each of the following fit measures is a weighted sum of $\hat{C}$ and d and can produce a distinct rank order of models. The specification search procedure reports each of them except for *CAIC*.

BCC

AIC

BIC

CAIC

Each of the following fit measures is capable of providing a unique rank order of models. The rank order depends on the choice of baseline model as well. The specification search procedure does not report these measures.

IFI $= \Delta_2$

PNFI

PCFI

The following fit measures are the only ones reported by Amos that are not functions of $\hat{C}$ and d in the case of maximum likelihood estimation. The specification search procedure does not report these measures.

GFI

AGFI

PGFI

Baseline Models for Descriptive Fit Measures

Seven measures of fit (*NFI*, *RFI*, *IFI*, *TLI*, *CFI*, *PNFI*, and *PCFI*) require a **null** or **baseline** bad model against which other models can be compared. The specification search procedure offers a choice of four null, or baseline, models:

Null 1: The observed variables are required to be uncorrelated. Their means and variances are unconstrained. This is the baseline *Independence* model in an ordinary Amos analysis when you do not perform a specification search.

Null 2: The correlations among the observed variables are required to be equal. The means and variances of the observed variables are unconstrained.

Null 3: The observed variables are required to be uncorrelated and to have means of 0. Their variances are unconstrained. This is the baseline *Independence* model used by Amos 4.0.1 and earlier for models where means and intercepts are explicit model parameters.

Null 4: The correlations among the observed variables are required to be equal. The variances of the observed variables are unconstrained. Their means are required to be 0.

Each null model gives rise to a different value for *NFI*, *RFI*, *IFI*, *TLI*, *CFI*, *PNFI*, and *PCFI*. Models *Null 3* and *Null 4* are fitted during a specification search only when means and intercepts are explicitly estimated in the models you specify. The *Null 3* and *Null 4* models may be appropriate when evaluating models in which means and intercepts are constrained. There is little reason to fit the *Null 3* and *Null 4* models in the common situation where means and intercepts are not constrained but are estimated for the sole purpose of allowing maximum likelihood estimation with missing data.

To specify which baseline models you want to be fitted during specification searches:

▶ From the menus, choose Analyze → Specification Search.

▶ Click the Options button ☑ on the Specification Search toolbar.

▶ In the Options dialog box, click the Next search tab.

The four null models and the saturated model are listed in the Benchmark models group.

Rescaling of AIC, BCC, and BIC

The fit measures, *AIC*, *BCC*, and *BIC*, are defined in Appendix C. Each measure is of the form $\hat{C} + kq$, where k takes on the same value for all models. Small values are good, reflecting a combination of good fit to the data (small $\hat{C}$) and parsimony (small q). The measures are used for comparing models to each other and not for judging the merit of a single model.

The specification search procedure in Amos provides three ways of rescaling these measures, which were illustrated in Examples 22 and 23. This appendix provides formulas for the rescaled fit measures.

In what follows, let $AIC^{(i)}$, $BCC^{(i)}$, and $BIC^{(i)}$ be the fit values for model i.

Zero-Based Rescaling

Because *AIC*, *BCC*, and *BIC* are used only for comparing models to each other, with smaller values being better than larger values, there is no harm in adding a constant, as in:

$$\text{AIC}_0^{(i)} = \text{AIC}^{(i)} - \min_i[\text{AIC}^{(i)}]$$

$$\text{BCC}_0^{(i)} = \text{BCC}^{(i)} - \min_i[\text{BCC}^{(i)}]$$

$$\text{BIC}_0^{(i)} = \text{BIC}^{(i)} - \min_i[\text{BIC}^{(i)}]$$

The rescaled values are either 0 or positive. For example, the best model according to AIC has $AIC_0 = 0$, while inferior models have positive AIC_0 values that reflect how much worse they are than the best model.

▶ To display AIC_0, BCC_0, and BIC_0 after a specification search, click ☑ on the Specification Search toolbar.

▶ On the Current results tab of the Options dialog box, click Zero-based (min = 0).

Akaike Weights and Bayes Factors (Sum = 1)

▶ To obtain the following rescaling, select Akaike weights and Bayes factors (sum = 1) on the Current results tab of the Options dialog box.

$$
AIC_p^{(i)} = \frac{e^{-AIC^{(i)}/2}}{\sum_m e^{-AIC^{(m)}/2}}
$$

$$
BCC_p^{(i)} = \frac{e^{-BCC^{(i)}/2}}{\sum_m e^{-BCC^{(m)}/2}}
$$

$$
BIC_p^{(i)} = \frac{e^{-BIC^{(i)}/2}}{\sum_m e^{-BIC^{(m)}/2}}
$$

Each of these rescaled measures sums to 1 across models. The rescaling is performed only after an exhaustive specification search. If a heuristic search is carried out or if a positive value is specified for Retain only the best ___ models, then the summation in the denominator cannot be calculated, and rescaling is not performed. The $AIC_p^{(i)}$ are called **Akaike weights** by Burnham and Anderson (1998). $BCC_p^{(i)}$ has the same interpretation as $AIC_p^{(i)}$. Within the Bayesian framework and under suitable assumptions with equal prior probabilities for the models, the $BIC_p^{(i)}$ are approximate posterior probabilities (Raftery, 1993, 1995).

Akaike Weights and Bayes Factors (Max = 1)

▶ To obtain the following rescaling, select Akaike weights and Bayes factors (max = 1) on the Current results tab of the Options dialog box.

$$\text{AIC}_L^{(i)} = \frac{e^{-\text{AIC}^{(i)}/2}}{\max_m [e^{-\text{AIC}^{(m)}/2}]}$$

$$\text{BCC}_L^{(i)} = \frac{e^{-\text{BCC}^{(i)}/2}}{\max_m [e^{-\text{BCC}^{(m)}/2}]}$$

$$\text{BIC}_L^{(i)} = \frac{e^{-\text{BIC}^{(i)}/2}}{\max_m [e^{-\text{BIC}^{(m)}/2}]}$$

For example, the best model according to *AIC* has $AIC_L = 1$, while inferior models have AIC_L between 0 and 1. See Burnham and Anderson (1998) for further discussion of AIC_L, and Raftery (1993, 1995) and Madigan and Raftery (1994) for further discussion of BIC_L.

Bibliography

Akaike, H. 1973. Information theory and an extension of the maximum likelihood principle. In: *Proceedings of the 2nd International Symposium on Information Theory*, B. N. Petrov and F. Csaki, eds. Budapest: Akademiai Kiado. 267–281.

_____. 1978. A Bayesian analysis of the minimum AIC procedure. *Annals of the Institute of Statistical Mathematics*, 30: 9–14.

_____. 1987. Factor analysis and AIC. *Psychometrika*, 52: 317–332.

Allison, P. D. 2002. *Missing data*. Thousand Oaks, CA: Sage Publications.

Anderson, T. W. 1957. Maximum likelihood estimates for a multivariate normal distribution when some observations are missing. *Journal of the American Statistical Association*, 52: 200–203.

_____. 1984. *An introduction to multivariate statistical analysis*. New York: John Wiley and Sons.

Arbuckle, J. L. Unpublished, 1991. Bootstrapping and model selection for analysis of moment structures.

_____. 1994a. Advantages of model-based analysis of missing data over pairwise deletion. Presented at the RMD Conference on Causal Modeling, West Lafayette, IN.

_____. 1994b. A permutation test for analysis of covariance structures. Presented at the annual meeting of the Psychometric Society, University of Illinois, Champaign, IL.

_____. 1996. Full information estimation in the presence of incomplete data. In: *Advanced structural equation modeling*, G. A. Marcoulides and R. E. Schumacker, eds. Mahwah, New Jersey: Lawrence Erlbaum Associates.

Attig, M. S. 1983. The processing of spatial information by adults. Presented at the annual meeting of The Gerontological Society, San Francisco.

Beale, E. M. L., and R. J. A. Little. 1975. Missing values in multivariate analysis. *Journal of the Royal Statistical Society Series B*, 37: 129–145.

Beck, A. T. 1967. *Depression: causes and treatment*. Philadelphia, PA: University of Pennsylvania Press.

Bentler, P. M. 1980. Multivariate analysis with latent variables: Causal modeling. *Annual Review of Psychology*, 31: 419–456.

_____. 1985. *Theory and Implementation of EQS: A Structural Equations Program*. Los Angeles, CA: BMDP Statistical Software.

_____. 1989. *EQS structural equations program manual*. Los Angeles, CA: BMDP Statistical Software.

_____. 1990. Comparative fit indexes in structural models. *Psychological Bulletin*, 107: 238–246.

Bentler, P. M., and D. G. Bonett. 1980. Significance tests and goodness of fit in the analysis of covariance structures. *Psychological Bulletin*, 88: 588–606.

Bentler, P. M., and C. Chou. 1987. Practical issues in structural modeling. *Sociological Methods and Research,* 16: 78–117.

Bentler, P. M., and E. H. Freeman. 1983. Tests for stability in linear structural equation systems. *Psychometrika*, 48: 143–145.

Bentler, P. M., and D. G. Weeks. 1980. Linear structural equations with latent variables. *Psychometrika*, 45: 289–308.

Bentler, P. M., and J. A. Woodward. 1979. Nonexperimental evaluation research: Contributions of causal modeling. In: *Improving Evaluations*, L. Datta and R. Perloff, eds. Beverly Hills: Sage Publications.

Bollen, K. A. 1986. Sample size and Bentler and Bonett's non-normed fit index. *Psychometrika*, 51: 375–377.

_____. 1987. Outliers and improper solutions: A confirmatory factor analysis example. *Sociological Methods and Research*, 15: 375–384.

_____. 1989a. *Structural equations with latent variables*. New York: John Wiley and Sons.

_____. 1989b. A new incremental fit index for general structural equation models. *Sociological Methods and Research*, 17: 303–316.

Bollen, K. A., and K. G. Jöreskog. 1985. Uniqueness does not imply identification: A note on confirmatory factor analysis. *Sociological Methods and Research*, 14: 155–163.

Bollen, K. A., and J. Liang. 1988. Some properties of Hoelter's CN. *Sociological Methods and Research*, 16: 492–503.

Bollen, K. A., and J. S. Long, eds. 1993. *Testing structural equation models*. Newbury Park, CA: Sage Publications.

Bollen, K. A., and R. A. Stine. 1992. Bootstrapping goodness-of-fit measures in structural equation models. *Sociological Methods and Research*, 21: 205–229.

Bolstad, W. M. 2004. *Introduction to Bayesian Statistics*. Hoboken, NJ: John Wiley and Sons.

Boomsma, A. 1987. The robustness of maximum likelihood estimation in structural equation models. In: *Structural Modeling by Example: Applications in Educational, Sociological, and Behavioral Research*, P. Cuttance and R. Ecob, eds. Cambridge University Press, 160–188.

Botha, J. D., A. Shapiro, and J. H. Steiger. 1988. Uniform indices-of-fit for factor analysis models. *Multivariate Behavioral Research*, 23: 443–450.

Bozdogan, H. 1987. Model selection and Akaike's information criterion (AIC): The general theory and its analytical extensions. *Psychometrika*, 52: 345–370.

Brown, C. H. 1983. Asymptotic comparison of missing data procedures for estimating factor loadings. *Psychometrika*, 48:2, 269–291.

Brown, R. L. 1994. Efficacy of the indirect approach for estimating structural equation models with missing data: A comparison of five methods. *Structural Equation Modeling: A Multidisciplinary Journal*, 1: 287–316.

Browne, M. W. 1982. Covariance structures. In: *Topics in applied multivariate analysis*, D. M. Hawkins, ed. Cambridge: Cambridge University Press, 72–141.

_____. 1984. Asymptotically distribution-free methods for the analysis of covariance structures. *British Journal of Mathematical and Statistical Psychology*, 37: 62–83.

Browne, M. W., and R. Cudeck. 1989. Single sample cross-validation indices for covariance structures. *Multivariate Behavioral Research*, 24: 445–455.

_____. 1993. Alternative ways of assessing model fit. In: *Testing structural equation models*, K. A. Bollen and J. S. Long, eds. Newbury Park, CA: Sage Publications, 136–162.

Browne, M. W., and G. Mels. 1992. *RAMONA user's guide*. The Ohio State University, Columbus, OH.

Burnham, K. P., and D. R. Anderson. 1998. *Model selection and inference: A practical information-theoretic approach*. New York: Springer-Verlag.

Burnham, K. P., and D. R. Anderson. 2002. *Model selection and multimodel inference: A practical information-theoretic approach*. 2nd ed. New York: Springer-Verlag.

Burns, D. D. 1999. *Feeling good: the new mood therapy*. New York: Avon Books.

Byrne, B. M. 1989. *A primer of LISREL: Basic applications and programming for confirmatory factor analytic models*. New York: Springer-Verlag.

_____. 2001. *Structural equation modeling with Amos: Basic concepts, applications, and programming*. Mahwah, New Jersey: Erlbaum.

Carmines, E. G., and J. P. McIver. 1981. Analyzing models with unobserved variables. In: *Social measurement: Current issues*, G. W. Bohrnstedt and E. F. Borgatta, eds. Beverly Hills: Sage Publications.

Cattell, R. B. 1966. The scree test for the number of factors. *Multivariate Behavioral Research*, 1: 245–276.

Chen, F., K. A. Bollen, P. Paxton, P. J. Curran, and J. B. Kirby. 2001. Improper solutions in structural equation models: Causes, consequences, and strategies. *Sociological Methods and Research*, 29:4, 468–508.

Cliff, N. 1973. Scaling. *Annual Review of Psychology*, 24: 473–506.

_____. 1983. Some cautions concerning the application of causal modeling methods. *Multivariate Behavioral Research*, 18: 115–126.

Cochran, W. G. 1952. The χ^2 test of goodness of fit. *Annals of Mathematical Statistics*, 23: 315–345.

Cook, T. D., and D. T. Campbell. 1979. *Quasi-experimentation: Design and analysis issues for field settings*. Chicago: Rand McNally.

Croon, M. 2002. Ordering the classes. In: *Applied Latent Class Analysis*: 137–162, J. A. Hagenaars and A. L. McCutcheon, eds. Cambridge, UK: Cambridge University Press.

Crowley, J., and M. Hu. 1977. Covariance analysis of heart transplant data. *Journal of the American Statistical Association*, 72: 27–36.

Cudeck, R., and M. W. Browne. 1983. Cross-validation of covariance structures. *Multivariate Behavioral Research*, 18: 147–167.

Davis, W. R. 1993. The FC1 rule of identification for confirmatory factor analysis: A general sufficient condition. *Sociological Methods and Research*, 21: 403–437.

Diaconis, P., and B. Efron. 1983. Computer-intensive methods in statistics. *Scientific American*, 248:5, 116–130.

Dolker, M., S. Halperin, and D. R. Divgi. 1982. Problems with bootstrapping Pearson correlations in very small samples. *Psychometrika*, 47: 529–530.

Draper, N. R., and H. Smith. 1981. *Applied regression analysis*. 2nd ed. New York: John Wiley and Sons.

Edgington, E. S. 1987. *Randomization Tests*. 2nd ed. New York: Marcel Dekker.

Efron, B. 1979. Bootstrap methods: Another look at the jackknife. *Annals of Statistics*, 7: 1–26.

_____. 1982. *The jackknife, the bootstrap, and other resampling plans*. (SIAM Monograph #38) Philadelphia: Society for Industrial and Applied Mathematics.

_____. 1987. Better bootstrap confidence intervals. *Journal of the American Statistical Association*, 82: 171–185.

Efron, B., and G. Gong. 1983. A leisurely look at the bootstrap, the jackknife, and cross-validation. *American Statistician*, 37: 36–48.

Efron, B., and D. V. Hinkley. 1978. Assessing the accuracy of the maximum likelihood estimator: Observed versus expected Fisher information. *Biometrika*, 65: 457–87.

Efron, B., and R. J. Tibshirani. 1993. *An introduction to the bootstrap*. New York: Chapman and Hall.

European Values Study Group and World Values Survey Association. *European and world values surveys four-wave integrated data file, 1981–2004*. Vol. 20060423. 2006.

Felson, R.B., and G. W. Bohrnstedt 1979. "Are the good beautiful or the beautiful good?" The relationship between children's perceptions of ability and perceptions of physical attractiveness. *Social Psychology Quarterly*, 42: 386–392.

Fox, J. 1980. Effect analysis in structural equation models. *Sociological Methods and Research*, 9: 3–28.

Furnival, G. M., and R. W. Wilson. 1974. Regression by leaps and bounds. *Technometrics*, 16: 499–511.

Gelman, A., J. B. Carlin, H. S. Stern, and D. B. Rubin. 2004. *Bayesian Data Analysis*. 2nd ed. Boca Raton: Chapman and Hall/CRC.

Gill, J. 2004. Introduction to the special issue. *Political Analysis*, 12:4, 323–337.

Graham, J. W., S. M. Hofer, S. I. Donaldson, D. P. MacKinnon, and J. L. Schafer. 1997. Analysis with missing data in prevention research. In: *The science of prevention: Methodological advances from alcohol and substance abuse research*, K. Bryant, M. Windle, and S. West, eds. Washington, DC: American Psychological Association.

Graham, J. W., S. M. Hofer, and D. P. MacKinnon. 1996. Maximizing the usefulness of data obtained with planned missing value patterns: An application of maximum likelihood procedures. *Multivariate Behavorial Research*, 31: 197–218.

Gulliksen, H., and J. W. Tukey. 1958. Reliability for the law of comparative judgment. *Psychometrika*, 23: 95–110.

Hamilton, L. C. 1990. *Statistics with Stata*. Pacific Grove, CA: Brooks/Cole.

Hamilton, M. 1960. A rating scale for depression. *Journal of Neurology, Neurosurgery, and Psychiatry*, 23: 56–62.

Hayduk, L. A. 1987. *Structural equation modeling with LISREL*. Baltimore: Johns Hopkins University Press.

Hoelter, J. W. 1983. The analysis of covariance structures: Goodness-of-fit indices. *Sociological Methods and Research*, 11: 325–344.

Hoeting, J. A., D. Madigan, A. E. Raftery, and C. T. Volinsky. 1999. Bayesian model averaging: a tutorial. *Statistical Science*, 14: 382–417.

Holzinger, K. J., and F. A. Swineford. 1939. A study in factor analysis: The stability of a bi-factor solution. *Supplementary Educational Monographs*, No. 48. Chicago: University of Chicago, Dept. of Education.

Hu, L., and P. M. Bentler. 1999. Cutoff criteria for fit indices in covariance structure analysis: conventional criteria versus new alternatives. *Structural Equation Modeling*, 6: 1–55.

Hubert, L. J., and R. G. Golledge. 1981. A heuristic method for the comparison of related structures. *Journal of Mathematical Psychology*, 23: 214–226.

Huitema, B. E. 1980. *The analysis of covariance and alternatives*. New York: John Wiley and Sons.

Ibrahim, J. G., M-H Chen, S. R. Lipsitz, and A. H. Herring. 2005. Missing data methods for generalized linear models: A review. *Journal of the American Statistical Association*, 100:469, 332–346.

Jackman, S. 2000. Estimation and inference via Bayesian simulation: An introduction to Markov chain Monte Carlo. *American Journal of Political Science*, 44:2, 375–404.

James, L. R., S. A. Mulaik, and J. M. Brett. 1982. *Causal analysis: Assumptions, models, and data*. Beverly Hills: Sage Publications.

Jamison, C., and F. Scogin. 1995. The outcome of cognitive bibliotherapy with depressed adults. *Journal of Consulting and Clinical Psychology*, 63: 644–650.

Jöreskog, K. G. 1967. Some contributions to maximum likelihood factor analysis. *Psychometrika*, 32: 443–482.

_____. 1969. A general approach to confirmatory maximum likelihood factor analysis. *Psychometrika*, 34: 183–202.

_____. 1971. Simultaneous factor analysis in several populations. *Psychometrika*, 36: 409–426.

_____. 1979. A general approach to confirmatory maximum likelihood factor analysis with addendum. In: *Advances in factor analysis and structural equation models*, K. G. Jöreskog and D. Sörbom, eds. Cambridge, MA: Abt Books, 21–43.

Jöreskog, K. G., and D. Sörbom. 1984. *LISREL-VI user's guide*. 3rd ed. Mooresville, IN: Scientific Software.

_____. 1989. *LISREL-7 user's reference guide*. Mooresville, IN: Scientific Software.

_____. 1996. *LISREL-8 user's reference guide*. Chicago: Scientific Software.

Judd, C. M., and M. A. Milburn. 1980. The structure of attitude systems in the general public: Comparisons of a structural equation model. *American Sociological Review*, 45: 627–643.

Kalbfleisch, J. D., and R. L. Prentice. 2002. *The statistical analysis of failure time data*. Hoboken, NJ: John Wiley and Sons.

Kaplan, D. 1989. Model modification in covariance structure analysis: Application of the expected parameter change statistic. *Multivariate Behavioral Research*, 24: 285–305.

Kendall, M. G., and A. Stuart. 1973. *The advanced theory of statistics*. Vol. 2, 3rd ed. New York: Hafner.

Kline, R. B. 2005. *Principles and practice of structural equation modeling*. 2nd ed. New York: The Guilford Press.

Kullback, S., and R. A. Leibler. 1951. On information and sufficiency. *Annals of Mathematical Statistics*, 22: 79–86.

Lee, S., and S. Hershberger. 1990. A simple rule for generating equivalent models in covariance structure modeling. *Multivariate Behavioral Research*, 25: 313–334.

Lee, S. Y., and X. Y. Song. 2004. Evaluation of the Bayesian and maximum likelihood approaches in analyzing structural equation models with small sample sizes. *Multivariate Behavioral Research*, 39:4, 653–686.

Lee, S. Y., and X. Y. Song. 2003. Bayesian analysis of structural equation models with dichotomous variables. *Statistics in Medicine*, 22: 3073–3088.

Linhart, H., and W. Zucchini. 1986. *Model selection*. New York: John Wiley and Sons.

Little, R. J. A., and D. B. Rubin. 1987. *Statistical analysis with missing data*. New York: John Wiley and Sons.

_____. 1989. The analysis of social science data with missing values. *Sociological Methods and Research*, 18: 292–326.

_____. 2002. *Statistical analysis with missing data*. New York: John Wiley and Sons.

Little, R. J. A., and N. Schenker. 1995. Missing data. In: *Handbook of statistical modeling for the social and behavioral sciences*, G. Arminger, C. C. Clogg, and M. E. Sobel, eds. New York: Plenum.

Loehlin, J. C. 1992. *Latent variable models: An introduction to factor, path, and structural analysis*. 2nd ed. Mahwah, New Jersey: Lawrence Erlbaum Associates.

Lord, F. M. 1955. Estimation of parameters from incomplete data. *Journal of the American Statistical Association*, 50: 870–876.

MacCallum, R. C. 1986. Specification searches in covariance structure modeling. *Psychological Bulletin*, 100: 107–120.

_____. 1990. The need for alternative measures of fit in covariance structure modeling. *Multivariate Behavioral Research*, 25: 157–162.

MacCallum, R. C., M. Roznowski, and L. B. Necowitz. 1992. Model modifications in covariance structure analysis: The problem of capitalization on chance. *Psychological Bulletin*, 111: 490–504.

MacCallum, R. C., D. T. Wegener, B. N. Uchino, and L. R. Fabrigar. 1993. The problem of equivalent models in applications of covariance structure analysis. *Psychological Bulletin*, 114: 185–199.

MacKay, D. J. C. 2003. *Information theory, inference and learning algorithms*. Cambridge, UK: Cambridge University Press.

MacKinnon, D. P., C. M. Lockwood, and J. Williams. 2004. Confidence limits for the indirect effect: distribution of the product and resampling methods. *Multivariate Behavioral Research*, 39:1, 99–128.

Madigan, D., and A. E. Raftery. 1994. Model selection and accounting for model uncertainty in graphical models using Occam's window. *Journal of the American Statistical Association*, 89: 1535–1546.

Manly, B. F. J. 1991. *Randomization and Monte Carlo Methods in Biology*. London: Chapman and Hall.

Mantel, N. 1967. The detection of disease clustering and a generalized regression approach. *Cancer Research*, 27: 209–220.

Mantel, N., and R. S. Valand. 1970. A technique of nonparametric multivariate analysis. *Biometrics*, 26: 47–558.

Mardia, K. V. 1970. Measures of multivariate skewness and kurtosis with applications. *Biometrika*, 57: 519–530.

_____. 1974. Applications of some measures of multivariate skewness and kurtosis in testing normality and robustness studies. *Sankhya*, Series B, 36: 115–128.

Marsh, H. W., and D. Hocevar. 1985. Application of confirmatory factor analysis to the study of self-concept: First- and higher-order factor models and their invariance across groups. *Psychological Bulletin*, 97: 562–582.

Martin, J. K., and R. P. McDonald. 1975. Bayesian estimation in unrestricted factor analysis: A treatment for Heywood cases. *Psychometrika*, 40: 505–517.

Matsumoto, M., and T. Nishimura. 1998. Mersenne twister: A 623-dimensionally equidistributed uniform pseudo-random number generator. *ACM Transactions on Modeling and Computer Simulation*, 8: 3–30.

Matthai, A. 1951. Estimation of parameters from incomplete data with application to design of sample surveys. *Sankhya*, 11: 145–152.

McArdle, J. J., and M. S. Aber. 1990. Patterns of change within latent variable structural equation models. In: *Statistical methods in longitudinal research, Volume I: Principles and structuring change*, A. von Eye, ed. New York: Academic Press, 151–224.

McDonald, R. P. 1978. A simple comprehensive model for the analysis of covariance structures. *British Journal of Mathematical and Statistical Psychology*, 31: 59–72.

_____. 1982. A note on the investigation of local and global identifiability. *Psychometrika*, 47: 101–103.

_____. 1989. An index of goodness-of-fit based on noncentrality. *Journal of Classification*, 6: 97–103.

McDonald, R. P., and W. R. Krane. 1977. A note on local identifiability and degrees of freedom in the asymptotic likelihood ratio test. *British Journal of Mathematical and Statistical Psychology*, 30: 198–203.

_____. 1979. A Monte-Carlo study of local identifiability and degrees of freedom in the asymptotic likelihood ratio test. *British Journal of Mathematical and Statistical Psychology*, 32: 121–132.

McDonald, R. P., and H. W. Marsh. 1990. Choosing a multivariate model: Noncentrality and goodness of fit. *Psychological Bulletin*, 107: 247–255.

Mulaik, S. A. 1990. An analysis of the conditions under which the estimation of parameters inflates goodness of fit indices as measures of model validity. Paper presented at the Annual Meeting, Psychometric Society, Princeton, New Jersey, June 28–30, 1990.

Mulaik, S. A., L. R. James, J. Van Alstine, N. Bennett, S. Lind, and C. D. Stilwell. 1989. Evaluation of goodness-of-fit indices for structural equation models. *Psychological Bulletin*, 105: 430–445.

Muthén, B., D. Kaplan, and M. Hollis. 1987. On structural equation modeling with data that are not missing completely at random. *Psychometrika*, 52: 431–462

Olinsky, A., S. Chen, and L. Harlow. 2003. The comparitive efficacy of imputation methods for missing data in structural equation modeling. *European Journal of Operational Research*, 151: 53–79.

Olsson, S. 1973. *An experimental study of the effects of training on test scores and factor structure.* Uppsala, Sweden: University of Uppsala, Department of Education.

Raftery, A. E. 1993. Bayesian model selection in structural equation models. In: *Testing structural equation models*, K. A. Bollen and J. S. Long, eds. Newbury Park, CA: Sage Publications, 163–180.

_____. 1995. Bayesian model selection in social research. In: *Sociological Methodology*, P. V. Marsden, ed. San Francisco: Jossey-Bass, 111–163.

Rigdon, E. E. 1994a. Calculating degrees of freedom for a structural equation model. *Structural Equation Modeling*, 1: 274–278.

_____. 1994b. Demonstrating the effects of unmodeled random measurement error. *Structural Equation Modeling*, 1: 375–380.

Rock, D. A., C. E. Werts, R. L. Linn, and K. G. Jöreskog. 1977. A maximum likelihood solution to the errors in variables and errors in equations model. *Journal of Multivariate Behavioral Research*, 12: 187–197.

Rubin, D. B. 1976. Inference and missing data. *Biometrika*, 63: 581–592.

_____. 1987. *Multiple imputation for nonresponse in surveys.* New York: John Wiley and Sons.

Runyon, R. P., and A. Haber. 1980. *Fundamentals of behavioral statistics*, 4th ed. Reading, Mass.: Addison-Wesley.

Salhi, S. 1998. Heuristic search methods. In: *Modern methods for business research*, G. A. Marcoulides, ed. Mahwah, NJ: Erlbaum, 147–175.

Saris, W. E., A. Satorra, and D. Sörbom. 1987. The detection and correction of specification errors in structural equation models. In: *Sociological methodology*, C. C. Clogg, ed. San Francisco: Jossey-Bass.

Schafer, J. L. 1997. *Analysis of incomplete multivariate data.* London, UK: Chapman and Hall.

Schafer, J. L., and J. W. Graham. 2002. Missing data: Our view of the state of the art. *Psychological Methods*, 7:2, 147–177.

Schafer, J. L., and M. K. Olsen. 1998. Multiple imputation for multivariate missing-data problems: A data analyst's perspective. *Multivariate Behavioral Research*, 33:4, 545–571.

Schwarz, G. 1978. Estimating the dimension of a model. *The Annals of Statistics*, 6: 461–464.

Scheines, R., H. Hoijtink, and A. Boomsma. 1999. Bayesian estimation and testing of structural equation models. *Psychometrika*, 64: 37–52.

Shrout, P. E., and N. Bolger. 2002. Mediation in experimental and nonexperimental studies: New procedures and recommendations. *Psychological Methods*, 7:4, 422–445.

Sobel, M. E. 1982. Asymptotic confidence intervals for indirect effects in structural equation models. In: *Sociological methodology,* S. Leinhart, ed. San Francisco: Jossey-Bass, 290–312.

_____. 1986. Some new results on indirect effects and their standard errors in covariance structure models. In: *Sociological methodology,* S. Leinhart, ed. San Francisco: Jossey-Bass, 159–186.

Sobel, M. E., and G. W. Bohrnstedt. 1985. Use of null models in evaluating the fit of covariance structure models. In: *Sociological methodology,* N. B. Tuma, ed. San Francisco: Jossey-Bass, 152-178.

Sörbom, D. 1974. A general method for studying differences in factor means and factor structure between groups. *British Journal of Mathematical and Statistical Psychology*, 27: 229–239.

_____. 1978. An alternative to the methodology for analysis of covariance. *Psychometrika*, 43: 381–396.

Spirtes, P., R. Scheines, and C. Glymour. 1990. Simulation studies of the reliability of computer-aided model specification using the TETRAD II, EQS, and LISREL programs. *Sociological Methods and Research*, 19: 3–66.

Steiger, J. H. 1989. *EzPATH: Causal modeling*. Evanston, IL: Systat.

_____. 1990. Structural model evaluation and modification: An interval estimation approach. *Multivariate Behavioral Research*, 25: 173–180.

Steiger, J. H., and J. C. Lind. 1980, May 30. Statistically-based tests for the number of common factors. Paper presented at the Annual Spring Meeting of the Psychometric Society, Iowa City.

Steiger, J. H., A. Shapiro, and M. W. Browne. 1985. On the multivariate asymptotic distribution of sequential chi-square statistics. *Psychometrika*, 50: 253–263.

Stelzl, I. 1986. Changing a causal hypothesis without changing the fit: Some rules for generating equivalent path models. *Multivariate Behavioral Research*, 21: 309–331.

Stine, R. A. 1989. An introduction to bootstrap methods: Examples and ideas. *Sociological Methods and Research*, 18: 243–291.

Swain, A. J. 1975. Analysis of parametric structures for variance matrices. Unpublished Ph.D. thesis, University of Adelaide.

Tanaka, J. S., and G. J. Huba. 1985. A fit index for covariance structure models under arbitrary GLS estimation. *British Journal of Mathematical and Statistical Psychology*, 38: 197–201.

_____. 1989. A general coefficient of determination for covariance structure models under arbitrary GLS estimation. *British Journal of Mathematical and Statistical Psychology*, 42: 233–239.

Tucker, L. R., and C. Lewis. 1973. A reliability coefficient for maximum likelihood factor analysis. *Psychometrika*, 38: 1–10.

Verleye, G. 1996. Missing at random data problems in attitude measurements using maximum likelihood structural equation modeling. Unpublished dissertation. Frije Universiteit Brussels, Department of Psychology.

Warren, R. D., J. K. White, and W. A. Fuller. 1974. An errors-in-variables analysis of managerial role performance. *Journal of the American Statistical Association*, 69: 886–893.

Wheaton, B. 1987. Assessment of fit in overidentified models with latent variables. *Sociological Methods and Research*, 16: 118–154.

Wheaton, B., B. Muthén, D. F. Alwin, and G. F. Summers. 1977. Assessing reliability and stability in panel models. In: *Sociological methodology*, D. R. Heise, ed. San Francisco: Jossey-Bass, 84–136.

Wichman, B. A., and I. D. Hill. 1982. An efficient and portable pseudo-random number generator. Algorithm AS 183. *Applied Statistics*, 31: 188–190.

Winer, B. J. 1971. *Statistical principles in experimental design*. New York: McGraw-Hill.

Wothke, W. 1993. Nonpositive definite matrices in structural modeling. In: *Testing structural equation models*, K. A. Bollen and J. S. Long, eds. Newbury Park, CA: Sage Publications, 256–293.

_____. 1999 Longitudinal and multi-group modeling with missing data. In: *Modeling longitudinal and multiple group data: Practical issues, applied approaches and specific examples*, T. D. Little, K. U. Schnabel, and J. Baumert, eds. Mahwah, New Jersey: Lawrence Erlbaum Associates.

Index